# A Geography of Italy

# D. S. WALKER

# A Geography of Italy

LONDON: METHUEN & CO LTD

First published 1958
by Methuen & Co Ltd
11 New Fetter Lane, E C 4
Second edition 1967
© 1958, 1967 D. S. Walker
Printed in Great Britain by
Butler & Tanner Ltd
Frome and London

# Contents

——⟨•⟩——

## PART IV: ECONOMIC GEOGRAPHY

# List of Plates

*between pages 244 and 245*

vii

# Maps and Diagrams

ix

# Tables

# Acknowledgements

The writer gratefully acknowledges his indebtedness to the authors of the books named in the bibliography and also to the following organizations which not only provided valuable material but made possible a more representative selection of photographs: the Ente Provinciale per il Turismo, Torino (pl. ia and via); the Ente Provinciale per il Turismo, Trento (pl. iiia and iiib); the Ente Provinciale per il Turismo, Venezia (pl. vii); the Ente Provinciale per il Turismo, Pisa (pl. xia); the Servizio Informazioni della Presidenza del Consiglio dei Ministri, Rome (pl. vib, xib, xva, b, c and d, and xxb); the Ente Nazionale Italiano per il Turismo, Rome (pl. xvib, xxia, xxib, and xxiib); the Ente Sila, Cosenza (pl. xixa); the Touring Club Italiano (pl. xxiiib); Fotocielo, directed by Dr Sergio Sostegni (pl. va, vb, ixa, xiv and xxiia); and the Consorzio Autonomo del Porto di Genova.

He also records his appreciation of the kindness of Prof. Mario Pinna of the University of Messina and Prof. Fiorenzo Mancini of the University of Florence for allowing their researches to be used to draw respectively the sketch map of aridity (fig. 13) and the sketch map of soils (fig. 19). Finally he wishes to express his gratitude to Mr F. Hume for his assistance with the photographs; to his brother, Mr H. P. Walker, for his valuable suggestions at the typescript stage; and to his wife for her practical help throughout.

# PART I

Some Geography and History

# SOME GEOGRAPHY AND HISTORY

Geography has been defined as the study of the relationship between Man and his environment. Over the centuries both the environment and Man's technique in coping with it have been undergoing continuous change. It is given to few generations to start with a clean slate in an untouched environment; each generation has to build on the good works or suffer from the mistakes of its predecessors, and this is more than ever true of a country like Italy which may claim to have been continuously and densely settled longer than any other European area. Twentieth-century Lombardy reaps the benefit of 1000 years of work and experience in the utilization of its waters for irrigation, and Basilicata struggles against the accumulated effects of 2000 years of deforestation. The environment changes, too, in the wider sphere of space relationships. The problems and opportunities presented to Italy in its Roman setting were different from those at the time of the Crusades, or during the Age of Discovery, or when the Suez Canal was cut or the Alps were pierced by tunnels. Without some appreciation of the geography of the past, the geography of the present is only partially intelligible. The purpose of this section is to give depth, a time dimension, to the study of modern Italian geography.

In some countries the effects of the forces of physical geography seem to be slow, imperceptible and remote; in Italy they are rapid, spectacular and recent, literally erupting into modern times. In Pliocene times Italy was a short, narrow peninsula terminating in an arc of small islands. The Po Valley and most of the modern peninsula were then under the sea, while the eruptions which built the volcanic zones of western Italy may well have delayed settlement in parts of that area.

Certain aspects of Italy's physical geography have been of the greatest human significance. The vulcanicity of Tuscany, Latium and Campania provided rich soils, valuable minerals and a variety of coastline which were conducive to the growth of civilization at an early date. Perhaps the most spectacular feature of the physical geography has been the work of rivers. In the North they have helped to build up the vast alluvial plain of the Po; in the South they have fretted the extensive erodible clays, marls and tuffs of the Apennines into a maze of steep valleys and gullies, sweeping down vast quantities of silt, often in disastrous floods, to form malarial marsh in the intermontane basins and on the coast. The acceleration caused by Man over the last 3000 years has converted the natural process of erosion into a wasting disease, and the gullied uplands of Lucania had their inevitable counterpart in the sterile marshes of the Gulf of Taranto. The introduction of malaria, probably in the Punic wars, added to the menace of these flats. At the head of the Adriatic the Po, Adige, Piave, Tagliamento and Reno have added a strip from four to twenty-five miles in width in the last three millennia. Adria, flourishing at the time of the Republic, had silted up by the decline of the Empire and is now sixteen miles inland. Ravenna, Ostia and Aquileia have suffered a similar fate. As inland waterways the rivers of Italy have never played the significant rôle of those of France, Germany, Russia, or even England; the conditions which contributed to the importance of Paris, Kiev or Rouen were absent in Italy. The best system, namely the Po, was only of modest importance because of seasonal fluctuations and silting. The rivers of peninsular Italy, with one or two exceptions, are short and swift, with silted mouths, and are dominated by regimes which fluctuate wildly from raging floods in winter to a mere trickle in summer. In the South even the route provided by the river was often of doubtful value, sometimes leading into marsh on the plain course and into difficult gorges with unstable sides in the mountains. This fact, and the lack of navigation facilities, emphasized the need for roads and may well have stimulated the road-building art in ancient Italy. Town sites too reflect the character of the rivers. There are very few sizeable towns on the middle and lower Po, and the important cities along the Via Aemilia are all near the Apennine tributaries, but few are on them.

Most important for the human geography have been the effects of the relationship between rock, climate, vegetation, soil and Man. The vital soil covering is maintained only when the loss by erosion is made good by the disintegration of the sub-soil and the accumulation of humus. On the steep slopes of peninsular Italy the parent rock is often easily erodible, and this together with the seasonal and torrential nature of the rainfall accelerates the destructive process. On the other hand the climate is not conducive to the replenishment of the topsoil from the subsoil, nor to the accumulation of the humus so essential for plant food and water storage; the Mediterranean vegetation is often woody and resinous and the rich surface layer, which in more northerly countries results from deciduous trees and a matting of grassy turf, is rarely found. When once the precarious stability of the soil has been disturbed by the action of Man in removing the natural vegetation, the all too frequent consequence has been a disastrous chain reaction – soil erosion, desiccation, flooding, silting and malarial marshes.

## SETTLEMENT AND COLONIZATION

The geological story of Italy is a short one but its human story is long. At the time of Augustus, when England can scarcely have had a population of a million, Italy was probably supporting 15 millions. The period roughly comparable to the Anglo-Saxon in England, when the broad pattern of agricultural settlement was being outlined, occurred 2000 years earlier in Italy, and in no country in Europe has the imprint of Man on the landscape, with its good and evil consequences, been so marked.

The Neolithic invaders of Italy found a landscape of forest, thicket and marsh, a vegetation grown up in response to the warmer and damper conditions following the Ice Age. The Northern Plain was a wilderness of forest laced with marshes, the most attractive sites for settlement being along the mountain margins where the gravels were better drained and less densely covered. The Peninsula too was largely forested. In ancient times the deciduous and evergreen forests of Cimino, Gargano, Apulia and Calabria, of which little survives, were renowned as sources of structural and shipbuilding timber. After the Pyrrhic wars Rome took over control of half the valuable forests of Bruttium as a spoil of war, and Latium is recorded as having exported beech and oak which must have been found extensively on the lower Apennine slopes. Cisalpine Gaul was famous for its timber and pork, the latter essentially a product of woodlands. The story of these forests, as elsewhere in Europe, has been one of steady destruction. Man has cleared them ruthlessly for agriculture and pasture, for ships and buildings, as reprisals in war and for fuel,[1] and the disastrous consequences began to appear early. The Campagna, once forested and later cleared to support a dense peasant settlement, had deteriorated by the first century BC into a sheep and olive area; sheep and goat pastures, already wasted and ailing, had replaced much of the forest of Lucania before the Romans took control of it. Once destroyed, recovery was difficult; high forest gave place to scrubby thickets of holm oak, wild olive, myrtle and laurel (macchia), or to garrigue or even to barren rock. In the Apennines there are few areas where the claws of erosion have not lacerated the landscape.

The origins and significance of the peoples of Italy over whom Rome became mistress are, not surprisingly, a matter of controversy. The earliest arrivals were Neolithic Mediterranean peoples from North Africa, filtering in through Sicily in the South (the Siculans), and through Spain, France and Liguria in the North (the Ibero-Ligurians). These pastoral peoples, whose impress on the landscape must have been slight, persisted in remote areas such as Liguria and Umbria long after they had been merged with, or destroyed by, later comers. More numerous and more important for the racial composition of ancient Italy were the Bronze Age folk who trekked in with their flocks and herds through the eastern Alps from the Danube Basin after about 1800 BC. In the Northern Plain archaeologists recognize a Terremare civilization characterized by villages of pile-dwellings built on dry land, whereas earlier pile-dwellings (*palafitte*) had been confined, more understandably, to the shores of the northern lakes. By 1000 BC much of Italy from the Po Valley down to a line joining Rome and Rimini was occupied by the Villanova peoples, a much more advanced group, skilled in the manufacture of iron for which Bologna remained famous even after the Villanovans had declined in the face of the Etruscan advance. The relationship of these early civilizations to the Latin and Sabellic tribes, who penetrated the eastern Alps and moved south to occupy the Peninsula between 1600 and 800 BC, is obscure. Both groups were farmers and herdsmen, familiar with the manufacture of bronze and later iron, and spoke Indo-European tongues. The Latins, who were distinguishable from

[1] The demand for firewood for the baths of Rome alone must have been considerable, and in the later Empire fuel was imported from North Africa for this purpose.

their Sabellian kindred by the practice of cremating their dead, concentrated in southern Etruria and Latium, while the Sabellians, with whom the Latins mixed to some extent, penetrated south along the Apennine backbone as far as Sicily. These two Indo-European farming peoples, who provided the bulk of the population of the Peninsula long before the traditional date of the founding of Rome (753), had much in common, and although much strife lay ahead, there was an underlying unity which was to become a political reality under Rome. Before that time arrived, however, Italy was to come under the influence of three civilizations, much more advanced and of a character different from anything so far experienced. These were the Etruscan, the Greek and the Carthaginian.

The Etruscans remain something of a mystery, but whether their origin is to be sought in Italy or beyond the Alps or in Asia Minor, it seems likely that, despite their distinctive racial contribution to the Italian population, they represented even in Etruria an aristocratic minority ruling over a subject native majority. At its maximum extent (*c.* 550) the Etruscan sphere extended southwards through Latium to northern Campania, northwards into the Po Valley, where they founded Felsina (Bologna), Parma, Mutina, Brescia and Verona, and overseas to the coastlands of Corsica. The Etruscans must have made considerable inroads into the original forest; apart from clearing for their serf-run agriculture, timber was vital for their trade and shipbuilding, and for the smelting of the copper of Volterrae, the tin of M. Amiata and M. Catini and the iron of Elba which together provided their main commercial asset. In contrast to the Romans, who despite their proximity to the sea were essentially 'land-minded', the Etruscans were metal workers, traders and pirates with their eyes fixed seawards to the Tyrrhenian. In the three-cornered struggle for the domination of that area, the Etruscans and Carthaginians frequently made common cause against the Greeks whose colonization north of Campania was consequently confined to the Massilian coast. Oddly enough, their mutual hostility did not prevent trading contacts, as the numerous Greek and Greek-inspired objects found on Etruscan sites testify.[1]

About 400 BC the Gauls overran the thinly held Po Valley and soon after Etruria itself. When the tide of invasion turned, the Etruscan cities, much weakened, fell more and more within the expanding Roman sphere, and by the beginning of the third century Etruria was virtually annexed and later so thoroughly Romanized that even the Etruscan language died out.

The Phoenicians, whose interests took them as far afield as the Atlantic coasts, were the first to appreciate the importance to a seafaring people of the waist of the Mediterranean in linking the complementary trading areas of the Eastern and Western Basins. Before the foundation of Carthage itself they had annexed Malta, Lampedusa and Pantelleria, and although many of their early trading posts on the Sicilian coasts disappeared in the face of the more systematic Greek coloniza-

---

[1] Recent excavations at Spina, near Comacchio, show that it was an important centre for the importation of Greek wares into the Etruscan territories by the Adriatic 'back door'.

tion, they established a firm base in western Sicily whence they frequently menaced the very existence of the Greek cities until they were finally expelled by the Romans. The first Greek settlement in Italy was at Cumae, which itself founded daughter colonies at Neapolis and Puteoli. During the eighth and seventh centuries numerous city colonies were established on the coasts of

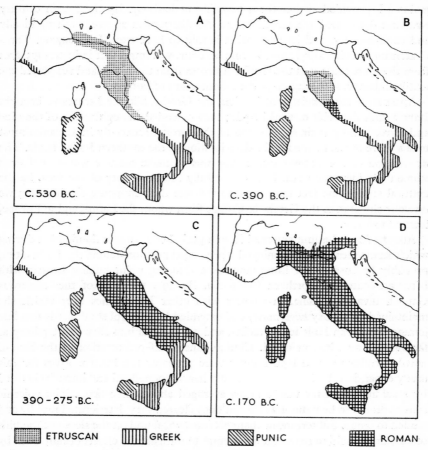

Fig. *1*. A – Spheres before the emergence of Rome. B – Spheres immediately before the Gaulish attack. C – Extended Roman sphere from the Gaulish incursion to the Pyrrhic Wars. D – Roman sphere 170 BC

Sicily up to the Punic zone, roughly east of a line joining Himera and Selinus; on the mainland others occupied the coast from Campania to Apulia and so thoroughly Hellenized the area that it became known as Magna Graecia. The almost notorious prosperity of these Greek cities was based on agriculture which provided a rich export of wine, grain, olive oil, flax, wool and timber. Some were able to exploit the commercial possibilities offered by their position; Zancle

(Messina) and Rhegium were well placed to control the important trade through the awe-inspiring Straits of Messina and their intransigent attitude encouraged Sybaris to develop an alternative route across Calabria to her colonies at Scidros and Laos. Foremost among the trading cities was Syracuse. Its original site was on the island of Ortygia, which together with the causeway joining it to the mainland, provided shelter for a magnificent harbour. By the fourth century Syracuse dominated the Greek central Mediterranean sphere, both politically and commercially, and its population is said to have exceeded 200,000. Taras (Tarentum), which also enjoyed a fine harbour, was important industrially; dyes from the murex fished in the Gulf and fleeces from the hinterland supported the textile industry, and local clays the manufacture of pottery.

Apart from their racial contribution, the Greeks, like the Etruscans, brought Italy within the orbit of world trade; they extended the cultivation of the vine and olive, and by their exploitation of the forests, especially in Lucania, must take a share of the blame for the deterioration of the southern Italian lands. The devastation of the Second Punic War was to make matters worse, and even Roman administration failed to restore fully the prosperity of the area. In the cultural sphere one fact may serve to indicate their immense significance; we owe our alphabet to the Greeks of Cumae from whom the Latins, and so Europe, learned to write.

About 510 BC Latium emerged from a period of Etruscan domination during which Rome seems to have enjoyed a privileged position among the Latin cities, probably because of her importance as a bridging point linking Etruria with Etruscan-controlled northern Campania. By 390, the year of the disastrous Gaulish invasion, Rome, in alliance with other Latin cities over which she maintained an uneasy hegemony, had extended her control southwards to a line joining the Alban Hills to Terracina, and northwards into Etruscan territory as far as the forest barrier of M. Cimino. Sheer self-preservation in the face of hostile neighbours and land hunger were probably the main motives for this costly expansion. Latium was apparently heavily populated and intensively tilled by a soldier-peasantry whose farms averaged about three acres. The volcanic soils appeared to be naturally rich but once cleared they deteriorated rapidly and tended to erode. Subterranean channels (*cuniculi*) found on the slopes of the hills of Latium are said to represent an attempt to mitigate the effects of rain-wash by carrying off the offending surface water underground. Other archaeological evidence suggest that much work was lavished on conservation measures which would only have been worth while in a land-hungry community.

The Gaulish invasion undid the work of a century; when the tide turned, Rome had to deal with a revival of hostility among the southern Etruscan cities, and even among some Latin ones, before re-engaging in the long and desperate struggle with the Sabellian tribes of the Apennines, most tenacious of which were the Samnites. By 283 the Roman sphere extended roughly from the Arno and Picenum in the north to southern Campania and Apulia in the south. Political and military control in this area was consolidated by the planting of colonies, which incidentally served to reduce social friction at home among the land-hungry Roman and Latin poor. Such were Hadria and Castrum Novum in Picenum, Cales in Campania and Beneventum in the Samnite territory. Other colonies safeguarded vital strategic roads, for example Terracina, Minturnae and Sinuessa on the Via Appia, Fregellae on the Sacco-Liri route, and Narnia on the Via Flaminia, while Ariminum was the first of a group of colonies to be built as a screen against the Gauls. Although in any attempt to explain the success of the Romans in dominating central Italy most weight must be given to their political and military ability, the unique strategic position of Rome must also be recognized. Three routes from the north, one along the coast (Via Aurelia), one across the volcanic plateau (Via Cassia) and one directly through the Apennines from Cisalpine Gaul (Via Flaminia), and two from the south, one along the coastal plain (Via Appia) and the other along the Sacco-Liri valley (Via Latina), concentrated inevitably at the best bridging point on the Tiber. From an early date the salt route inland from the Tiber marshes (Via Salaria) was also important. No other site in central Italy had such possibilities; it was Rome's achievement that she exploited them fully by laborious and systematic road-building and colonization.

In Rome's expansion southwards into the central Mediterranean Hellenic sphere two phases may be recognized; in the first she became mistress of Magna Graecia after the costly Pyrrhic War (280–275 BC), which began with a seemingly unimportant quarrel with Tarentum; in the second she fell heir, almost inevitably, to the Greek enmity towards the Carthaginians. After a long struggle, during which Rome became almost reluctantly a naval power (First Punic War 264–241 BC), Sicily was cleared of the Carthaginians and came under the control of Rome and her Greek allies. Taking advantage of Carthage's domestic troubles, Rome later rounded off her dominion of the Tyrrhenian by annexing Corsica and Sardinia.

During this period Rome seems to have outrun her capacity to colonize in the systematic manner pursued earlier in central Italy. The newly acquired islands became tribute-paying provinces and the land was left largely in native hands, or when forfeited to the state was hired out in large blocks to Roman capitalists. Some colonization continued but the north proved more attractive than the south and islands. In particular, sizeable tracts of the Ager Gallicus (the former Gallic territory on the Adriatic south of the Rubicon) were distributed by C. Flaminius to poor settlers. A few more colonies were planted at strategic points, among them Spoletum and Brundisium.

Since their unmolested withdrawal from Rome in 390, the Gauls had frequently menaced the Peninsula from their base in the Po Valley. In retaliation for renewed attacks the Romans began the subjugation of the area but their work was soon interrupted by Hannibal's descent from the Alps in 218.[1] Only after the

[1] The pass he used has long been a matter of speculation; tradition favours the Little St

bloody trial of the Second Punic War was Rome in a position to renew the attempt. Those Celts who remained south of the Alps were subjugated and a steady influx of Italian settlers claimed the area for Latin civilization. In the east of the Plain the territory of the friendly Cenomani and Veneti was peacefully occupied; in the west the Ligurian tribes were steadily pacified. The abandoned colonies of Cremona and Placentia were re-settled and others planted at Parma, Mutina and Bononia along the Via Aemilia; Aquileia's function was to thwart barbarian attacks from Illyria and from the Pannonian Basin through the low Carnic and Julian Alps. All these northern colonies were big (Cremona and Placentia comprised 6000 families each) and the grants of land, graded according to rank, were unusually generous.[1]

The Roman settlement of Italy briefly outlined above was to last without serious challenge for 700 years, and even afterwards, despite numerous folk invasions, the Latin stamp of people and culture was never to be effaced. This was particularly important in the rich Po Valley, so attractive to invaders and so vulnerable in spite of the deceptive Alpine barrier. But for the thorough Italian settlement in the second and first centuries BC the area might well have remained part of the central European Celtic sphere. In the islands too, despite repeated foreign occupations and Sicily's strong Hellenic traditions, Latin culture emerged triumphant.

## ROMAN GEOGRAPHY

Roman and Latin civilization, despite later urbanization, was in many ways basically agrarian; no civilized ancient people seems to have been less interested in trade and industry. Even when Rome controlled the Mediterranean and the neighbouring countries to the north and east of it, the Romans did not exploit their central position at the waist of the Mediterranean, nor the opportunities for the exchange of manufactures and raw materials with the barbarian northerners. The trading potentialities of Massilia, Syracuse and Messana had been grasped by the Greeks, and those of Gades and Carthage by the Punic peoples, but the Romans with their yeoman traditions and ideals continued to regard agricultural land as the soundest form of wealth. For the senatorial class, whose models were Cincinnatus and Cato, trade was considered unworthy, and even forbidden by law. Land speculation and the pickings offered by pro-consular offices in the provinces were the normal means of enrichment. At no time was a serious attempt made to make Italy or Rome the manufacturing and trading centre of the Empire. In fact, even in Italy as time went on, trade and manufacture were taken over more and more by foreigners, chiefly Greeks, and even the

---

Bernard but Sir Gavin de Beer makes out a convincing case for the Col de la Traversette, at the headwaters of the Po. See *Alps and Elephants*.

[1] Formerly the grant for the ordinary settler seems to have been about five jugera; at Bononia it was fifty (thirty-one acres).

shipping bringing the vital corn supply to Rome was normally of Greek origin.

The traditional Roman farmer, whose passing was so lamented by the statesmen and poets of the Empire, was a peasant proprietor with military obligations in time of war. He farmed normally anything between two and fifteen acres, largely on a subsistence basis, his family, possibly helped by a slave, providing the labour. The main crops were wheat, barley, spelt and beans, and among the richer farmers, vines and olives. Pigs, sheep and goats were the common livestock, and mules, and particularly oxen, were the chief draught animals. Such small holdings provided little opportunity for a numerous family, and in the early days of Rome's expansion there was no shortage of settlers for the colonies founded throughout the Peninsula. Although regarded as the source of the Roman virtues, the Italian small farm had its disadvantages. The bare living it afforded encouraged overcropping, a tendency well illustrated in the Campagna, which even before the influx of cheap grain, was switching over from wheat to grazing and the less exacting olive. Like all small units it was vulnerable to the misfortunes of weather, while the absence of the farmer on military duty, or worse, his death, must have resulted in the selling up of many holdings. There was, therefore, a constant tendency for the breakdown of the egalitarian structure of the nation of peasant farmers. Holdings became bigger and fewer as members of the more prosperous classes competed to invest in land. At the same time the increasing number of landless freemen either drifted into the cities or, after the Marian reforms, enlisted in the hope of a reward in land which would restore their fortunes. The provision of lands for veterans became one of the major worries of the successful general and in the case of Sulla and Octavian led to large-scale confiscations.

The First Punic War not only took a further heavy toll of the yeoman but worsened his economic position. When Sicily was annexed the old colonizing policy was not applied, possibly because of a temporary shortage of settlers, and wealthy Romans took control of large blocks of the available state lands. These became virtually their property and were farmed with slave labour for wheat and wool, to the detriment of olives and vines. The maximum holding was legally fixed at 500 jugera (about 312 acres) but the treasury was glad to tolerate larger holdings in order to maintain revenue, especially as many of the bidders were owed large sums lent to the state during the war. The switch of the Sicilian grain surplus from its former market in Greece to Italy was welcome in Rome where the increasing urban population was taxing local supplies in the Campagna, but elsewhere in accessible coastal areas grain producers found it difficult to compete. The situation was somewhat similar to that in England in the nineteenth century when the English farmer was faced with the competition of American grain.

Latifundia were not confined to Sicily. The consolidation process continued in Apulia, Latium, Etruria, Lucania and Campania, while in the Ager Gallicus in particular large areas of state lands were acquired by capitalists. These estates were not particularly efficient. Slave manpower in the third and second centuries was cheap but wasteful, and could only be used on routine manual tasks needed in grain production and herding; for the more skilled work on vines, olives and fruit trees, free labour had to be hired. Perhaps the greatest asset of slave labour was that it was immune from military service, but the frequent absence of the owner did not make for efficiency, and much depended on the quality and zest of the bailiff, himself usually a freedman. Perhaps the worst feature of the latifundia was the lack of personal interest or responsibility for the land itself which resulted in the 'running down' of many areas suited to grain production. When large-scale grain imports became available, not only from Sicily but also from Sardinia, Africa and Egypt, big producers in Italy tended to switch to sheep, cattle and goat rearing. Huge areas of Apulia, Lucania, and even Sicily, became sparsely populated ranches run by barbarian slave herdsmen (usually Gauls) who formed the backbone of slave revolts in the first century BC. The ancient system of transhumance between the summer mountain pastures and the winter lowland areas (e.g. between the Samnite hills and Apulia) was extended and the special drover routes were protected by law. This development could not fail to have a detrimental effect on the forests.

Fortunately the latifundia did not blanket Italy completely. The Po Valley was largely spared, as were inaccessible areas away from the main routes and the coast, and elsewhere a sprinkling of small and medium-sized farms flourished particularly in the areas suited to the more specialized arboreal culture, e.g. Campania. Even so, between the First Punic War and the time of Augustus, the outstanding feature of Italian agriculture was the squeezing out, not only of the small proprietor, but also of the free labourer from the countryside by non-Italian slaves who were sometimes freedmen set up as squatter tenants on the estate. Of the 15 million inhabitants of Italy at the beginning of the first century AD probably a quarter were of foreign origin, and the tendency for smaller families among the Italian rich, which so alarmed Augustus, was later to spread down the social scale. The cause of the small farmer was not without its champions. Flaminius had advocated the settlement of the Ager Gallicus by the landless poor, but unfortunately this state land ended up, as in Sicily, in the hands of larger owners. The most spectacular attempt to stem the economic flood and rehabilitate the small farmer on former state lands, now firmly in the hands of large owners, was made by the Gracchi, with only modest results. Even the settlement of veterans in Italy was a mixed blessing. Usually the land was acquired by confiscation from political enemies (e.g. Sulla in Campania and Etruria) and existing tenants were ejected, and very often an indifferent farmer replaced a good one. In time veterans' land often found its way back on to the market and the accretion process was resumed. From the time of Marius it became customary for veterans to receive their grants of land in the provinces, thereby further reducing the native-born element in Italy.

These gloomy trends in the Italian countryside, which were to continue and add their share to the social and economic instability of the Empire, should not be allowed to cloud the solid achievements of the Romans in agriculture nor give the impression that sound husbandry was unknown. The relentless attack on the forest was perhaps less completely beneficial than the drainage enterprises of the Romans. The temperamental Lake Fucinus was first drained to the Liri by Claudius, while the Pontine Marshes received the attention in turn of Appius Claudius, Caesar Augustus, Nerva and Trajan, but their efforts were only partially successful. In the Po Valley the Romans continued the work first begun by the Etruscans. The area between the Po and the Apennines east of Placentia was first tackled by Aemilius Scaurus, the road builder, and later efforts in the rest of the valley must have been very successful to judge from the size and prosperity of its many cities and from the wide distribution of centuriation, that typically Roman chessboard system of fields, roads and ditches whose kinship with the modern field pattern is revealed in air photos.

The Italians of the Empire grew a wide variety of crops, the chief gaps in the ancient list of products compared with the modern being maize, rice, oranges, lemons, potatoes, sugar beet, silk and tomatoes. Wheat and barley were the chief grain crops grown to a greater or lesser degree throughout the country where altitude and drainage allowed; rye and millet flourished in the North; oats seems to have been unimportant. Among the fibres, flax was the most important and was grown chiefly in the Po Valley. The widespread growth of tree crops, often on terraces, was very sound in that it not only provided food but counteracted to some extent the evil effects of deforestation. The olive, then as now, was not only useful in providing a crop for rundown stony areas, but because of its small leaf cover, allowed field crops to be grown in its shade in the better regions. Of the fruits, apples (for which the Aquileia area was noted), pears and figs were common from a very early date, and were later supplemented by the introduction from South-east Asia of the apricot, peach, plum, cherry, pomegranate and citron. As today, Campania was famous for intensive irrigated fruit-growing. The vine which the Greeks first popularized in peninsular Italy grew in importance until its further extension was forbidden by the Emperor Domitian (c. AD 90), probably in the interests of grain cultivation. There were few areas in Italy which did not produce some wines but those of Campania (Vesuvian, Pompeian, Faustinian, Falernian, Sorrentine), Latium (Alban Hills, Ardea, Cervetri, Fregellae) and eastern Sicily were particularly renowned. Then as now the Mediterranean climate of the Peninsula presented the farmer with the twin problems of moisture conservation and the recuperation of the soil. The technique widely adopted was to leave arable land in fallow which was kept clear of weeds and ploughed three times in the winter to pulverize the topsoil and so prevent the loss of moisture beneath. The attendant dangers in a country so prone to erosion are obvious. Oddly enough, unless the drainage was good, waterlogging often rendered the soil cold and prevented the germination of winter wheat. Fallowing assured a minimum recuperation but for better yields manuring was vital, and that presented a problem. Despite a surprising variety of fodder crops, which included clover, lucerne (introduced from Persia via Greece), beans, pulses, peas and lupins, as well as hay and tree leaves, the difficulty of providing fodder all the year in a Mediterranean climate limited severely the amount of stock on the farm. The widespread practice of transhumance was no answer as the vital manure was lost to the corn lands. On the better farms, folding, the spreading of wood ash, liming, marling and the ploughing in of green crops and compost was practised to some extent, and the growth of legumes must have helped to maintain fertility, but the development of systematic rotations had to wait many centuries. In the north the fodder problem was easier because of the cultivation of water-meadows and the feeding of barley and spelt to stock. The need for draught animals (and incidentally manure) was met by the ox, mule and horse, although the hoe was as important as the plough even on big farms. Horses were more important militarily than agriculturally, and those of Venetia, Apulia and the Reate Basin were in great demand. As mentioned above, large-scale cattle and sheep rearing became a feature of Roman Italy, particularly in the southern Peninsula, Emilia and central Sicily, and the same areas had the largest concentration of goats. The evil reputation of the latter where trees were concerned was realized by Varro, who recommends owners to forbid goat-grazing on their tenants' land in the interests of saplings. The Italian pig very largely fended for itself in the chestnut and oak forests and was very important in the North.

The agricultural malaise, whose symptoms had been recognized as far back as the Gracchi, became steadily worse under the Empire. The free labourer and free proprietor became increasingly rare as economic pressure continued and as the declining birth rate made itself felt among the poorer classes. The government found itself in the position of having to maintain a policy with contradictory aims. On the one hand political and social necessity demanded the continued import of cheap grain, which was the very policy which had helped to eliminate the free peasant and encourage the spread of latifundia and the disastrous switch to large-scale animal rearing. Even the important exports of oil and wine had declined in the face of provincial production and in the absence of a mercantile policy in favour of the Italian grower. On the other hand it was widely realized that the health of Italy and the Empire depended on the protection of what was left of the small farming class and on the maintenance of agricultural production at a high level in case of a disruption of the overseas grain supply. Even the big estates were feeling the pinch because of the difficulty of obtaining free labour and the increasing expensiveness of slave labour. As long ago as the first century BC Varro had advocated a policy of allowing landless freemen to squat on small plots of the estate in order to have on hand a permanent supply of labour. Under the later Empire this policy became general, the only difference being that, in the absence of adequate free squatters, slaves were freed on the understanding that they remained on the estate. Under Constantine the freeman squatter was finally tied to the land and forced to pay his rent in kind and in labour, and so a system not unlike serfdom was established in the Italian countryside. 'To displace the free peasant by the slave, then the slave by the small tenant, only to end by converting the small tenant into a serf, was part of the Roman fate' (W. E. Heitland). Successive Emperors had tinkered with the problem. Vespasian ceased recruiting in Italy; Domitian tried to check the unhealthy concentration on viticulture; Trajan prohibited Italian emigration to the provinces; Hadrian tried to breathe new life into the old Roman policy of founding colonies in Italy and encouraged squatter tenants on Imperial waste lands; Marcus Aurelius and Aurelian planned to settle barbarians on the waste lands under a military tenure. All these efforts were unavailing against the mounting economic crisis.

The Italy of Augustus was heavily urbanized,[1] and it was a heavy importer not only of wheat, but also of raw materials and manufactures of all kinds. It might be assumed, therefore, that in order to maintain some sort of balance of trade, Italy was herself a correspondingly great exporter and an exploiter of the trading position which geography and politics presented now that the whole Mediterranean Basin and beyond was the Roman sphere. That does not seem to have been the case. We must conclude, therefore, that the necessary invisible exports took the form of tribute, booty, the proceeds from the sale of slaves, provincial lands and mines and revenues from the provinces.

In ancient times the risks and cost of transport were great. Consequently the everyday needs (pottery, textiles, utensils, implements, etc.) were produced by local craftsmen on a small scale or in the home itself, and if an article was to control a large market, it had to be very cheap or vastly superior to the local product. Italy produced comparatively few things which fell into the latter category. The metal industries based on the iron, copper and tin of Etruria, and on local charcoal, remained largely where Etruscan and Greek enterprise had located them; iron smelting at Populonium, Cales, Puteoli, Minturnae (all well placed for the shipment of Elba ore), and Bononia in the north; bronze at Praeneste, Capua and Nola. To judge from its plentiful use in Roman plumbing, lead was cheap and it frequently yielded silver as a by-product of the smelting. One of the main markets for metals was of course the army, but as the legions were stationed more and more on the frontier the manufacture of weapons was undertaken gradually by the provinces. In Italy itself one of the main centres was Arretium, which was also famous for its Arretine ware, one of the few Italian products with a wide overseas market. This pottery, which was also made at Puteoli and in the Po Valley, finally declined in the face of provincial competition. Brick-making and tile-making were carried on universally, but especially at Rome, and the main glass centres were in northern Campania. Except in the case of bricks and tiles the units of production were very small and the workmen, either slaves or freedmen, often of Greek, Asiatic or African origin. It was

[1] Rome itself had nearly 2 million inhabitants, and there were a dozen cities, e.g. Patavium, Verona, Aquileia, Mediolanum and the Campanian ports, which must have approached or passed the 100,000 mark.

common practice for a master to free a craftsman slave and set him up in business as an investment.

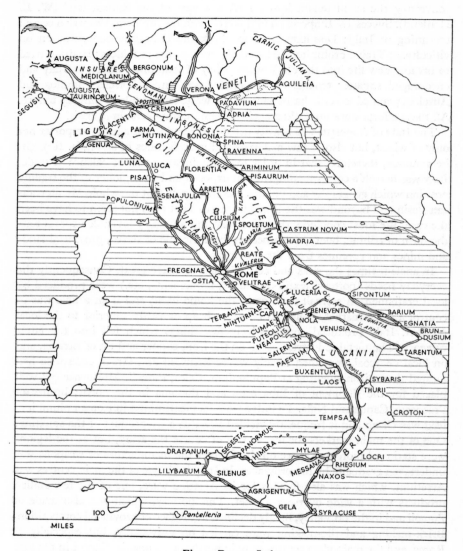

*Fig. 2.* Roman Italy

The main foodstuffs exported from Imperial Italy were oil and wine (and even these faced fierce provincial competition), and the main raw materials marble (Luna), sulphur, alum and salt. There was a good deal of internal trade of course (e.g. Po Valley pork, pitch, flax and timber to the south of Italy and Rome) but it is generally true to say that Italy possessed few outstanding advantages in raw materials, labour or technique which could support a large manufacturing export, or agricultural surpluses or specialities which could not be produced elsewhere in the Mediterranean.

There was another reason for the paucity of Italian exports: the Romans were emphatically not a nation of shopkeepers.[1] The absence of metallic ores in the Campagna, the lack of harbours and navigable rivers, the inland position of Rome, and the preoccupation of all classes with territorial expansion had all helped to prevent the rise of a trading interest. Even the powerful knight class was more interested in contracting, tax farming and land speculation than in ordinary trade, and one of the dangerous aspects of this attitude was the dependence of Rome on foreign shipping. Rome itself was a poor port, and relied on Puteoli until the improvement of Ostia by Claudius; in fact the busiest Roman ports were those of Campania because of the agricultural and manufacturing prosperity of their hinterland. With the complete control of such a vast trading area a mercantile policy favouring Italian industry and agriculture by the setting up of monopolies in certain products would have seemed natural enough, but in the event there were no such safeguards against provincial competition, and in consequence Italian trade suffered. Low tariffs between the provinces made possible the existence of an almost free trade area, and Rome's attitude to trade under the Empire seems to have been as lacking in enthusiasm as when in 348 BC she made a very disadvantageous treaty with Carthage, whose mercantile policy we may guess would have been very different from Rome's had she had the latter's opportunities.

Roman Italy seems to have deprived itself of nothing which could be imported; hides, skins, wool and slaves from Germany through the Alpine passes; fleeces, pork, timber and tin from Gaul through Massilia; tin from Britain via Gades; glass, paper, linen, silks, spices and wild animals through Egypt and Syria; and of course grain from Sicily, Sardinia, Africa and Egypt.

The crisis of the fourth century was of complex origin but revealed itself particularly in its military, fiscal and economic aspects. Prices were rising rapidly as a result of the interruption and shrinkage of trade and insufficient production. The reforming Emperors attacked the problems with legal weapons. Diocletian fixed commodity prices by edict (with the questionable results one would expect in the absence of complete supervision), and in an attempt to force each group in the community to shoulder its Imperial burdens, froze the occupational pattern. In future the craftsman was to remain at his bench and the sailor on his ship; the city patrician could no longer avoid the duties of honorary magistrate, tax-gatherer and recruiting agent; above all the countryman was to remain on the land, whatever his rank, to ensure the production of adequate food. The large landowner too became an agent of the Imperial government, and as conditions deteriorated assumed the rôle of rural aristocrat to whom the countrymen looked

[1] Tarentum had a silver coinage about three centuries before Rome.

for help and protection. In an age devoid of mechanical invention, production depended more directly on manpower, and under Constantine the peasant was shackled to the soil and the mass of the cultivated land of Italy was tilled by countrymen who, whatever their status, were dependent legally or practically on their local lord. Agricultural specialization declined as the trading horizon shrank, and all too often the efficient landowner became the target of the tax-gatherer.[1] And yet despite all these troubles city life in Italy, with its squalor and luxury, its baths and its doles, seems to have flourished up to, and in some cases long after, the onslaught of the barbarian.


## ITALY DURING THE DARK AGES

The twilight of the Empire emphasized the inadequacy of the Alpine barrier as a defence against invasion without the strong arm of a Marius or a Stilicho to confirm it. The low Julian and Carnic Alps were forced in 408 by Alaric's Visigothic host and again in 452 by the Huns under Attila. Ostrogoths, Lombards and Magyars were to reinforce the lesson. Similarly the events of the period underlined the vulnerability of peninsular Italy to a strong sea power. In 440 Sicily had fallen to the Vandals who sacked Rome itself in 455. In the sixth century Sicily and much of the coastland of peninsular Italy were to come under the control of another naval power, Byzantium, and thereafter of the Saracens and Normans. In fact Sicily and at times the adjoining peninsular coast, both of which we tend to regard as essentially part of Italy, lived an existence independent of it. For many centuries to come Sicily was less of an outpost of Italy than a Mediterranean halfway house, as in pre-Roman times, a prize for the dominant sea power whether based in Europe or Africa. The divorce of Sardinia from Italy, until the Middle Ages, was if anything more complete.

The reign of Odovacar was challenged in 489 by Theodoric the Ostrogoth, who, armed with a mandate from the Eastern Emperor, overthrew the Herulian and established an Ostrogothic kingdom which remained secure till his death in 526. This is a convenient point at which to pause and examine the changes wrought by the first century of barbarian invasions on the geography of Italy.

The unity of the Mediterranean trading world had been shattered. The shores of the Western Basin were controlled by barbarians, the most powerful of which on the sea were the piratical Vandals of North Africa, and only in the Eastern Basin did trade continue in any volume under the protection of the Byzantine navy. Italy in the fifth century was thrust back on its own resources. The Egyptian grain export was monopolized by Constantinople, and until Theodoric retook the island, the fields of Sicily were under Vandal domination. Similarly the corn of North Africa and Sardinia was denied to Italy until Justinian's counter-attack in the sixth century. The Alpine passes into Gaul, southern Germany and the

---

[1] Italian land was first taxed in the second century AD, and this reflects a stage in the worsening fiscal conditions of the Empire.

Danubian lands, formerly Roman provinces, were as likely to bring invaders as traders to the populous north Italian towns, although there was a temporary amelioration under Theodoric who controlled the central and eastern Alps.

In the countryside the Roman landowner remained and the Roman system of tillage was to continue little changed in fundamentals until the Middle Ages. Not that he was left undisturbed. Raiding, requisitioning and brigandage were the normal hazards of the time, and in the more settled periods wherever barbarian troops happened to be established they were allotted a third of the land.[1] This affected the northern landowners most as the Northern Plain was the main area of barbarian settlement, and to some extent acted as a spillway for the flood of barbarian rapacity, thus indirectly protecting the Peninsula. It is impossible to gauge accurately the extent of early barbarian settlement and its effect on the racial composition of Italy. The Visigothic and Hun raids certainly had little permanent influence, and the varying estimates of Theodoric's host never exceed 250,000 and many of their descendants were to be uprooted for ever from Italian soil as a result of the Byzantine 'triumph' in the Gothic War (536–53). It may well be that the most important pre-Lombard barbarian element was furnished by those mercenaries who were settled on wastelands during the last two centuries of the Empire, and who were well established and partially Romanized by the fifth century.

It seems certain that the population of Italy during the fifth century, although denser than anywhere else in Europe, was at best static, and probably on the decline. The descendants of slaves of Greek, Asiatic, Syrian, African and Spanish origin probably represented a higher proportion than those of Germanic stock. War, famine, and above all plague had played their allotted rôle. Even in the ordered and, by ancient standards, sanitary Empire of the second century a virulent epidemic of smallpox caused cities to be abandoned in the reign of Antoninus; in 250 bubonic plague and in 313 anthrax had depopulated the countryside. The influx of invaders from the plague spots of eastern Europe (e.g. the Huns), the filth of warfare and the decay of Roman public works caused epidemics to be almost a yearly risk, and worse was to follow in the sixth century when the ghastly plague of Justinian (bubonic) raged intermittently for fifty years. Extensive areas reverted to waste particularly in the North, where to the decay of the drainage system were added natural disasters, as in 589 when the Adige at Este shifted its channel nine miles southwards. The laudable efforts of Theodoric to drain the Pontine Marshes and restore Roman public works, particularly the corn ports and the aqueducts (e.g. at Ravenna), were not typical of the period as a whole. The barbarians contributed nothing to agricultural technique, and specialization tended to decline as transport difficulties increased and the trading horizon shrank.

Bearing in mind the decay of the economic, social and administrative conditions which had encouraged their growth, the surprising thing is, not that the cities

---

[1] Some historians maintain this refers only to the public lands.

declined, but that their decline was not more rapid. The cities of the Northern Plain which felt the initial fury of invasion time after time, descended into the Dark Ages by a series of steps rather than in one great leap. In quieter periods they often regained some of their importance as the countryside recovered and trade trickled back. The ponderous machine of Roman administration, which was made use of by the barbarians, was centred on the towns and ploughed on by sheer momentum long after the original motive power had gone. Many of the northern cities rose many times from their ruins because of the natural richness of their surroundings and the permanent importance of the routes they controlled. Such was Milan, originally a Celtic foundation which in the fourth century had rivalled Rome in size, and, as the home of St Ambrose, in ecclesiastical influence. Sustained by the rich farms of Lombardy, it lived through sack by Visigoths and Huns, and became one of the centres of the Ostrogothic and later the Lombard power. Padua, which in Roman times was little less important than Milan, survived to become one of Europe's centres of learning. The strategic importance of Verona assured its continuance and it was for a time a favourite residence of Theodoric. Pavia was privileged to be chosen as an Ostrogoth and later as a Lombard capital, and maintained a law school which trained the administrators the barbarians lacked. Aquileia was exceptional in that it was destroyed by the Huns never to rise again. On the other hand refugees flying from the Huns found safety in the islands of the Adriatic lagoons, and so laid the foundations of Venice, while Ravenna which had been a major Roman naval base became increasingly important. Practically impregnable from the landward side, it controlled the Via Aemilia route westwards into Lombardy and southwards into the Peninsula. Honorius, Odovacar and Theodoric were at pains to possess it, and under the Byzantines it became the pivot of their power in Italy. Ravenna's rise underlined the decay of Rome, now no longer the capital of the Empire nor even of Italy. For centuries it had lived less on its immediate surroundings than on the corn and tribute of distant lands, and if it survived into the Middle Ages, shrunken within its ruins, it did so because of new-found subsidies from all Christendom. The classical city received its *coup de grâce* when the Goths besieging Belisarius cut the aqueducts. The uncontrolled waters contributed to the degeneration of parts of the Campagna into a malarial wilderness.

The defeat and expulsion of the Goths from Italy by the Greeks between 536 and 553 reduced the cities and countryside to desolation. This was Italy's nadir even in the Dark Ages. Byzantine control had barely lasted a decade when the Germanic Lombards under Alboin invaded North Italy through the vulnerable Friuli march (568), and for roughly two centuries Italy was to be divided between the hostile powers of Lombards centred on Pavia with semi-independent duchies of Friuli, Spoleto and Beneventum, on the one hand, and the Greeks entrenched at Ravenna and a number of isolated areas round the coast, on the other.

Unlike the Ostrogoths the Lombards came unashamedly as conquerors. There was no pretence of restoring the Empire and the Italians were regarded not as 'hosts' but as the vanquished. Fewer in numbers than the Ostrogoths they can have altered the racial make-up of Italy very little except possibly in their main stronghold round Pavia, Monza and Milan. A semi-nomadic people settled in clans (*fara*) at strategic points, for decades they remained scornfully aloof from the Italians. How far their demands were satisfied by the extensive wastelands left by the Gothic wars it is impossible to say. Church foundations, which had become the biggest landowners, certainly suffered in the early days, but by the eighth century the Lombards had mellowed, and having forsaken Arianism became generous benefactors of the Church. Unlike their predecessors the Lombards eventually took to town life, and those settlements whose names end in -*engo* and -*fara* owe them their origin.

The political decline of the Lombards came in the mid-eighth century when the Papacy invited the Catholic Franks into Italy, but Beneventum remained virtually independent till 840. After the end of the Carolingian line in 888, Lombard power revived and was not extinguished until 962 when Otto asserted his Imperial rights in Italy. By that time the Lombards had mingled with the Italians and their own language had become extinct without influencing greatly that of the Italians.

The intrusion of the Lombards shattered the unity of Italy so painfully built up by the Romans. Not only did they occupy the North and most of the Centre, but those areas left to the Byzantines were now oriented eastwards and seawards into the orbit of the greatest existing commercial and maritime power. Sicily was administered independently from Syracuse as a theme of the Empire; Sardinia (and Corsica) came under the Exarch of Africa, and the scattered districts of the peninsula, under the Exarch at Ravenna, turned their backs on the Lombard interior. From bases on both sides the Byzantines controlled the Adriatic sea lane, and from Sicily and Calabria they dominated the waist of the Mediterranean like the ancient Greeks before them. In the northern peninsula their power depended on holding the Via Flaminia route between Rome and Ravenna which isolated the Duchies of Spoleto and Beneventum from the main centre of Lombard power in the North.

Until the Saracen threat developed in the ninth century, the Byzantine areas enjoyed participation in the trading sphere of the Eastern Empire. As in the days of Magna Graecia, Apulia exported her wines, oil, wool and grain (often in Venetian bottoms); Sicily her grain, fleeces, timber, oil, alum, sulphur and papyrus; Calabria her ship timber. Linen manufactures flourished at Naples on local flax, and silk-weaving in Syracuse and other Sicilian cities after the introduction of the silk-worm (the mulberry had already been established by the Ancient Greeks). Increasing commitments elsewhere caused the Byzantines to lean heavily on local militias led by native notables who sometimes became *de facto* hereditary rulers, over whom Constantinople exercised only a shadowy suzerainty. These conditions favoured the emergence of such trading cities as Naples, Gaeta, Amalfi, and above all Venice, and a beginning was made in the commercial development of Italy which was to replace the Greek by the Italian as the middle-man of Europe. The Campanian cities traded with Sicily, Africa and the Levant, and missed few opportunities to enrich themselves whether at the expense of

*Fig. 3.* The Byzantine lands *c.* 600 are shaded; the variety of shading indicates to whom the territories were lost

Christian or Infidel. In those troublous times, when slaves were considered a normal article of commerce, the margin between war and piracy, trade and treachery, was a narrow one.[1] After a brief period of brilliance during which she

[1] In 843, the Neapolitans helped the Muslims to reduce the Byzantine fortress of Messina.

developed the compass and produced a body of mercantile law (Tabula Amalfitana) Amalfi, like Gaeta, submitted to the Normans and eventually declined in the face of Pisan competition. Venice, isolated in her lagoons, had built up a near-monopoly in the salt trade, and thanks to the privileges received from the Emperor, had developed trading connections with the eastern Mediterranean by the ninth century, and proved herself strong enough to keep open the Adriatic lifeline against both Saracen and Dalmatian pirates.

Harassed by Lombard, Frank, Saracen and Norman, the Byzantine grip on Italy loosened. Liguria succumbed early to the Lombards (642); by 756 most of the Ravenna–Rome strip had come under Papal control and Sicily fell to the Saracens between 829 and 902. By 1000, apart from her nominal suzerainty over Venetia and the Campanian cities, only Calabria and Apulia remained, and these were frequently harassed and even occupied by the Muslims.

The Muslim period in southern Italy and Sicily, like the Byzantine, further emphasized the Mediterranean, non-Italian, geographical associations of the area. On the mainland, where the Saracens were never firmly enough established to be more than pirates in force, the Saracen experience was one of unrelieved catastrophe. From bases in Bari (taken 840) and Taranto they plundered and terrorized the southern Peninsula until the fortunate revival of Byzantine power in the later ninth century. Their last stronghold (on the Garigliano) was destroyed by the Pope only in 915. In Sicily, after the initial period of slaughter and destruction the island settled down under Muslim rule and reached a standard of prosperity and cultural brilliance unequalled since the Hellenic period.

Like the Phoenicians, the Muslims landed in the west, took Palermo in 831 and by 878, when Syracuse fell, the island was practically theirs. The immigrants who came over from Africa, chiefly Arabs in the Palermo area and Berbers in the south and east, were numerous enough to modify the racial composition of the island, and they brought with them new crops and techniques. Intensive irrigated cultivation revived and diversified Sicilian agriculture, and the newly introduced crops, sugar, dates, cotton, oranges, lemons and rice, were added to the traditional exports of wheat, fleeces, oil and timber. In the towns the manufacture of silk, linen, leather and metal goods and the building of ships flourished as never before. Palermo, particularly famous for its metal work and shipbuilding, became the most prosperous port on the Tyrrhenian and replaced Syracuse as the capital, an honour it retained under the tolerant and capable rule of the Normans.

## ITALY DURING THE MIDDLE AGES

By the eleventh century the West had absorbed and tamed her barbarian invaders; the new pattern of Europe in which Catholic civilization provided the

---

In 849 their participation in the battle off Ostia helped to save Rome from a second Saracen plundering.

dominant motif was beginning to emerge from the obscurity of the earlier centuries; the Germans were on the offensive in the east, the Spaniards and Normans in the south. In Italy, Byzantine and Muslim control in the south had come to an end, and an improving economic situation in northern Europe and a more favourable strategic position in the Mediterranean made possible a revolution in the geography of the country, the most important features of which were a growth in the population, and the emergence of prosperous trading and manufacturing cities rivalling those of Roman Italy in size and surpassing them in wealth.

Medieval Italy was fortunate in that she lay between the Levant termini of the great Asiatic trade routes on the one hand, and the main market in north-west Europe on the other. Her access to the Levant was made easier by the counteroffensive of the Christian powers against the Muslims which found its most obvious expression in the Crusades, while the market for luxury goods in the towns and courts of Europe, both lay and ecclesiastical, expanded with more cultivated tastes and more settled times. Of the return trade the most important commodities were English wool, and later, woollens, Flemish linens and cloth, slaves from east German frontier wars, furs and metal. Vast fairs were held in Champagne and Brie to facilitate exchange between Europe's two most economically developed areas, north Italy on the one hand and north France, the Low Countries and south-east England on the other. These fairs lost much of their importance in the fourteenth century because of the wars between Flanders and France and the development of the sea route from Italy to the Channel. What Rheims and Troyes lost London and Antwerp gained.

A compelling influence in the rise of Italian trade and industry was the growth of population in the country, in common with most of the rest of Europe, despite the catastrophic setbacks with which the period is studded. Although Italy was already (c. 1000) the most heavily populated sizeable area in Europe, she lacked the plentiful wastelands of France and England and the expansible frontier of Germany and Spain. The numerous unprovided sons of the lesser nobility sought their opportunity in trade and finance, which came to be regarded not only as a lucrative activity but also as an honourable one. Similarly the surplus rural population swelled the artisan classes of the towns, which in turn provided a demand for specialized commercial products such as flax, silk, wool and hides. The Italians became the middlemen of Europe, and were found wherever a deal could be made from London to Pekin, and from the Baltic to the Niger. They managed the opulent finances of the Vatican, acted as advisers to foreign kings[1] and successfully challenged the Jewish banking monopoly. Humbler folk found an outlet for their talents as mercenary soldiers, sailors and artisans.

Economic developments were very unevenly spread over Italy. With the exception of Venice, the early pioneer cities of the Italian commercial revival,

---

[1] The Florentine Franzenzi brothers to Philip the Fair; the Genoese Pessagno to Edward II of England.

Amalfi, Naples, Gaeta, Bari and Salerno, began to decline relatively in the twelfth century. Too remote from the main new centres of activity in the North, they were absorbed politically in to the Norman kingdom whose enmity with the Eastern Empire excluded them from the valuable privileges of trading in that sphere. Amalfi, crippled by a Pisan attack (1135), was finally laid low by the great storm and earthquake of 1343. Ravenna had succumbed to the Franks and was steadily silting up. Even Palermo was no longer so well placed now that the commercial centre of gravity of Europe had shifted northwards. The future lay with Pisa, Genoa and Venice.

In the tenth century the Western Basin of the Mediterranean was almost a Muslim lake. Spain south of Barcelona, all North Africa, Sicily and most of Sardinia and Corsica, and even Garde Fresnet on the Provence coast, were still in the hands of the Infidel. Not that the Muslims were united, nor was trade with the Christians entirely at a standstill, but in the eleventh century a radical change in the situation was accomplished which was to end with the restoration of all but the African coast to the Christian powers. In this revolution Pisa and Genoa were the most powerful agencies.

Pisa, unlike its early rival Amalfi, had not enjoyed the benefit of Byzantine connections, and in the tenth century was almost entirely agricultural. As late as 1004 the Saracens had sacked the town, yet within sixty years of that event Pisa and her ally, Genoa, had driven the Muslims from Corsica and Sardinia, attacked the Tunisian corsair base of Mehdia, and assisted the Norman conquest of Sicily by capturing Palermo. These operations were followed by trading ventures in the Levant and as a result of the First Crusade (1095) Pisa secured trading quarters in Constantinople, Laodicea, Sidon, Alexandria and Cairo whence came the riches which built the city's architectural glories. Unfortunately this splendid prosperity was insecure. A traditional Ghibelline stronghold, she was prevented from fully exploiting the natural advantages of her position by the jealous enmity of Guelf Lucca and Florence. Overseas, after crushing Amalfi (c. 1135) she lost ground to Genoa and the defeat of the Pisan fleet at Meloria (1282) was decisive.[1] Florence became increasingly implacable, and in 1406 bought and developed Leghorn as the natural outlet of Tuscany.

Genoa possessed an excellent deep-water harbour, was sheltered to some extent by the Apennines, through which the low Giovi and Bocchetta passes gave access to the rich Po basin, and, unlike Pisa, had no rival within the immediate environs. Unfortunately medieval Genoa did not have the unhindered communications with central Europe and the Rhinelands which the modern city enjoys. Some Genoese traffic did use the Mt Cenis and St Bernard passes to Champagne when political conditions were favourable in Piedmont, but tolls made the route increasingly expensive, while the central Alpine routes were monopolized for Milan's benefit. Furthermore, Genoa's position in relation to

---

[1] The danger of silting on the lower Arno was increased by the action of the Genoese in dropping stone blocks at the mouth.

north-west Europe tended to be outflanked by the Rhône waterway route. It is not surprising therefore that Genoa pioneered the all-sea route to Bruges, Antwerp and London, which was first used about 1277. The immediate hinterland was not greatly productive but the decline of the Saracens at the beginning of the eleventh century enabled Genoa to bring Corsica and Sardinia within her orbit and open up trade with southern France, Spain, Sicily and North Africa. Genoa's first convoys to the Levant sailed in 1065, and her assistance in the First Crusade was rewarded by the establishment of factories. The presence of Genoa's fleet in the eastern Mediterranean not only earned the enmity of Pisa, but also of Venice, particularly when the Genoese began to poach in the latter's special preserve, Egypt.

In the mid-thirteenth century Genoa thrust herself into the lucrative Black Sea trading area where Venice had enjoyed a near-monopoly since the Latin seizure of Constantinople in the Fourth Crusade (1204). The restoration of the Greeks to power in 1261 enabled the Genoese to replace their Venetian rivals, and they later so dominated the truncated Empire from their fortified suburb in Galata, that they were able not only to usurp the normal Black Sea trade but also the local fisheries, the privilege of victualling the capital and the very tolls of the Bosphorus itself. For centuries Constantinople had been the mart for the raw materials of southern Russia and the luxuries of the East arriving overland through numerous intermediaries. About 1250 the Black Sea trading horizon was vastly and miraculously extended. For almost a century priests and merchants were able to travel to Cathay across the Mongol Empire straddling Eurasia from the Carpathians to the Pacific. At the western terminal of this Mongol route the Genoese established factories at Tana and Kaffa, the fatal city from which the Black Death spread to Europe. By the end of the fourteenth century the curtain had already fallen again.

Meanwhile Genoa persevered in other spheres. Sailings to Sicily and Spain, to the Balearics, Ceuta and Tunis continued. In Cyprus, whose importance was enhanced by the loss of the last of the Crusader footholds on the mainland, the Genoese for a time monopolized the entrepôt trade with the neighbouring coast; ventures beyond the Mediterranean brought them to the Canaries (discovered 1277) where sugar became the most important crop, and to the Channel ports where wool and cloth were exchanged for oriental and Italian luxuries. But by 1400 the star of Genoa was waning fast. The prolonged struggle with Venice had sapped her strength, and, worse still, faction within the city had invited the intervention of Milan and France. Venice was left supreme.

Venice pre-dated and outlived all her Italian rivals. The refugees from the prosperous mainland cities who fled before the waves of barbarian invaders between the fifth and eighth centuries found safety in the lagoons and islands which stretched from Grado to Comacchio, where their persecutors, with their eyes on easier game, thought it unwise or unprofitable to follow, and where the sea power of the Eastern Empire managed to preserve a vestige of its authority.

26

Of the numerous coastal settlements, Grado, Heraclea and Malamocco[1] seem to have been pre-eminent in turn until the concentration of population in the Rialto–Giudecca group of islands, which was to be Venice, in the eighth century.

Given the conditions of the time, seldom has a city enjoyed greater geographical advantages or exploited them more skilfully. Its strong defensible position, its isolation and at first its insignificance, gave a certain immunity from interference from the mainland and allowed its inhabitants to develop on their natural element, the sea. A small tidal range helped to keep the channels in the lagoon free from silt, and rendered it comparatively healthy by discouraging the breeding of mosquitoes. For a time, however, water supplies were a problem and this necessitated expensive well-digging and storage.[2]

Venice's earliest trade was in fish, salt from the lagoons, and amber from the Baltic, a traffic in which she seems to have been heir to Aquileia. The disreputable trade in slaves (chiefly Slavs imported through Pola from the German-Slav frontier lands), often sold to Muslims, contributed largely to Venice's wealth despite Papal thunderings and some hypocritical legislation. The Byzantine connection soon provided opportunities in the carrying trade and an introduction to Eastern commerce. At this time Venice had the best of both worlds. She was in Italy but not of it; she enjoyed the advantages of the Eastern Empire without its onerous exactions.

The quickening tempo of trade which began to be felt in the tenth century revealed the wider geographical advantages of her position. The Adriatic itself provided a prosperous field in Dalmatian ship timber and in Apulian oil, wool and grain, much in demand in Constantinople, with which city it was so essential for Venice to maintain uninterrupted communications. The Adriatic sea lane (the Sea of Venice) was her most vital concern and involved her in successful wars with pirates from the Dalmatian coast, with Saracen corsairs based on Bari, and with the Normans who succeeded the Byzantines in Apulia and who more than once threatened to occupy permanently both sides of the Gulf of Otranto. The acquisition of the coastline and islands (with the exception of Ragusa) from Istria to Cattaro was a necessary condition of her eastward expansion and was achieved in the eleventh century, although frequently challenged afterwards.

Venice's hinterland offered opportunities which she had seized from the earliest times, and which became even more precious with the economic developments of the eleventh and twelfth centuries in north-west Europe on the one hand, and the Levant on the other; and she managed to do this without sacrificing the advantages of her isolation.

Although far from ideal navigable rivers, the Po, Brenta and Piave carried a large volume of traffic, and were to be preferred to the roads. Charlemagne, Lothaire and Charles the Fat, by granting Venice special navigational privileges,

---

[1] The Malamocco referred to here was situated on the Po delta.
[2] Montaigne in 1580 remarked on the boats bringing water for drinking and dyeing into the city at a crown per load.

had enabled her to establish merchant 'colonies' on the mainland at an early date, while her seaboard rivals in the river traffic, Comacchio and Chioggia, were brought under control and their interests subordinated to those of Venice.[1] A speech by the Doge Tomaso Mocenigo (1413–23) gives us a glimpse of the importance of the Po Valley trade in the heyday of the city. According to him,

> The Florentines bring to Venice each year 16,000 bales of the finest cloth which is sold in Naples, Sicily and the East. They export wool, silk, gold, silver and sugar to the value of 392,000 ducats in Lombardy. Milan spends annually in Venice 90,000 ducats; Monza 56,000 ducats; Como, Tortona, Cremona 104,000 ducats each; Bergamo 78,000, Piacenza 52,000; Alessandria della Paglia 56,000, and in their turn they import into Venice cloth to the value of 900,000 ducats.

Although interested in all the Alpine passes, it was in relation to those of the eastern Alps that Venice was particularly favoured. The Brenner, the gateway to Germany, could be approached either up the Adige or up the Val Sugana or up the Piave and so along the Puster Thal. The Adige was navigable for small boats below Rovereto, but the easy route it provided could not be fully exploited until the difficult section near Chiusa had been improved (*c.* 1320) and until Venice controlled Verona in the early fifteenth century. Along these routes the Venetians sent not only their oriental wares,[2] but also their own manufactures, in particular glass, and gold and silver ware, and salt. Metals, wool, wine, foodstuffs, and in the later Middle Ages, fustians for re-export from Venice, provided the return traffic.

The expansion of Venetian power overseas falls into four main periods. In the first Venice, still careful to maintain the valuable Byzantine connection, succeeded in dominating the Adriatic in the face of Moslem, Narentine and Norman opposition. In the second, that of the early Crusades, she secured trading privileges in Tyre, Sidon, Acre and Constantinople, and considerable earnings as the major carrier of the Crusaders. In the third, Venice revenged herself on her ancient protector, Byzantium, for the ill-treatment of the large Venetian merchant community in Constantinople, by turning the Fourth Crusade against the Greek Empire, and so acquired strategically placed islands (e.g. Crete, Negroponte and the Cyclades) and ports of call in the Morea and elsewhere, as well as a dominating position in the Straits. These gains furnished excellent bases for the Levant,

---

[1] In 1142 the diversion of the Brenta which threatened to silt up the lagoon involved Venice in war with Padua, and eventually the river was canalized to do the minimum of harm.

[2] A selection of the oriental wares so frequently referred to may be helpful:

Textiles: Persian and Chinese silks; damask; Byzantine velvets and taffeta; Indian cottons and muslins; Cypriot cloth of gold; Persian carpets; Syrian purples.

Spices: South-east Asian cloves, cinnamon, cassia, ginger, cardamon, saffron, sugar, nutmeg.

Textile raw materials: Asia Minor alum; Indian indigo and logwood.

Jewels: Persian pearls; Indian stones.

Perfumes etc.: Red Sea incense, myrrh, spikenard; Tibetan musk; South-east Asian camphor, sandalwood.

Also Russian furs, wax; South-east Asian ivory and ebony.

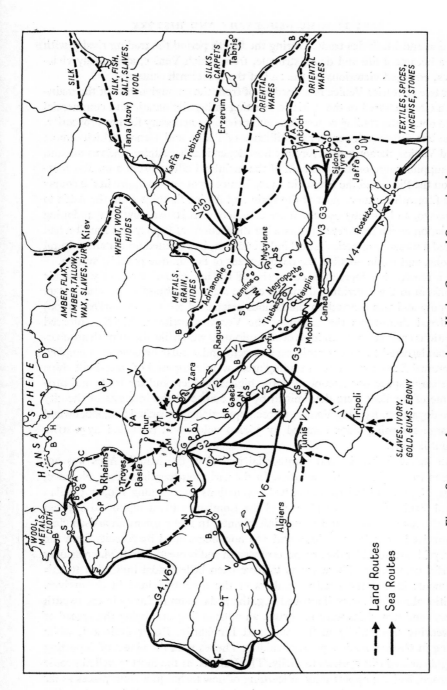

*Fig. 4. Summary of routes concentrating on Venice, Genoa and Constantinople*

V1 Dalmatia (timber, slaves, fish). V2 S. Italy and Sicily (oil, grain, wine, timber, sulphur). V3 Levant (textiles, alum, spices, jewels). V4 Egypt (incense, spices, jewels). V5 Constantinople and Black Sea (Oriental manufactures, silks, salt, slaves, grain, fish). V6 Flanders and England (wool, woollens, metals). V7 N. Africa (ivory, slaves, gold, gums). G1 Corsica and Sardinia (timber, wools, metals). G2 S. Italy, Sicily, N. Africa. G3 Cyprus and Levant. G4 S. France, Spain and Channel. G5 Constantinople and Black Sea

Egyptian and Black Sea trade. During the fourth period the trading rivalry with Genoa became a life and death struggle, from which Venice, after many vicissitudes, emerged victorious by the end of the fourteenth century.

For five centuries Venice remained aloof from the entanglements of the mainland, a city anchored in the Adriatic, trusting in her diplomatic and commercial skill to obtain the trading concessions and privileges necessary for her prosperity. In the late fourteenth century the alliance of Padua and Genoa, which almost ruined Venice, demonstrated forcibly how dependent her Alpine trade routes and food supplies were on the goodwill of the mainland cities. From a modest foothold on the Piave and the Brenta in 1400, Venice went on to acquire in the course of the fifteenth century, most of the Plain and Alpine foothills from the Adda to the Isonzo, and thereby became more completely an Italian power, abandoning an isolation which had served to spare her the factions of Papacy and Empire, had ensured a measure of ecclesiastical independence, had opened up distant cultural horizons, and made possible the development of her unique political system.

To a remarkable degree the enterprise of the individual merchant was made to conform to the overriding demands of the state. Shipbuilding became a state monopoly and was centred on the famous arsenal whose 16,000 workers (1400) considered themselves the cream of the Venetian artisans. Rigidly enforced regulations ensured the soundness of all equipment which like the ships themselves was standardized to ensure rapid replacement and similar behaviour in convoy. The annual fleets for the main trading areas were composed of state-built ships whose cargo space was auctioned to the highest bidder, and the route and programme of the fleet were determined by the Senate in the interests of the city before departure. By 1400 Venice, whose population approached 200,000, owned 330 large sea-going ships manned by 36,000 sailors and regulated by a strict mercantile code.

The Italian industrial and commercial revival in the Middle Ages was not confined to the great maritime cities. In the early fourteenth century Florence, Genoa, Naples and Palermo each had populations approaching 100,000; Milan rivalled Venice for the first place, and the Lombardy Plain supported a dozen cities of between 20,000 and 50,000 inhabitants. In many towns an artisan class had survived since Roman times and was now augmented by recruits from the countryside attracted by the prospects of wealth and protection in the increasingly powerful communes. There seems to have been little feudal inhibition to this movement; indeed the needy members of the nobility joined in themselves. Traditional methods were improved (e.g. the pedal loom in Lucca in the twelfth century) and new skills were imported, an outstanding case being the spread of silk-weaving from Sicily to Tuscany and Lombardy. Roger Guiscard, while warring in Greece, made a point of raiding Thebes with the object of deporting its highly skilled silk workers to Sicily. The Italians, as the most travelled people of Europe, had the opportunity of learning of new techniques from places as far apart as Damascus and Bruges, and received the stimulus to design and quality which came from handling the best in merchandise from the whole civilized world. The Church, the numerous petty but none the less luxurious courts, and the most prosperous bourgeoisie in Europe, provided a substantial home market, while experienced merchants, who knew where to place Italy's wares, afforded the financial machinery for export and manufacture.

The wool industry had been important in Roman times, based on local but not particularly high-grade fleeces, and it had survived the centuries of invasions. The industry was widespread, but as with industry as a whole, the main concentrations were to be found on the Northern Plain at Como, Bergamo, Brescia, Mantua, Treviso, Venice, Parma, Modena, and not least, Milan. Tuscany provided a second concentration at Siena, Pisa, Prato and Florence. It was only in the fourteenth century that Italian output seriously challenged that of Flanders and northern France. Until then the emphasis had been on the finishing and dyeing of imported cloth from northern Europe and on the production of coarse cloths for the Eastern market. Genoa, Florence and Lucca were noted in this trade. Better quality demanded better raw materials from England, Spain and Portugal, and it is significant that Papal dues were often paid in wool and their collection was frequently farmed out to Italian merchants operating from London, Bruges and Antwerp. The wool industry of Florence deserves special mention, not only because powerful banking houses were based on its transactions, but because its profits provided the means of converting the city into one of the foremost artistic and architectural centres of all time. As elsewhere the finishing industry, using north European cloth, pre-dated the weaving industry, and was organized by the Calimala Guild taking its name from the Calle Mala.[1] In the thirteenth century the production of all-Italian cloths increased under the aegis of the Wool Guild and by 1400, 30,000 workers in 300 workshops were producing 100,000 pieces yearly, compared with the 20,000 pieces of the Calimala. The opposed interests of the two guilds engendered a conflict which resulted in the banning of cloth imports in the fifteenth century and so in victory for the local producers. The prosperity of the Wool Guild, whose patronage contributed largely to the building of the cathedral, was far from untroubled. Quite apart from natural catastrophes like the Black Death, the embargo on the export of English wool necessitated a switch to other sources; foreign competition, especially from England, became increasingly severe; and the Hundred Years War damaged Florentine banking and wool interests in an area where they were particularly committed. Second in importance among the textiles was the manufacture of silk. The technique had been imported into Sicily by the Byzantines and had been developed by the Moslems particularly at Palermo. By the thirteenth century it had spread to Pisa, Genoa, Venice and Lucca. The latter's early pre-eminence was later challenged by Florence, Venice and Milan. Gradually Italy replaced the Levant as the chief source of silk cloths, and in the interests of home producers Venice put an embargo on imported silks in 1490.

[1] Ugly street.

Linen was manufactured in the two main flax producing areas, Campania and the Po Valley, which also produced hemp.

Iron smelting, based on small local deposits and on imports, flourished at the main ports, particularly at Venice, but Brescia, Bergamo, and above all Milan achieved a European reputation for weapons and armour in the later Middle Ages. Venice dominated the shipbuilding industry although Genoa and the Ligurian ports, Naples, Bari and Palermo contributed their share. Soap manufacture based on olive oil was widespread in Tuscany and the South, and Sicily was noted for its leather. The prosperity of the little town of Fabriano was based on paper-making, for which its waters were particularly suitable.

Industrial and commercial development in medieval Italy were very unevenly spread and despite the early brilliance of Amalfi, Naples, Bari and Palermo, the balance tipped steadily in favour of the North. A similar tendency with which it is not unconnected may be observed in the agricultural development. The South provided tracts of fairly easily won land which had been worked from very early times. Under the Romans a pattern of agriculture had evolved and this pattern remained essentially unchanged throughout the Middle Ages. The Roman latifundia, worked by inefficient serf labour and concentrating on wheat and olive production, changed little in fundamentals when a Norman or Angevin feudal lord took over control. The dangers of Saracen incursions, the continental wars and general lawlessness of the times resulted in the concentration of agricultural population in villages and small towns, usually built round the lord's castle for defence and high up to avoid the fevers of the lowlands, and this remains a feature of settlement in many southern areas. Transhumance and the old-established extensive sheep-rearing industry remained firmly entrenched and were protected by Byzantine, Norman and Hohenstaufen alike. Of the intensive and diversified areas Campania 'Felix' remained the most important. Sicily reached a peak of prosperity under the Normans and Ferdinand II, growing even sugar and cotton, only to slump back gradually into its earlier rôle as producer of grain, hides and skins, timber and wine.

Land in the North was less easily won, particularly in the Arno and Po Basins, but once cultivated it gave a generous reward. The Romans had gone far in taming the latter area, but during the Dark Ages much of it had reverted to marsh and forest, and engineering works once destroyed were seldom replaced. During the Middle Ages, despite frequent catastrophes, as when in 1151 the detritus load of the torrential Panaro diverted the mass of the Po's waters from the Po di Volano into the more northerly Po Grande channel, the lost ground was more than made good. Small-scale drainage and clearance were effected by landowners who offered the reclaimed areas to tenants at low rents or rewarded their labours with part of it as an outright grant, but reclamation in these areas lent itself less to isolated ventures than to large-scale organization, and in this the religious orders, especially the Cistercians, and the increasingly powerful municipalities, played a major part. In the twelfth century the course of the lower

Brenta was straightened and controlled by levees, and about 1300 the Po was newly dyked from its junction with the Oglio to Ostiglia. On higher ground above the fens where irrigation was possible the Cistercians built the Chiaravalle Canal near Milan and the commune of that city had completed the La Muzza Canal by 1239 and the Naviglio Grande soon after. In 1400 the Milan–Pavia Canal was constructed by the orders of Gian Galeazzo Visconti. Reclamation was not confined to the Po Valley; much of the fen round Lucca was drained; attempts, albeit unsuccessful, were made to reopen the Roman conduits draining Lake Fucino in 1240; Popes Boniface VIII and Martin V made efforts to reclaim parts of the Pontine Marshes; and in 1341 by digging channels to the Arno the commune of Arezzo began the long struggle to drain the Val di Chiana to the north. The

*Fig. 5.* Irrigation canals in the Northern Plain

industrial cities were a great stimulus to agriculture; they drained off the surplus rural population, provided the drive and money for reclamation, and encouraged the intensive cultivation of foodstuffs and raw materials, e.g. Romagna flax and hemp, Sicilian and Calabrian silk, Abruzzi wool and saffron. The intensification demanded in the neighbourhood of the big towns was made possible not only by the natural fertility of the alluvial soils, but also because irrigation enabled large numbers of livestock to be kept which provided the manure, the lack of which had always been a problem in the purely Mediterranean area farther south. Green manuring, too, was advocated as early as the thirteenth century by Pietro dei Crescenzi. In contrast to the South where feudal tenures were more firmly established, many cultivators in north-central Italy were virtually peasant proprietors by the thirteenth century. *Mezzadria* in various forms also became increasingly widespread in the Middle Ages. The demesne land was usually worked by tenants who paid higher rents for the privilege, and then, as now, the

33

land worked by any one peasant was seldom consolidated. The labour situation in the countryside was rudely disrupted in the later fourteenth century by the Black Death. Temporarily at least much land went out of cultivation, and in the territories of Florence married men were exhorted to rent land and farm it on their own account rather than work as labourers.

## FROM THE RENAISSANCE TO THE EIGHTEENTH CENTURY

With the passing of the glorious Quattrocento the petty Italian states were reduced to pawns in the struggle between the French and Imperial forces as a result of which Italy was subjected to Spanish domination for nearly two centuries. Of no less importance than the political eclipse of Italy was the gradual change in her geographical significance in the world. The Age of Discovery, which ironically enough her scholars and practical seamen had done so much to promote, was slowly shifting the commercial centre of gravity to the Atlantic seaboard and opening new horizons from which Italy was excluded. Until the opening of the Suez Canal the Mediterranean was reduced to a commercial backwater. Worse still, the power and riches of Venice were being bled by the continual struggle with the relentless Turk astride the Near East trade routes. The glorious episodes which illumined her decline were no substitute for the loss of Constantinople (1453), Cyprus (1571) and Crete (1669), and although some decades passed before Venice felt the full effect of the Portuguese voyages, 'La Dominante' gradually declined into just another Italian port. By the seventeenth century Dutch and English interlopers were quarrelling for supremacy in the waters once monopolized by the Venetians, and visitors to the city were less likely to be interested in cargoes than in art and architecture, publishing and the theatre. Fortunately during the fifteenth century Venice had vastly increased her possessions on the mainland, and their importance increased relatively as the overseas empire declined. By the eighteenth century the Venetian nobleman was as much a landed proprietor as a merchant venturer, and was as likely to be found in his Palladian villa as on the Rialto. And yet although Italy had already become Metternich's 'geographical expression', the tremendous energy released in the Renaissance was far from spent. She was the wonderland to be visited by every civilized gentleman whether his inclinations led him to the basilicas of the Eternal City, the spas of Tuscany, the court of the Medici, the universities of Padua or Bologna, the mercenaries' barracks or adventures in the decadent society of Venice. Venice's case was far from typical, and the attention usually given to the fortunes of her cities has tended to obscure the overriding importance of agriculture in the contemporary geography of Italy. Of those foreign travellers who have left an account of their journeyings the majority passed through the Lombardy Plain, and even those whose interest in the countryside was incidental were impressed with the fertility of the area. Thomas Coryat (1608) was enchanted, 'for as Italy is the garden of Europe, so is Lombardy the garden of Italy. . . . It is wholly plaine, and beautified with such an abundance of goodly rivers, pleasant meadowes, fruitfull vineyards, fat pastures, delectable gardens, orchards, woodes, and what not, that the first view thereof did even refollicate my spirits, and tickle my senses with inward joy.' The plain of Piedmont he describes as 'wonderfully replenished with corne, vineyards, orchards, and a singular exuberancy of all manner of fruits'. Nearly two centuries after, Arthur Young from a vantage point overlooking the same plain described it as 'the finest farmer's prospect in Europe'. The improvements in the Po Valley during the Middle Ages had been continued by the men of the Renaissance to whose energies and talents the control of water presented a lively challenge. The brothers Domenico of Viterbo developed the double-gate lock and Leonardo himself was engaged in controlling the waters of the Ticino and Adda in the interests of Milan. Apart from the absence of maize and large-scale rice-growing,[1] the countryside of Piedmont and Lombardy must have looked much the same as today with its rows of elms, mulberries and fruit trees lining the fields. Great intensity was achieved and double cropping for wheat was practised in some areas. The manure problem was less difficult in the Lombardy Plain because of the large numbers of cattle which had long ago given Piacenza, Lodi and Parma a reputation for cheeses. Furthermore as the Scottish traveller Fynes Morison (1594) noted, 'neither do they give the ground rest by laying it fallow, as we do, but each second year they sow part of it with Beans and Pulse, yielding plentifull increase, and then burying the stubble to rot in the ground, make it thereby fat to beare wheate againe'.

Tuscany too aroused the enthusiasm of the northern traveller. Montaigne (c. 1580), the motive for whose journey was to visit the famous Italian spas, approached Florence from Urbino. 'I was bound to admit,' he writes, 'that neither Orleans, nor Tours, nor even Paris, can boast of environs so richly set with villages and houses as Florence; which with regard to fine houses and palaces, comes first without a doubt.' Around Lucca, whose baths he visited, 'all about the cornfields are rows of trees, each tree being attached to its neighbour by vines, wherefore these fields have all the appearance of gardens'. Certainly Tuscany was fortunate in being ruled for centuries by a dynasty which rose to power through commerce and which included many agricultural improvers.[2] Montaigne notes that the alluvial lands round Pisa had an evil reputation for 'unhealthy air, but this is vastly improved since Duke Cosimo has drained the marshes by which it is surrounded'. Seventy years later, about 1625, Sir Robert Dudley was commissioned by Ferdinand II to drain the marshes between Pisa and Leghorn. Unfortunately not all the good works in the Arno Basin were successful. Near Lucca a system designed by a Fleming named Raet 'to drain and

---

[1] This crop seems to have been grown first in the Arno basin in the sixteenth century.
[2] John Evelyn (1644) was surprised to find the Duke of Tuscany himself engaging in the wine trade.

render fertile the marshes' was already derelict three years after its construction. Elsewhere the story was the same. Early success was followed in a few decades by ruin. Alfonso II d'Este, the patron of Tasso, drained the marsh between the Po Grande and the Po di Valano, but within eighty years the area had reverted to its former state. In this case as in most others the initial drainage was so successful that the land surface fell by shrinkage thus reducing the fall of the channels, and in the absence of efficient pumping equipment the area inevitably reverted to marsh.

Until the late eighteenth century the traveller bound for Rome from Florence avoided the unhealthy Val di Chiana route, preferring the Via Cassia across the smiling, well-tilled uplands of south Tuscany. Few travellers failed to be shocked by the treeless, barren and deserted Campagna, and this at a time when Rome itself was growing in magnificence with every princely pope. As late as 1780 John Moore wrote,[1]

> This, I am convinced is the only country in the world, where the fields become more desolate as you approach the capital. After having traversed the fertile and cultivated valleys of Umbria, one is affected with double emotion at beholding the deplorable state of poor neglected Latium. For several posts before you arrive at Rome, few villages, little cultivation and scarcely any inhabitants are to be seen. In the Campagna of Rome . . . no trees, no inclosure, nothing but scattered ruins of temples and tombs, presenting the idea of a country depopulated by pestilence.

And yet the Papal State was not without its improvers. After unsuccessful attempts by his predecessors Pope Clement VIII drained the Rieti Basin by reopening in 1598 the original Roman channels built in 272 BC, and the energetic Sixtus V was one of several popes who struggled to reclaim the Pontine Marshes.

Most northern travellers got no farther than Naples, if as far. Fynes Morison (1594) described the country between Capua and Naples as 'a most fruitfull plain of corne and vines growing high upon elm trees according to the tillage of Lombardy'. Rice, flax, hemp and sugar-cane were common crops. The fertility of the Campania only emphasized the miserable condition of the rest of the kingdom; most of Apulia was sacrificed to pastoralism; the system of tenure was nearer to medieval serfdom than the *mezzadria* practised elsewhere in the Peninsula; and the continued wastage of the forest cover in the interests of transhumance promoted the deterioration of the soil on the erodible hill lands. Manpower was under-employed and inefficiently distributed in large villages where defence was available against local bandits and North African raiders. How different from the Florentine countryside where the health and contentment of the peasantry impressed the eighteenth-century visitor, and where 'the country all around is divided into small farms, with a neat farm house on each'. In the Neapolitan kingdom the curse of the latifundia lay heavily on the land. While the serf-like peasantry lived in brutish poverty, the produce of the estates

[1] *A View of the Society and Manners in Italy.*

went, not in improvements, but to maintain the absentee landowner at court in Naples. If the Campania was productive it was so in spite of its rulers. Dr John Moore, a keen and sympathetic observer, prescribed just the sort of medicine one would expect of an enlightened eighteenth-century Englishman.

> If the land was leased out to free farmers, whose property was perfectly secure, and the leases of a sufficient length to allow the tenant to reap the fruits of his own improvements, there is no manner of doubt that the estates of the nobility would produce much more. The landlord might have a higher rent paid in money, instead of being collected in kind, which subjects him to the impositions of a steward; and the tenants, on their parts, would be enabled to live much more comfortably, and to lay up, every year, a small pittance for their families.

Nearly two centuries after, such a modest ambition can scarcely be said to have been achieved. It was certainly not of the agriculture of the Two Sicilies that Arthur Young was thinking when he wrote, 'Water, clover, cows, cheese, money, and music! These are the combinations that string Italian nerves to enjoyment and give lessons in government to northern politicians.'

The period from the fifteenth to the eighteenth century produced very few startling changes in the industrial and commercial pattern of Italy. Genoa's decline had preceded that of her rival and coincided with the loss of political independence; she did not come into her own again until the development of railways. The outstanding development among the Italian ports was the rise of Leghorn, a creation of the Medici. In 1551 the town had only 759 inhabitants. A century later it had surpassed Pisa in size and importance. Not only were the necessary physical improvements driven through, but the liberal policy adopted towards religious and political refugees, in particular Jews and English Catholics, established useful connections abroad. Furthermore, Leghorn was a free port. Of the southern ports Naples remained pre-eminent, but as unfortunate in her rulers as Leghorn was fortunate. The economic basis of this inflated capital was insecure.

> Though Naples is admirably situated for commerce, and no kingdom produces the necessaries and luxuries of life in greater profusion, yet trade is but in a languishing condition; the best silks come from Lyons and the best woollens from England.

In the mid-eighteenth century the city is said to have had 350,000 inhabitants, and was notorious for its noise, its crowds and the number of its unemployed.

> There is not perhaps a city in the world, with the same number of inhabitants, in which so few contribute to the wealth of the community by useful, or by productive labour as at Naples; but the number of priests, monks, fiddlers, lawyers, nobility, footmen, and beggars is to surpass all reasonable proportion; the last alone are computed at thirty or forty thousand.[1]

Silk, stockings, soap, snuff boxes, ornamental furniture, marble, embroidery,

[1] Moore.

37

liqueurs, macaroni and confections are mentioned among the city's industries. Of the inland cities those of the Northern Plain retained their importance despite the Spaniards. The manufactures of Bologna were fairly representative and reflect the close link with agriculture; they included silk, woollens, hemp, linen, soap, sausages, macaroni, liqueurs and essences. The woollen and silk industries were the most important on the Plain as a whole. The iron industry was widespread but on a small scale. In Tuscany the Medici fostered this ancient industry, and Duke Cosimo in particular set up mills near Fucecchio. Arms manufacture was old-established at Venice, Brescia, Cremona and Ferrara.[1] In those industries requiring skilled craftsmanship and taste the Italians were still unsurpassed. Apart from textiles, work in precious metals, jewellery and glass was a speciality in which Florence and Venice were outstanding. Montaigne noted in Florence 'certain men engaged in counterfeiting Eastern jewels, and working crystal'. Of the Murano glass industry Evelyn makes an interesting comment. 'It is white flints they have from Pavia, which they pound and sift exceedingly small, and mix with ashes made out of sea-weed brought out of Syria, and white sand which causes the manufacture to excel.'

Of the overseas trade of Italy in the late sixteenth century there is no better short account than that left by Morison.

English Merchants bring into Italy Tinne, Lead, Herrings (especially dried which they esteeme among dainties), Conny skins, Veches, Kersies, and sometimes English Corne. They also bring thither divers commodities from Dantzk, as Cordage, Hemp, Caviale, Tallow, Waxe, Indian Hides, and like commodities of Poland and Muscovy. The Netherlanders bring into Italy dried fishes, and the commodities of all Nations. Into England, Netherland, and other parts, the Italians send Velvets of Genoa, Taffities of Florence and Lucca, Sattens of Bologna, and other cities, Stuffs of Milan as Fustians, and divers kinds of Silk woven and in thread, Gold and Silver, Alom, and like commodities brought to Venice out of Turkey. From the islands of the Mediterranean sea subject to Venice, they send to us Malmsies and Muscadine wines of Candia, Corrands of Zant and Cephalonia. The ships of our parts which bring Corne or any victuals into Italy, are received with all courtesie, especially by the Duke of Florence in the haven of Ligorno, and even by the Pope in Civita Vecchia.

Had the account been written a century and a half later the only major change would have been the increase in the amount of English manufactures imported.

Then as now the tourist trade flourished despite plagues, administrative delays and searches for heretical literature. The foreign visitors to Rome alone numbered hundreds of thousands annually. Roads varied from state to state but were generally better in the North. The condition of the Alpine passes before Napoleon's time was lamentable; even on the popular Mt Cenis passengers were carried over by chairmen and their coaches had to be dismantled and reassembled on the other side.

[1] The swords of Ferrara were particular favourites with Scottish Highlanders.

# ITALY IN THE NINETEENTH CENTURY

Throughout the eighteenth century Austria's grip on the Peninsula tightened as Spain's relaxed, but during the twenty years before Waterloo, Italy was forced to recognize a new master in Revolutionary France. This was no mere change of garrison. With the French armies came new ideas sweeping away the inertia and stagnation of centuries, and putting into motion a series of upheavals which was to end in nothing less than the triumph of Italian nationalism and the emergence of a unified Italy in 1870. By previous standards French administration was honest and efficient and serious attempts were made to further the economic development of the country. Agricultural schools were established and, particularly in Naples, feudal tenures were reformed. Peasant proprietors were settled on communal and confiscated church land, and tillage was extended, particularly in Apulia, as the rights of graziers were curtailed. Grandiose schemes for the repopulation of La Sila and for the control of the Po and Tiber were prepared, and work was actually begun on the Pontine Marshes, but little enough was actually achieved. The most lasting concrete improvements made by Napoleon originated from his strategic needs. To ensure better communications with France Piedmont was annexed and vast sums were expended on the building of gently graded roads suitable for wheeled traffic over the Mt Genevre, Mt Cenis and Simplon Passes. In Italy itself the roads were improved but many of the more ambitious projects, e.g. the Cisa Pass over the Apennines, were left unfinished when the French withdrew. With the fall of Napoleon and the restoration of the petty kingdoms of Italy under the protection of an Austria now more firmly rooted than ever in Venetia and Lombardy, it seemed that the clock had been safely put back. Actually this was the uneasy calm before vast political and economic changes which revolutionized the geography of Italy. Little more than fifty years after the Restoration, Italy had become a political and economic unit, the Alps had been pierced to link Calais and Brindisi, the Suez Canal had changed the Mediterranean into a vital world trade route, and the population had grown from 18 to 26 million. This last fact is of the greatest significance, and it is against the background of a steadily and rapidly rising population that the changing geography of Italy in the nineteenth century must be reviewed.

Throughout the century Italy remained predominantly agricultural. The extension of the cultivated land continued, but at a quickened tempo. The climate of much of the country is such that cereals and vines may be grown at quite high altitudes, commonly to three or four thousand feet, consequently the cultivated zones moved up at the expense of the forests, already seriously depleted for grazing, fuel and charcoal. In Sardinia in 1820 one-fifth of the area was classed as woodland; a hundred years later this had declined to one-twentieth. Continuous deforestation had been largely responsible for those intractable marshes which now presented such a promising field of agricultural extension in the nineteenth century. Great progress had already been made but there were certain chronic areas in the Po delta, the Maremma, Lazio and the Val di Chiana, where the most enthusiastic efforts had proved unavailing. Broadly two methods had been employed. The first involved straightening out waterways or replacing them by levels in order to give a steeper gradient, and building feeder cuts on a rectangular pattern. As pointed out above the shrinkage of the land reduced its surface level and so the channels became less efficient. Furthermore the restriction of the rivers between levees resulted in a rise in the bed, and made drainage into it by a natural fall impossible. Attempts were made as early as the sixteenth century to devise lifting machinery, and later pumps worked by windmills were introduced, but not until steam power was applied to them was a really efficient means available to polder the very low land. The second method is known as *colmate naturali* or natural filling up. The idea (which is associated with the name of Leonardo, and more particularly Torricelli[1]) was to direct the load of the torrential rivers in spate so that it spread over a restricted area and gradually built up the surface level. This was a very slow process, but in some cases the results had proved more permanent than the polder method.

In the nineteenth century the first notable advances in reclamation were in Tuscany. Leopold II, in happy contrast to the other rulers of the Peninsula, was an enlightened monarch and possessed in Count Fossombroni an enthusiastic and efficient minister. It was on the latter's initiative that serious reclamation was begun in the Maremma and the Val di Chiana. The Maremma had developed as a result of vast quantities of silt brought down by the Tyrrhenian rivers building up behind *tomboli* or wave-constructed offshore bars of Quaternary and modern date. These *tomboli* prevented effective drainage to the sea. For centuries, except for occasional forts built against North African raiders, settlement had shunned these pestilential flats, and their only economic value was as winter pasture for upland sheep. The main method here was *colmate* combined with cuts through the slightly raised coastal zone to the sea. The results were remarkably good and settlement crept down into areas abandoned since Roman times. The work was far from complete and today we are witnessing the further rehabilitation of the area under the auspices of the Ente Maremma. The other intractable area to which Fossombroni turned his attention was the Val di Chiana. The first efforts had been made by the Commune of Arezzo in 1341 when channels were dug to take surplus water to the Arno. Two hundred years later Cosimo I built the Canale Maestra, which claimed still more of the uncertain watershed for the Arno, and by the end of the sixteenth century only the stretch from Faiano to the Paglia was really stagnant. In this area Torricelli attempted colmate without great success as the carrying capacity of the tributary streams from the west had been over-estimated. After 1870 the work was continued by building an artificial watershed still farther south at Chiusi and by Fossombroni's efforts to control the Tuscan tributaries. The reclamation has continued into the present century. In 1930 the Castiglion Fiorentino area was drained by tunnelling

[1] A pupil of Galileo and the inventor of the barometer.

through the barrier which prevented direct access to the main drains. Even now much remains to be done. The other difficult areas in Tuscany lay in the middle and lower Arno valley where the Fucecchio district and the Bonifica[1] di Coltano (between Pisa and Leghorn) had raised many false hopes; the former was finally tamed in the 'eighties' and the latter only in 1920.

In the Po Valley lay the greatest hydraulic problem in Italy, and also the greatest opportunity. The annual load of the river near its mouth has been estimated at 40 million tons, and the annual advance of the delta at between 30 and 80m. The raising of the bed between levees, severe floods, and shrinkage where poldering had been attempted, had hindered reclamation in the very low areas, but with the application of new techniques successful drainage was now possible. In the 'eighties' the work was began on the Bonifica Ferrarese, between the Po Grande and the Po di Volano, the Bonifica di Burano west of the Panaro's junction with the Po, and the Bonifica Parmigiano-Moglia lying between the Secchia, Crostolo and Po rivers. This work which involves hundreds of thousands of acres has continued to the present. From the very nature of the area holdings are extremely large and heavily capitalized. In the lower Reno area the *colmate* method has been applied successfully.

Two other reclamation areas deserve special mention, the Fucino Lake, and the Pontine Marshes. The Romans had achieved some success with L. Fucino, but the conduits to the Liri had soon become blocked and attempts to free them in the Middle Ages were fruitless. The lake level had always been subject to fluctuations because of connections with the underground drainage of the surrounding limestone, but in 1852 it rose alarmingly to 9m above normal. Two years later Prince Alessandro Torlonia engaged the Swiss engineer Montricher to drain the lake to the Liri and reclaim the area for tillage. The project, completed in 1875, was remarkably successful, and an area of 15,500 hectares was drained and divided into tenant farms of varying sizes, organized and financed by the Torlonia estates. The Pontine Marshes presented a tougher problem. The area lies between the Lepini and Ausoni Mountains and the coast from M. Circeo to a point a mile or two south of Anzio. This covers 80,000 hectares, of which 50,000 were pestilential fen, and 30,000 consisted of Quaternary spits and dunes along the coast, largely covered with macchia. It was this low ridge which barred the path of the mountain streams and turned such drainage as existed south-eastwards. The short streams issuing from the limestone hills had insufficient load to furnish colmate and almost all the schemes had as their basis the improvement of the drainage south-eastwards by main canals and feeders. Such was the Rio Sisto constructed by Sixtus V (*c.* 1590) along the eastern margin of the dunes and the ambitious Linea Pia built by Pius VI (*c.* 1777), which followed the line of the Via Appia and received feeders from the east at mile intervals to take the surplus mountain water. Although the work continued spasmodically throughout the nineteenth century descriptions of the area at the

---

[1] *Bonifica* means any area improved by man.

turn of the century might well have been written of some South American swamp.[1] The wild, fever-ridden inhabitants lived a semi-nomadic life of utter squalor and hopelessness. Only in 1918 was an overall plan evolved; it was later executed at immense expense by the fascist government which settled some thousands of peasants from all parts of Italy in smallholdings. The area was organized as the province of Littoria with its capital at the new town of the same name (now changed to Latina).

All these efforts at reclamation involving a vast expenditure of labour and money reflect the growing pressure of population on the land. The same is true of the extension of irrigation. Using the water of the Alpine rivers and the *fontanili*, every century since the Middle Ages had added its contribution to the increasingly close network of irrigation channels. From the mid-nineteenth century, Cavour, himself a successful progressive landowner, gave new drive to the movement. The Marzano Canal, the Naviglio Grande, the Cavour Canal and Villoresi Canal made possible the perennial irrigation of vast areas particularly for rice and fodder crops (fig. 28). Yields of maize and grain on land to which water was applied increased as much as five-fold, and on the *marcite* (irrigated meadows) of Lomellina at least seven crops are taken annually. These improvements made possible an extension of the livestock industry and between 1881 and 1908 the number of pigs increased 115% and cattle 30%.

The same period witnessed other important developments in which Emilia may claim to have been a pioneer. Agricultural newspapers, technical schools and co-operatives were established; the use of artificial fertilizers became widespread and mechanization had advanced sufficiently by the turn of the century to cause unrest among landless labourers whose numbers rose with the growth of population, the increasing fractioning of holdings and the failure of smallholders in the face of price fluctuations, the misfortunes of weather and the depredations of pests.[2] Not least among the changes of the century was the cultivation of new crops. Rice became almost a monoculture in Polesine and the Vercelli area; the tomato acreage increased rapidly in Emilia and Campania; maize challenged wheat as the main cereal of Veneto and Emilia and as the chief article of diet of the Venetian peasantry must be held partly responsible for the prevalence of pellagra in the years before 1914. Sugar beet, too, increased in popularity, and refineries, the first of which was built at Rieti in 1887, became a common feature of the Northern Plain. Progress over the country as a whole was patchy. While some of the great landowners like Cavour and Torlonia set the pace in improvements, all too many, particularly in the South, were content to stagnate. Although large areas, particularly in the Centre and South, remained on a semi-subsistence basis or served only local markets, most districts became increasingly interested in satisfying the demands for food and raw materials of the rapidly expanding

[1] See Arnaldo Cervesato 'Roman Campagna'.
[2] Notably phylloxera and the olive fly.

northern cities and the specialized needs of north-west and central Europe. This was only possible because of the improvements in communications, and it is to this aspect we must now turn.

The lessons Napoleon had given in road-building had not been lost on the Austrians. The Adige route was improved, and in 1825 the 3000m Stelvio Pass was made 'coachable' to provide an alternative route to the centre of Austrian administration in Italy, Milan. In the twenties several passes focusing eventually on the same city were constructed, viz. the Splugen (1821), St Bernardino (1823), Julier (1826), and St Gotthard (1820-32). The Maloja followed in 1840. Many of the modern tourists passes could scarcely claim the name of roads until the turn of the century. The Little St Bernard dates from 1871, the Furka from 1894 and the Great St Bernard from 1905. As late as 1899 Baedeker still classed the Septimer as a bridle path. On these roads passengers and mail provided most of the traffic and their importance was mainly strategic. The revolution in goods transport came with the railways.

In England it might be said that railways started in response to an immediate industrial need – to shift coal; in Italy they pre-dated any major industrial developments. Strangely enough the first railway in Italy was built in the most backward state, the Kingdom of the Two Sicilies. Constructed by a French engineer, Bayard, with French capital and using English locomotives, the line ran from Naples to Portici, a residence of the King. The first lines in Lombardy-Venetia (Milan–Monza 1840) and in Piedmont (Turin–Moncalieri 1848) had a similar purpose, but Tuscany built her first track, more practically, from Leghorn inland to Pisa in 1844, and extended it to Florence four years later. Once the military implications of railways were appreciated each state built according to its strategic needs; Austria directed her railways up the Adige from Venice and Milan; Piedmont towards the port of Genoa via the fortress of Alessandria. Both of these lines involved a notable engineering feat; the first the building of the viaduct across the lagoon; the second the negotiation of the Giovi Pass. The Italian nationalists recognized in railways an irresistible ally[1] and while Cavour was putting all his energy behind railway expansion in Piedmont, he looked forward to the time when Italy would have a unified system from the Alps to the Gulf of Taranto. Such sentiments were not lost on Pope Gregory XVI, and the Papal States' first line (Rome–Frascati 1856) was not constructed until after the election of the more liberal Pius IX. Three years later Rome was joined to its port, Civitavecchia.

When the Kingdom of Italy emerged only Piedmont had a real network, and the Venetian and Roman systems were still in alien hands, but from 1865 began a decade of feverish building. That year the stretch from Susa to Brindisi was completed, but the development of the shortened route to India via Calais, Brindisi and Suez had to await the opening of the Canal (1869) and the Mt Cenis Tunnel (1871). By that time Rome was free to assume her natural rôle at the centre of

---

[1] See Petitti's *Strade Ferrate Italiane*, published in exile in 1845.

the system. Bologna, Florence, Turin and Milan had already developed as great railway centres, and the last named was destined to still greater importance with the opening of the St Gotthard Tunnel in 1882 and the Simplon in 1906. Such rapid progress was not achieved without some false starts and administrative mistakes. When the new kingdom was only two years old the state ceased railway building and the task was handed over to concessionaries who operated within such a tight schedule that much of the work was of poor quality. In 1865 the railways were handed over completely to private enterprise and three main companies, Alta Italia, Meridionali and Romane, took over the system in the North, South and Centre, respectively. As a result of the failure of the Alta Italia and Romane a new administrative and financial reshuffle took place in 1885. Henceforth the track was state-owned, but the operation and development were in the hands of two big private companies, the Mediterraneo and the Adriatico. The roughly longitudinal division of their spheres was intended to emphasize the unity of North and South, and to distribute track mileage, traffic and ports equally between the two systems. The networks overlapped at several points, notably Milan (they shared the St Gotthard route), Piacenza, Florence, Leghorn and Naples. A third company operated in Sicily. This strange arrangement which lasted until the final nationalization in 1905, worked better than might have been expected. A second Giovi line was opened to Genoa in 1889, and the skeleton system of the South and Sicily was completed, including a train ferry across the Messina Straits. It was left to the nationalized railways to carry through the revolution of electrification between the wars.[1]

The topography of Italy was scarcely favourable to railway construction. Few countries can boast more spectacular – and costly – tunnels. Their total length is 910 km. When the Bologna–Prato line was built in the 'thirties' to supplement the overloaded Pistoia route, the difficulties involved in building the second longest tunnel in the world included landslips, quicksands, underground water and natural gas. Bridging, too, has been expensive. The system in 1955 included 78 km of iron bridges, and 242 km in masonry and cement.

The economic consequences of the growth of railways cannot be traced in detail, but one or two effects may be mentioned in passing. Markets for the specialized agricultural products of Italy, Sicilian citrus fruits, Emilian stone fruits and Campanian vegetables, were now more easily accessible; the whole character of Apulian agriculture changed radically with the demand for wines in France and later Austria-Hungary. Among the ports none benefited more than Genoa (fig. 15). Not only the Northern Plain but a good deal of Switzerland and south Germany was brought within its hinterland, and between 1885 and 1905 the tonnage handled rose from 2·7 million to over 6 million. Not least of the advantages of the railways was the stimulus they provided to the tourist trade. Baedeker in hand, the middle classes of England and Germany flocked to inspect the palaces of Florence and the ruins of Rome. Lastly, although railways in Italy

[1] The Lecco–Chiavenna–Sondrio line was the first in Italy to be electrified (1902).

44

*Fig. 6.* The Italian railway network, 1848 and 1861

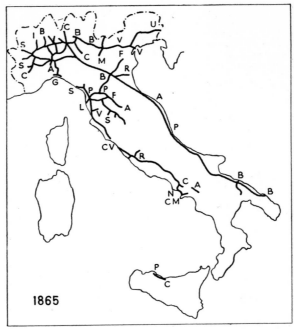

1865

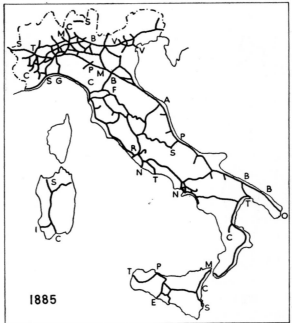

1885

*Fig. 7.* The Italian railway network, 1865 and 1885

preceded any wide-scale industrialization, they inevitably provided one of its essential elements.

Until 1850 Italian industry maintained its traditional craft pattern specializing in agricultural products, textiles, glass and artistic metal goods. The notable extractive industries were marble and sulphur, the latter almost an Italian monopoly until the opening up of the Texas deposits. Given the lack of coal and the paucity of iron ore supplies there seemed little prospect of great industrial advance, but in Piedmont, Cavour, with the example of France and England before him, set out to reform the economic conditions of his country. The customs barrier between the mainland and Sardinia was abolished to the great advantage of the extractive industries of the island; the tariff which had protected small inefficient iron producers was removed so that only large-scale modern plants could survive. The hardheaded Genoese and Piedmontese middle classes responded, and with the aid of foreign capital and techniques, some of the great names of Italian industry made their appearance even before the unification. By 1865 Ansaldo of Genoa had designed and built the first all-Italian locomotive and in the same city Orlando had begun building iron ships. The engineering firms of Robertson and Ballaydier were already established at Sampierdarena, and before long shipyards, foundries and engineering shops were dotted along the Ligurian coast from Savona to Spezia. The latter, like many other Ligurian towns, benefited from the demand for modern armaments. The raw materials for these developments, particularly English coal, came from abroad. Elba was producing about 100,000 tons of iron ore in 1870, but almost all of it went to England and Holland until the turn of the century, when plants were established at Piombino and Follonica on the mainland. Early industrial ventures were not confined to the Kingdom of Sardinia. Modern cotton mills were established at Pisa in 1850 and even in Bourbon Italy railway repair shops, arsenals and shipyards were established. The demand for railway equipment provided a great stimulus from which Milan, Bologna and Genoa benefited particularly. The emergence of a unified Italy in 1870 extended the industrial opportunities and generated new enthusiasms which were all too often accompanied by booms and slumps.

By the end of the century the pattern was fairly clear. Heavy industry, largely dependent on government orders, was severely limited by the lack of coal and other minerals, and the industrial centre of gravity remained firmly in the North. The really important revolution in Italian industry, the development of hydro-electric power and its application to the textile, light engineering and chemical industries, lay in the next century.[1]

All these developments in the field of agriculture, industry and trade must be considered against the background of a population rising sufficiently fast to double itself in the century (fig. 8). The cultivated area had been notably extended and its use intensified by means of irrigation, fertilizers, better methods and the growing of cash crops, but distress remained almost everywhere in the

[1] The first large-scale hydro-electric plant in Italy was built at Paderno sull' Adda in 1898.

countryside. Unemployment, and in those areas of seasonal work, under-employment, gave rise to widespread unrest. Industry had attracted many, not necessarily those in the poorest circumstances, but the absorptive capacity of Italian industry at the turn of the century was still very limited. The state's main

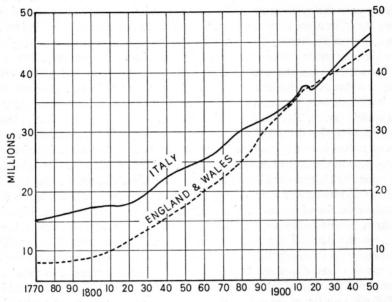

*Fig. 8.* Estimated population growth of Italy (present area) and England and Wales 1770 to 1950

contribution was to provide jobs in the civil service and semi-military organiza-tions with the result that petty bureaucracy has become recognized as a necessary evil. Given these conditions there is little wonder that a major emigration move-ment developed towards the end of the century, reaching its peak in the years before and after the 1915–18 war and dwindling in the 'twenties' as the receiving countries closed their doors.

# PART II

# Some Physical Geography

PRESSURE, AIRMASSES AND WINDS. Since, to an extent which is not generally appreciated, Italy does not escape those day-to-day uncertainties we call the weather, it would seem logical to outline first the more significant features of the changing atmospheric pattern to which the country is subjected and whose effects, in generalized form, provide much of the substance of the conventional climatic description. Inevitably this task involves some consideration of the thermal and pressure situations over Eurasia, the Atlantic and North Africa as well as over the Mediterranean itself.

Although interrupted by peninsulas and islands which sometimes develop their own, usually weak, pressure systems, the Inland Sea offers an easy route for easterly moving depressions, but its outstanding characteristic is its warmth in winter, the consequence in large measure of the homothermal layer (13·5°C) which extends from about 100m to the sea bed. The positive temperature anomaly so created contrasts strongly with the thermal conditions over the European mainland and this contrast is sharpened by the barrier imposed by the Pyrenees, the Massif Central, the Alps and the Dinaric ranges. This shield against the more rigorous conditions to the north is frequently overridden or is penetrated through gaps or lower sectors, notably the Carcassonne gap, the Rhône corridor and the narrow Julian Alps. When this occurs, the intimate juxtaposition of cold northerly air and warmer, rather stagnant Mediterranean air creates conditions favourable to the formation of frontal depressions. Indeed, some 70% of all depressions forming over the Mediterranean have their origin along the axis which passes through the Gulf of Lions, the Ligurian Sea, the Po Valley and the northern Adriatic. Many of the Po Basin depressions are of the lee type, that is a low-pressure system formed on the sheltered side of a barrier against which an airmass is being pressed. The rôle of the Apennines is less important but they do tend to guide depressions south-eastwards and their position athwart the incoming systems is of great significance in the distribution of precipitation in the peninsula.

WINTER PRESSURE CONDITIONS. During most of the cool season (October–March), the western Mediterranean basin is flanked on the north-east by the Eurasian high and on the south by the Saharan high. The basin itself, whose warmth tends to encourage the development of a regional airmass composed very largely of modified Polar maritime air, forms a broad convergence zone orientated north-westwards. This zone is invaded by three neighbouring airmasses; most frequently by Polar maritime air from the north-west, quite often by Polar continental air from the north-east, and more rarely by Tropical continental air from the south. The commonest Polar maritime incursion occurs when the cold front at the rear of a deep depression moving eastwards into central Europe swings round to encounter the Alpine barrier. Checked in this manoeuvre it causes heavy precipitation in the northern Alps and may encourage the formation of a lee depression in the Po Basin: at the same time its right and left flanks wheel round to enter the Mediterranean through the Rhône corridor and over the Julian Alps respectively. Over both the Ligurian Sea and the upper Adriatic the intruding airstreams form the rear sectors of depressions whose main characteristic is a well-developed cold front. Such systems may move eastwards into the Balkans and beyond, but the commonest tracks are south-eastwards parallel to the Apennines. The original pulsation down the Rhône 'funnel' may give rise to the *mistral*, particularly if its descent southwards is encouraged by the northerly winds in the rear of a depression already located over the Ligurian Sea. In its Italian guise, as the *maestrale*, it causes strong squally winds over the Gulf of Genoa and on the northern coasts of the Tyrrhenian islands. Similarly the Adriatic intrusion may cause the *bora* (see below). Once the original cause of these disturbances (the easterly trending depression in central Europe) moves on, the pulsations into the Mediterranean basin die out until a similar pressure situation builds up again.

The intrusion of Polar continental air is particularly significant for Friuli-Venezia Giulia, the Po Basin and the Adriatic flank of the peninsula. In its most violent form it occurs as the *bora* whose descent from the Carso is accelerated by the presence of a depression over the northern Adriatic. Over the land the wind, which frequently exceeds 110 km.p.h., is usually accompanied by clear skies, but as it fans out over the sea, losing some of its force in the process, it absorbs moisture and brings cloud and rain to the coastlands between Venezia and Ancona. Although adiabatically warmed by its descent, the loss of altitude is insufficient to temper its severity as it blusters through the streets of Trieste and paralyses traffic in the port. The offending airstream rarely exceeds 1000m and if it undercuts a warm stagnant layer, heavy cloud and rain may result. This is the *bora scura* – the dark bora. Not infrequently the *bora* continues over the Apennines as a north-easterly airstream on a wide front, precipitating snow on the mountains but descending to the Tyrrhenian Sea with the clear skies but keen air of the *tramontana*. Polar continental air sometimes invades the cul-de-sac of the Po Valley causing heavy snow in Piedmont as it attempts to escape.

The intrusion of Tropical continental air is induced by winds on the front of a depression over the Tyrrhenian Sea. This is the *scirocco*. In North Africa it is feared for its dusty parching breath, rendered more stifling by its descent from the Saharan interior. By the time it reaches Italy it has usually absorbed a great deal of moisture and it is associated there with hot and humid weather accompanied by poor visibility and occasionally by light rain; the latter may be muddied by the dust aloft. The *scirocco* is a frequent visitor to Sicily, where it may recover some of its Saharan character as it descends to the northern coastlands, but its influence is also felt as far north as Friuli. It often happens that the same depression which introduces the *scirocco* in the south is at the same time reinforcing incursions of cold air over the Ligurian Sea.

Not all depressions affecting Italy have their origin over the Mediterranean basin. Sometimes the country is invested by a well-developed system of the Atlantic type which has formed along the Polar Front and moves in from the Bay of Biscay. Others which enter the Mediterranean through the Straits of Gibraltar are of particular significance to the south of Italy where the sharp rise in relief causes heavy rainfall. Occasionally Sicily comes under the influence of depressions which have their origin to the south of the Atlas.

SUMMER PRESSURE CONDITIONS. The transition from winter to spring in Italy is usually a halting and uncertain one, for the systems which have dominated the winter situation release their grip irregularly, almost reluctantly. By April the Eurasian High has faded, but the Azores High, which has usually extended itself over north-west Africa by May, does not establish beyond the northern Mediterranean shore till August. In the meantime Polar maritime air still affects north-central Italy for short periods but the decline in the temperature anomaly over the sea helps to establish more settled weather. By August there is a steady pressure gradient over the country towards the south and east, that is towards the Saharan Low and the south-western sector of the Asiatic Low. The result is a northerly or north-easterly drift of air with long periods of dry, sunny weather. North Italy is still not entirely immune from Atlantic influences, and thermal lows, accompanied by convectional storms, develop over heated land surfaces such as the Po Valley, Apulia and Sicily. On the other hand a weak high pressure sometimes establishes itself over the Tyrrhenian Sea, causing light westerly winds (the *ponente*) on the western coast. Throughout this season onshore breezes, which station cumulus clouds over the coastal relief, are part of the rhythm of a summer's day.

Compared with spring the onset of autumn is predictable. As the land cools while the sea retains its heat, the thermal contrast between the Mediterranean and its northern hinterland becomes more marked and the conditions conducive to frontogenesis described above re-establish themselves.

AVERAGE TEMPERATURE CONDITIONS. Once summer conditions have set in towards the end of June, the thermal situation over Italy at low altitudes is remarkably uniform and there are few places whose July means do not fall between 23° and 25°C. In the same month the maximum recorded temperatures for most stations are likely to be about 36° and the minimum about 12°C. The highest maxima and the highest minima may be expected in the south, and places on the coast do tend to be a degree or two cooler than those in the interior in the same latitude (Genoa 24°C, Bologna 25·4°C; Viareggio 23·1°C, Florence 24·5°C), and the impression of airiness is heightened by sea breezes. But to escape from the heat successfully one must go into the mountains and even there the lower valleys can be oppressive (Sondrio 21·9°C) and higher up care must be taken not to expose oneself too long and too quickly to the strong insolation. Cortina (1275m) averages 15·8°C in July, Bormio (1225m) 17·3°C and Capracotta (1421m) 18·2°C.

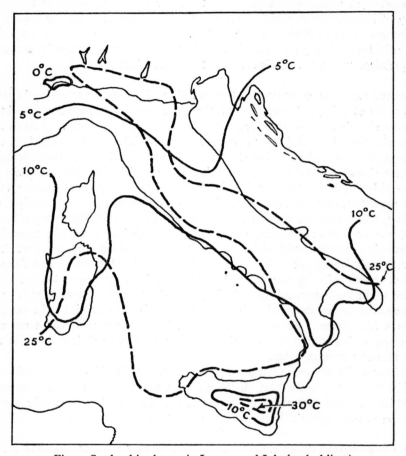

*Fig. 9.* Sea level isotherms in January and July (pecked lines)

In winter the average temperature situation reveals a strong contrast between the more maritime Mediterranean peninsula and the continental North. The latter is exposed to cold Polar maritime and Polar continental airstreams and in anticyclonic periods the Po Valley in particular is susceptible to temperature inversion. In fact the winter in that area, though short, can be thoroughly unpleasant. Milan can expect some 60 days of frost and as many days with fog, and with the increasing pollution of the atmosphere by industry, the city's 'smogs' are becoming notorious. The January mean at Milan is 1·2°C, at Turin 0·3°, and at Bologna 2·5°; and temperatures may fall to −7°C for short spells. Coastal stations on the Adriatic enjoy somewhat milder winters (Trieste 5·3°C, Venice 3·8°C).

The distribution of temperature within the Alps lends itself less to generalization; apart from altitude, much depends on aspect, the orientation of relief in relation to cold northerly airstreams, the incidence of the *föhn*, and the proximity of lakes, which tend to mitigate the winters (Salò Jan. 4°C and only 27 frosts). In the deeper valleys temperature inversion is a common occurrence and the floor is frequently blanketed in fog while the upper slopes are bathed in sunshine. Sondrio (295m), for example, has an average of 85 frosty days, and at Bormio (Jan. −1·4°C) temperatures of −15° are not unusual. The climate above about 1000m may be classed as Alpine and up to 150 frosty days may be expected.

In the peninsula and islands temperatures reflect the proximity of the sea as well as latitude and altitude (Bari 8·4°C, Foggia 6·3°C). The Tyrrhenian shores, which are less exposed to chilling Polar continental influences and benefit thermally from the effects of a deeper sea, are milder than those of the Adriatic (Leghorn Jan. 8·0°C; Ancona 4·8°C). On the Calabrian and Sicilian coastlands severe frosts are rare but temperatures may fall to zero three or four times a year. Much of the Apennine zone may be classed as Sub-Alpine in temperature and prolonged frosts are normal; in the intermontane basins temperature inversion is frequently experienced. Aquila (785m) has a January mean of 2·1°C and Capracotta (1421m) of 0·1°C.

Throughout the whole country to a lesser or greater degree maritime influences are recognizable in the warmth of the autumn compared with spring, and in the length of both intermediate seasons. It should be noted that Italy, in spite of its enviable climatic reputation, is no more immune than its northern neighbours from freak weather; the severe winter of 1956 was particularly disastrous even in the south of the country.

HUMIDITY AND PRECIPITATION. It will be apparent from the brief remarks made above on the changing pressure situation from season to season that the vast majority of the rainfall experienced over Italy is of cyclonic origin, and that the distribution will be largely determined by the height and orientation of relief while the periodicity will depend on the frequency of depressions along the various tracks at each season. The heaviest rainfall occurs in the Alps and the Pre-Alps, the Ligurian Apennines, and western-most massifs of the Abruzzi and Campanian Apennines, and the mountains of Calabria and north-east Sicily. The rest of Sicily, Sardinia and Apulia are particularly dry (see fig. 10).

As regards regime the fundamental distinction is between the North (Liguria excepted), which receives more than half of its rainfall in the summer half-year (April–September), and the peninsula and islands which receive the majority in the winter half-year. On these two major themes there are numerous variations. In the northern zone winter (Dec., Jan., Feb.), and summer are generally the driest seasons, and autumn and spring the wettest. Of these two peaks that in spring is, on average, the more important in Piedmont, while in eastern Lombardy and Veneto it is the autumn one. Towards the Alpine watershed the first

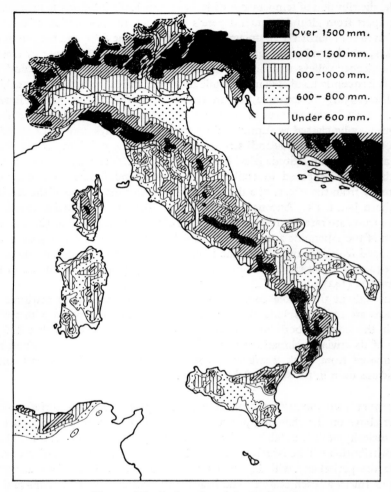

Fig. 10. *Distribution of precipitation in Italy*
Note the close association with relief.
(Adapted from the Atlante Fisico Economico d'Italia del TCI)

peak arrives later in spring and the second earlier in autumn so that eventually an Alpine type with a single summer maximum is recognizable. In the larger islands and in the extreme south of the peninsula the regime approximates to the 'typical' Mediterranean type with a simple maximum in winter. In the rest of peninsular Italy summer is also the driest season (though less markedly so than further south) and there are two rainy periods, one in autumn and the other either in spring (mainly in the north and the interior) or in winter (mainly on the coastlands further south).

The significance of mean annual rainfall figures for stations in Italy should be assessed with caution. Both in England and Italy they vary from about 500 mm in the driest areas to about 2000 mm in the wettest, but such a crude comparison masks a contrast in the effectiveness of the rainfall from the farmer's point of view. Firstly, the rainfall in Italy is obviously much more seasonal in character. This is not necessarily a misfortune. In fact, the greater incidence in the cool season is most opportune; the same totals distributed throughout the year would serve only to increase the proportion of moisture lost by evaporation in the summer and to soak the subsoil less thoroughly in winter. Secondly, the rainfall in Italy occurs more frequently than in England in the form of short, heavy showers which are conducive to soil erosion and are particularly destructive when accompanied by hail, as is often the case with convectional storms and with cold front disturbances. Furthermore, such brief rainy spells merely punctuate much longer periods of strong insolation and intense evaporation. Thirdly, Italy's rainfall is unreliable both in its seasonal incidence and in the annual totals received. For example, Milan received 466 mm in 96 days in 1921, and 1782 mm in 110 days in 1951; for the same years the totals for the three

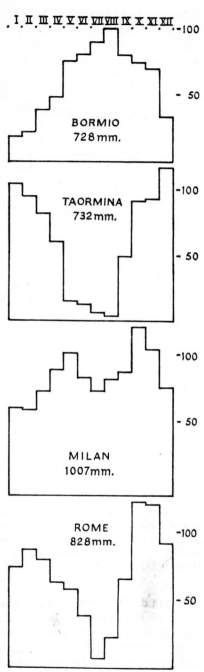

*Fig. 11.* Seasonal distribution of rainfall in millimetres for Bormio (type 1 on fig. 12), Milan (type 2), Rome (type 3) and Taormina (type 4)

57

autumn months (normally the wettest) were 45 mm and 539 mm respectively. Similarly between 1951 and 1955 the annual totals at Rome varied between 306 mm (70 days) and 970 mm (116 days), at Florence between 444 mm (52 days) and 1493 mm (110 days) and at Bari between 365 mm (65 days) and 774

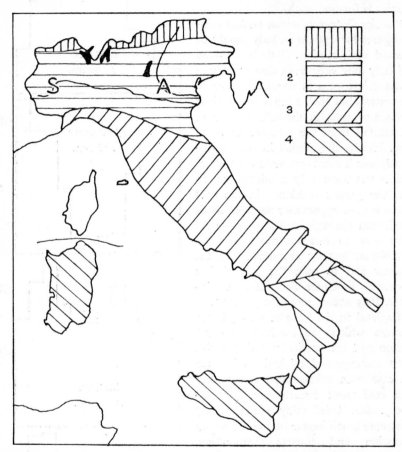

*Fig. 12.* The distribution of rainfall regimes. 1 - Summer maximum, winter minimum; 2 – Some rain throughout the year but minimum in winter and maximum in autumn and spring; A – autumn predominating. S – spring predominating. 3 – summer minimum; autumn and either winter or spring the wettest seasons. 4 – Winter maximum, summer minimum

mm (113 days). Scarcely a year passes without a freakish downpour somewhere in the country; 1500 mm in three days were measured in Calabria in 1951 and 469 mm in 24 hours have been recorded at Viu (Piedmont). It can scarcely be a matter for surprise if floods and landslips frequently reach disaster proportions and if fluctuating yields and local crop failures are commonplace occurrences.

In Italy, especially Mediterranean Italy, the availability of water for plant life
and for domestic, irrigation and industrial uses is often of such critical importance

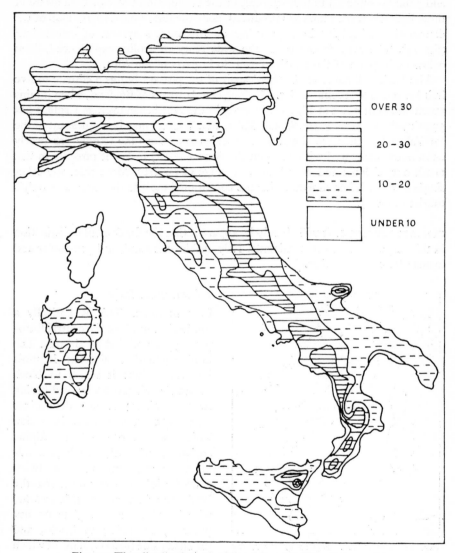

OVER 30

20 – 30

10 – 20

UNDER 10

*Fig. 13.* The distribution of aridity (after M. Pinna) (see p. 60)

that it gives particular significance to attempts to express aridity in scientific
terms. Such calculations are beset with practical difficulties; no factor can be
incorporated in the index to offset the capricious nature of the precipitation, and

it is almost impossible to set a value on the contribution of dew and mist to the humidity total or estimate the effects of plant transpiration, surface permeability and wind (as opposed to temperature) in the evaporation process. Well aware of these limitations M. Pinna has produced, none the less, a most useful map of the distribution of aridity in Italy using de Martonne's system of calculation[1] (fig. 13). The map demonstrates the wide range of aridity experienced, from below 10 in parts of the South to over 80 in parts of the Alps.

The Italian climate may be the despair of the peasant but as a climate to live in it has much to recommend it. The long cloudy weeks of England, when it rains much and shines not at all, are rare even in the North. On average Cagliari has 59 rainy days a year, Rome 82 and Milan 102. Winters may be unpleasant in the Po Valley but they are short. The abundance of sunshine (Rome has nearly 2400 hours compared with 1700 on the Sussex coast) makes it possible to live much out of doors and even blunts the edge of poverty. More than any other single factor it is her climate which has contributed most to the success of Italy's tourist industry.

CLIMATIC REGIONS. It will already be apparent that the fundamental distinction in this respect is between continental Italy, on the one hand, and peninsular and insular Italy on the other.

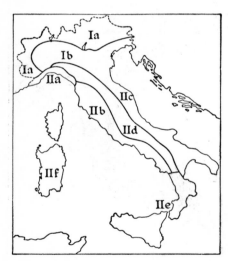

*Fig. 14. The climatic regions of Italy: for explanation see pages 60-62*

**1** *Continental Italy*

**Ia** THE ALPS. This is basically a southerly variant of the central European type, modified by altitude. The local orientation of relief is most important since it serves to block or canalize airstreams from differing source regions; it also determines aspect and the amount of insolation which can be received. In Alpine regions, particularly in valleys trending east–west, there is almost always a discernible contrast between the land use of the sunny side (*solatio*) with its vines, arable plots or hay pastures, according to height, and the shady side (*ombria*) most of which is wooded. There is also a clear cor-

[1] Aridity index $= \left( \dfrac{P}{T + 10} + \dfrac{12 \cdot p}{t + 10} \right)$ where $P$ = the mean annual precipitation in mm; $T$ = the mean annual temperature in degrees C; $p$ = the precipitation for the driest month; and $t$ = the mean temperature for the driest month.

relation between precipitation and relief; most areas over 1000m receive between 1000 and 2000 mm, while the lower valleys are decidedly dry (Aosta 585 mm, Bormio 728 mm, Merano 660 mm). The central and eastern Alps, which are particularly exposed to the effects of cyclonic disturbances over the Valle Padana and the northern Adriatic, are in general wetter than the western Alps, and the Pre-Alpine fringe, though lower, receives almost as much precipitation as the interior Alps (2000 mm). The latter have a continental regime with wet summers and dry winters. Elsewhere winter is still the driest season but the rainfall peaks occur in autumn and spring. In the central and eastern Alps and in the Pre-Alps the autumn peak is the more important while in Piedmont May is usually the wettest month. To the embarrassment of winter sports hôteliers, the extent, depth and duration of the snow cover vary considerably from year to year. Generally speaking over 1500m the mountains are covered from November till late April, while at 2000m the high pastures can only be exploited between June and September. At Cortina (1275m) the snow reaches a depth of two metres and lies continuously for some 100 days. The mantle of snow, which is usually more abundant in the eastern than in the western Alps, is normally thickest between 2000 and 2500m and the snowiest period is from February to April. The permanent snowline varies from about 2500 to 3000m according to aspect and relief. Small glaciers persist within the Italian frontier from M. Ambin to the Vetta d'Italia, but except in the Pennine Alps, the Bernina group, the Adamello–Presanella group and on the Tirol watershed, they rarely occupy more than a few square kilometres; in fact, for nearly a century, despite minor oscillations, they have been in retreat and many have disappeared altogether.

The contrast between the upper mountain slopes and the valleys is not only a matter of precipitation: on the former the rarefied atmosphere and strong insolation encourage a wide thermal range at ground level but the air temperature range is usually much less than in the valleys. At Bormio in July the downward drift of cold mountain air may reduce the temperature to 2°C at night when during the day it has been as high as 23°C. In winter temperature inversion fills the valley with mist and keeps the thermometer below zero; the Piave valley is a good example. At the head of Lake Garda in summer thermally induced pressure gradients cause down-valley winds in the morning and up-valley winds, often accompanied by heavy showers, in the afternoon. During anticyclonic spells in summer up-valley winds may reach considerable force in the Dora Riparia and Dora Baltea valleys causing widespread haze over the upper mountain slopes. A southerly blowing *föhn* is frequently experienced, especially in March, and interior valleys are also subject to it from the opposite direction.

In the vicinity of the larger lakes a recognizable sub-type (the Insubric) emerges. Warmed by the presence of large bodies of water, sheltered from the east and north, and high enough to escape the cold blanket of air which so often envelopes the plain, this discontinuous zone enjoys mild winters which tolerate Mediterranean species as well as those more typically northern. This

Mediterranean *nuance*, as suggested by the presence of the ilex and by the cultivation of the olive and lemon, is most obvious in the Garda area with its lower rainfall, its more abundant sunshine and its calcareous rock surface.

**Ib** THE VALLE PADANA. The main characteristics of this area have already been noted. In the short winter temperature inversion causes prolonged foggy and frosty spells; but snow rarely lies for more than a day or two. The rainfall regime and the long growing period are favourable to agriculture but convectional disturbances with severe hailstorms are a serious menace in autumn.

**II** *Insular and peninsular Italy*

**IIa** THE RIVIERA LIGURE. This is an extraordinarily mild area benefiting to the full from the winter warmth of the Ligurian Sea. Although subject to the *maestrale* from time to time, on the whole it is sheltered and most winds reaching it from the north are warmed adiabatically. The Riviera di Ponente is decidedly drier and somewhat milder than the Riviera di Levante (San Remo 678 mm, Spezia 1140 mm).

**IIb** THE TYRRHENIAN COAST. The northern half compares unfavourably with the Riviera in winter and is drier than the southern half because of the screening effect of Corsica. Towards the south the autumnal maximum gives way to a winter one.

**IIc** THE ADRIATIC COAST. This is less mild in winter than the corresponding latitudes on the Tyrrhenian coast because it is more exposed to the north-easterly continental influences. Southwards the total rainfall decreases (cf. Tyrrhenian) and the length of the summer drought increases (Ancona 120 mm in the three summer months, Bari 76 mm).

**IId** THE APENNINES. This zone still exhibits the characteristically Mediterranean summer drought, longer and more unbroken towards the south, but the winters, which eliminate the olive, are longer and more severe than on the neighbouring coastlands. Over 1500m snow is frequently experienced and may lie for weeks; the crests, especially in the Abruzzi, are usually capped till April. In intermontane basins temperature inversion is common.

**IIe** SICILY and **IIf** SARDINIA. The most 'typically' Mediterranean zones with a long summer drought and a simple winter rainfall peak.

## VEGETATION

An appreciation of the vegetational tapestry of Italy invites consideration of three contributory influences, namely, the climate now, the climate in the past and the influence of Man.

With worsening conditions at the end of the Pliocene, the subtropical vegetation, which till then had covered much of the European mainland, began to retreat southwards. In contrast with North America where the retreat could take place unhindered, the presence of mountain barriers and the limited extent of the land mass resulted in the elimination of many species. During the ensuing glacial periods the peninsula was invaded by more northerly types including steppe grasses and conifers (*Pinus sylvestris*), some of which have since found refuge in the Alps and Apennines, as they did in the interglacial periods. These more fortunate interludes were warm enough for the mesothermal vegetation to re-establish itself over the lowlands at the expense of the northern intruders, and even during the post-glacial period there have been climatic oscillations (as evidenced by the pollen in peat bogs) of sufficient magnitude to cause widespread distributional fluctuations. Thus the beech, which prefers a humid, maritime environment, seems to have been much more widely represented at one time and the *P. sylvestris* to have been crowded from the Po Valley into the more continental recesses of the Alps. Similarly, the Mediterranean element in the Insubric zone may well represent a survival from a warmer post-glacial interval when this type of flora, probably spreading up from Liguria, was more widely distributed.

Until recently Man's rôle in the vegetational story has been almost entirely a destructive one. Of the forests which in prehistoric times covered all but the summits, four-fifths have been replaced by arable, pasture and waste; and of the rest, which is classed as woodland, only a minority is composed of trees which are spared Man's interference sufficiently to attain their full stature. Whereas in England the forest tree is useful only when it is felled, in Italy, it has often to pay its way during its lifetime; the willow is pollarded for its withies, and the elm is mutilated to support the 'married' vine and provide leafy fodder for the oxen team; every seven years the cork is robbed of its bark and the pine is often tapped for resin. Oakwoods, both deciduous and evergreen, are frequently stunted in appearance because they are regularly lopped for firewood or charcoal, and the beechwoods of the Pre-Alps and Apennines are often no more than head-high thickets struggling against Man's constant meddling. Such worked-over woodlands are classed as *cedui* (coppice), as opposed to the *fustaie* composed of better developed trees, often in stands. Although less exploited than formerly, the oak, beech and chestnut provide good pannage, and the last-named still makes a contribution to the peasant table. In fact, the chestnut (*Castanea sativa*) illustrates the selective character of Man's intervention; as the *albero del pane* it has survived better than most. Even so it is often found in the degraded *ceduo* form; the 'suckers' from the boles of felled trees growing rapidly to 10m or more are valuable for making vine supports.

But Man's intervention does have its positive side. Through him new species have been profitably introduced. From Latin America came the agave and the prickly pear, the latter a useful cover plant for arid land and a source of fodder for mule and donkey in the droughty Sicilian summer. The vigorous and now widely dispersed *Robinia pseudo-acacia* was imported from the same area; it has proved useful for stabilizing unconsolidated slopes and quickly takes possession of waste ground. Although the mulberry, which was brought in from the Near East in the late Middle Ages to support the silk industry, has lost much of its economic importance and is probably doomed to disappear with the spread of mechanization, it still makes a pleasing contribution to the mixed cultivation of the Piedmont and Venetian plains. The ailanto, a native of southern Asia imported for the same purpose in the eighteenth century, is found wild throughout the length of Italy. Perhaps the most valuable introduction has been the graceful and quick-growing eucalypt which provides material for paper-making and is a useful ally against wind and water erosion. Since the turn of the century, with the wider appreciation of the evils of deforestation, large areas have been replanted both by private bodies and by the state. The depopulation of many mountain areas should provide still greater scope for the restoration of the original cover.

So all-pervading has been Man's intervention that to speak of 'natural vegetation' is somewhat unreal, but by making use of such remnants as survive and of the obvious relationship between the vegetation of an area and its climate, relief and soil, an approximate picture of the original cover can be reconstructed. From the geographer's viewpoint this is perhaps best described on a threefold basis – the Alps, the Valle Padana, and the Mediterranean peninsula and islands.

THE ALPS. On a local scale the study of Alpine vegetation must assess the effects of a host of micro-climatic and edaphic factors but, in the more generalized picture, altitude, and to a lesser degree, aspect and continentality emerge as the most important influences. The increasing degree of continentality towards the Alpine watershed tends to thin out the beech, which finds its most favourable habitat on the humid south-facing slopes of the Pre-Alps, and favours the conifers, particularly the *Pinus sylvestris*. The effect of aspect is to lower the upper tree limit on north-facing slopes and to create conditions suited to the less demanding species. For example, on the southern side of the col between the Presanella and Brenta groups, the red fir (*Picea excelsa*) is dominant, but once over the watershed the hardier larch (*Larix decidua*) takes its place. The contrast between the two sides of valleys trending east and west is well exemplified in the Graian and Cottian Alps (Val Maira, Val Varaita, Valle del Chisone, Valle di Susa, etc.) and further east in the Val Venosta, in the Val di Sole, and perhaps best of all, in the Valtellina. Here forests of red fir and larch, briefly interrupted by pasture, look across to terraced vineyards and chestnut woods above which hayfields and patches of arable penetrate the pinewoods almost to the limit of trees (1850m).

Before generalizing about the main vegetation zones, which are broadly related to altitude, two facts, neither of them easily explained, should be noted. Firstly, the upper limit of trees is actually higher in the interior Alps than on the Pre-Alps; and secondly, the vegetational strata, whether nearer the watershed or the plain, are inclined to the east. The decline is particularly sharp in Carnia where the limit of trees is some 500m lower than in the central Alps. The snow-line and the limit of cereal cultivation (up to 1850m in the Piedmontese Alps) exhibit a corresponding tendency. Similarly, the higher tree line towards the Alpine interior is accompanied by a rise in the limit of cereal cultivation.

Bearing in mind all these reservations, three main zones may be recognized – a piedmont zone up about 1000m, a mountain zone to about 2100m and a culminating zone as far as the permanent snowline.

In the piedmont zone almost all the spontaneous vegetation has been replaced by cultivation, especially of vines and fruit trees. As mentioned above, at low levels near the lakes and in the Euganei and Berici hills favourable micro-climates have permitted the survival of numerous Mediterranean species includ-

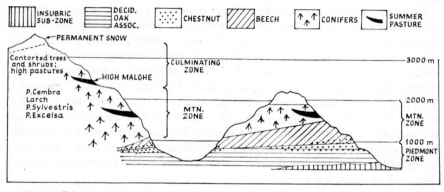

*Fig. 15.* Diagrammatic representation of the vegetational altitude zones in the Alps and Pre-Alps

ing the ilex, olive, laurel, cistus and rosemary. This Insubric sub-zone is more typically Mediterranean on the shores of Garda. On the better watered slopes surrounding Maggiore and Como, especially where crystalline rocks occur, acid-loving plants – laurels, magnolias, rhododendrons, azaleas, and tree heather – are more characteristic. Elsewhere the dominant association was that of the deci-duous oaks, particularly the two species found in northern Europe (*Quercus robur, Q. petraea*). In this woodland, with its dense undergrowth, ash-elms (*Fraxinus ornus*), limes, sycamores, wild cherries and plums were also repre-sented. Towards the upper limit of the piedmont zone the oak association gives way to that of the chestnut, a tree which is happiest on well-watered crystalline slopes. It is best exemplified in the Piedmontese foothills.

The lower stratum of the mountain zone is occupied by the beech (*Fagus sylvatica*) and its associates which prefer the fresher more humid slopes between 1000 and 1500m where really severe winter temperatures are exceptional. It occurs widely in the Piedmontese Alps and in the Pre-Alps but towards the watershed it is discouraged by the *föhn* and may be eliminated altogether (the upper Valtellina). Without any clearly defined break the beech stratum merges into the conifers among which the noble red fir, with its reddish bark and long tight cones, is a favourite with the forestry authorities. It shelters an undergrowth which includes myrtles, rhododendrons, heather and a variety of edible fungi. The hardier larch is content with less favourable situations on northern slopes or rocky ground. Although a conifer, it is not an evergreen; the shedding of its needles no doubt reduces the transpiration loss and enables it to struggle on in insolation well beyond the limit of the forests proper. It is sometimes accompanied by the *Pinus cembra* whose survival is threatened because of the popularity of its seeds with forest fauna. In the more continental Alpine interior the *Pinus sylvestris* occupies exposed stony slopes where evaporation and the percolation of water defeat most other conifers.

Between 1900m and 2100m the habitat deteriorates and the forest thins out. Only those trees and shrubs which can dispense with the protection of their fellows survive; six or seven months of snow, a short growing period, fierce temperature fluctuations at ground level, strong desiccating winds and a soil composed of little but scree are all elements of this daunting environment. Among patchy thickets composed of contorted mountain pines (*P. montana*), junipers, rhododendrons, myrtles and alders (*Alnus viridis*) only the larch, the pioneer of the forest, stands erect; the rest cower over the rocks to escape the wind and conserve warmth and moisture. Further up across the scree to the permanent snowline only the humble Alpines survive; their long roots, hairy leaves and cushion-like form help them to withstand violent temperature fluctuations and excessive loss of moisture.

THE VALLE PADANA. Of the vast forest of the Valle Padana (Cisalpine Gaul to the Roman colonists under whose axes it first began to retreat extensively) practically nothing remains; the last sizeable remnant, the oaks of Montello, so long protected by the conservationist legislation of the Venetian Republic, disappeared in the 1890s. A reconstruction would probably reveal oaks (*Q. robur* and *Q. petraea*) spreading down from the piedmont and dominant over most of the plain. In response to local drainage conditions they would be associated with the elm, ash, willow, alder and poplar. On the higher morainic arcs of Piedmont, especially where *ferretto* has rendered the crystalline detritus more impermeable, a few stands of chestnut and beech have survived, but this habitat is also proving attractive to that vigorous foreigner the robinia.

Along the northern margin of the plain, the fans of very coarse fluvio-glacial debris support a heath vegetation known generally as *brughiere* and locally in Piedmont as *vaude* or *baragge*. Heather, gorse, silver birch and the *Pinus sylvestris* are characteristic, this last the straggling rearguard of a post-glacial retreat. Traditionally the summer grazing grounds of transhumant flocks, which have contributed to the degradation of the vegetation, the *brughiere* have dwindled with the extension of irrigation and the overspill of industry. In Veneto and Friuli where the corresponding deposits are largely of calcareous origin and are even more porous and arid, the vegetation of the *magredi* is nearer to steppe than heath.

In parts of the Po delta, in the *valli* of Comacchio and along the alluvial Adriatic littoral sizeable areas of aquatic vegetation persist, increasingly halophytic in character towards the lagoons where it has an important rôle in the accretion of silt. Since classical times Man has utilized the coastal dunes for plantations of maritime and stone pines; the most famous of these *pinete* lies along the Ravenna shore. By the banks of the Po and its tributaries and in the *bassa* of Veneto and Friuli, wherever the danger of flooding discourages cultivation, plantations of quick-growing poplar have been established; they stabilize the silt, reinforce the levees and provide a profitable return from the paper, rayon and match industries.

THE MEDITERRANEAN PENINSULAS AND ISLANDS. The outstanding characteristic of the plant life here is its ability to adapt itself to high temperatures accompanied by long rainless periods. The aridity of summer and to a less degree the coolness of winter tend to induce repose, while autumn and especially spring are the seasons of active growth. A prodigious root development tapping the subsoil and the disappearance of starch in the leaves and twigs in favour of sugar enable plants to make the best use of the available ground water, while woody and resinous stems and leaves, which may be shiny, hairy, very small or thorny, serve to reduce transpiration. Many of the humbler plants hug the ground or assume a cushion-like form and others conserve water in bulbous roots or fleshy stems.

The increasing aridity in Italy towards the south and east is reflected in a corresponding rise in the vegetational zones. On the coastlands this means that towards the south a stratum composed originally of xerophilous plants (the carob, wild olive and lentisk association) insinuated itself below the stratum of evergreen oaks, which is more generally characteristic of the Mediterranean lowlands. Despite its trespass into Biscayan France, the ilex association is considered by some experts to be more valuable than the olive in delimiting the Mediterranean habitat. In early classical times it covered vast areas up to 600m in the peninsula and to over 1000m in Sicily and Sardinia. Except in one or two nature reserves the evergreen forest, in its original form, no longer exists, but patches of evergreen oakwood, *in ceduo*, are common enough. In general it has been replaced by arable, much of it in the form of *coltura promiscua* in which fruit trees are an essential element. Other important trees which fall within the ilex stratum are the cork oak, the maritime pine, the stone pine and the Aleppo pine. The cork oak (*Q. suber*) does best on crystalline soils and in an oceanic atmosphere – hence its preference for the western Mediterranean basin; it occurs on the Tyrrhenian coastlands but is most extensively represented in Sardinia. Of the 'umbrella' pines, the stone pine (*P. pinea*) has a wider distribution than the maritime pine (*P. pinaster*); both are found along the sandy stretches of the Tyrrhenian littoral, as well as on the northern Adriatic sandpits. The Aleppo pine (*P. halipensis*), a pioneer tree capable of withstanding wind and drought, is best represented on the dunes of Sicily and Sardinia. The kermes oak (*Q. coccifera*) the most drought-resistant of the genus, is of little importance in Italy.

At an early date Mediterranean Man evolved a system of agriculture which was adapted to the peculiarities of the climate and at the same time capable of providing a sound diet. While wheat, beans and other field crops, sown in November and harvested in early summer, relied on the rainfall of the cool season, tree crops exploited the moisture of the subsoil. Unfortunately, in spite of the conservational rôle of tree crops, the clearing of the evergreen forest resulted in the general deterioration, and in some areas the almost complete destruction of

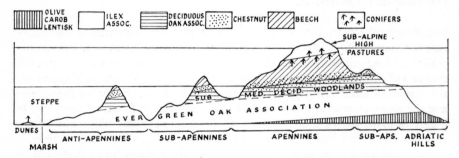

*Fig. 16.* Diagrammatic representation of the vegetational altitude zones in central Italy. In fact the olive–carob–lentisk zone included here is found only in the southern peninsula and islands

the soil cover. Even when abandoned by the cultivator, the climatic conditions, the lack of shade and humus, and the evil effects of grazing militated against the natural regeneration of the forest. In its place various vegetational associations established themselves; most of them fall within the broad categories of *macchia* (*maquis*), *gariga* (*garrigue*) or steppe.

Although macchia may well have been the primary vegetation in a few areas, it is generally safe to assume that it is the consequence of Man's intervention. Its appearance is infinitely varied; in some places it is a stunted woodland dotted with oaks and conifers, the survivors of a nobler vegetation; in others it is an immense shrubbery or a tangled thicket so laced with briars, ivy and convolvulus as to be almost impenetrable. It may be patchy or continuous but almost everywhere woody evergreen shrubs provide the most important element. Macchia is classified roughly according to the characteristic or dominant plant. For example, there is an evergreen oak macchia (which is usually associated with the lentisk, arbutus, myrtle and privet), a wild olive–lentisk macchia, a euphorbia macchia and an erica macchia. The constituent plants are often very sensitive to variations in soil and moisture; the oleander is usually restricted to the banks of ephemeral torrents while the laurel prefers deep-cut valleys offering moisture and shade. Gorse, broom and cistus are usually an indication of siliceous soils. Macchia, which has made its contribution to the shrubberies of gardens all over Europe, is most attractive in spring when the greys and dark greens are cheered by masses of predominantly yellow blossom. Left undisturbed it might well develop the biotic conditions conducive to the regeneration of the original forest; unfortunately its meagre resources are repeatedly exploited for grazing, firewood, tannin, basket material and even as long-term fallow.

In fact, outside Sardinia, the area covered by macchia is small; garrigue (or the infinite variations between it and macchia) is much more common. It consists of an assemblage of low tufty or bushy plants, rarely providing a complete cover, and capable of tolerating thin stony soils, high ground temperatures and desiccating winds. It may represent the degeneration of macchia or it may be the direct successor of the original forest, but in either case it is generally considered to be the outcome of human intervention. Sometimes a few survivors of the forest, a stone pine or a kermes oak, struggle on, and representatives of the forest undergrowth (gorse, broom, dwarf palms) are common, but thyme, lavender, rosemary and other aromatic herbs (labiates) constitute the biggest element. In the absence of true soils the nature of the parent rock is of great importance; broom, gorse, lavender and bramble flourish on siliceous soils while rosemary, thyme and cistus prefer a calcareous parent rock. Garrigue is of meagre value as pasture and repeated grazing tends to eliminate those plants most acceptable to sheep and goats. In some areas, for example the Murge of Apulia, this process of deterioration by animal selection results in the disappearance of all but the asphodel.

The dividing line between garrigue and steppe is a narrow one. Generally steppe is more typical of recent alluvium spread over arid coastal plains, for example the Tavoliere di Puglie. All such areas have been over-grazed and the characteristic vegetation is a discontinuous cover of tufty grass and halophytes, the latter most common near the coastal lagoons. In spring this desolation may be brightened by short-lived grasses and the unprofitable asphodel.

THE SUB-MEDITERRANEAN DECIDUOUS WOODLANDS. Above the evergreen oak forests (or its degenerate successors), where the summers are fresher and the winters wetter, a stratum composed of mixed deciduous trees is recognizable. In central Italy it lies between about 500 and 1000m and it is best preserved on the volcanic areas of the Anti-Apennines. In these woodlands box, ash-elm and walnut are represented but oaks are the dominant group. They include the two northern European species as well as those more typically southern (*Q. pubescens*, *Q. cerris*, *Q. macedonica*). It is climatically significant that towards the upper limit of this stratum olive cultivation becomes marginal and it is widely replaced in the economy by the almond and the hazel nut.

THE MOUNTAIN ZONE. The chestnut horizon which extends up to about 950m in Lazio and 1350m on the slopes of Etna, may be regarded as transitional to the mountain zone proper. The chestnut's preference for crystalline soils has already been noted and it is best exemplified in the slopes of Monte Amiata, Monte Cimino, Monte Vulture and the Sila plateau. At full stature its fresh green leaves filtering light into a moist undergrowth of ferns and bracken make a welcome change from the duller hues and tinder-dry litter of the Mediterranean woods below. But the Apennine mountain tree *par excellence* is the beech; in central Italy it extends from about 900 to about 1800m, that is practically to the limit of trees. Its very dense leaf cover discourages undergrowth and its only competitor is the white fir (*Abies alba*), which has suffered even more than the beech at the hands of Man. Where conifers are found in any numbers in the Apennines they are usually the fruit of re-afforestation. The beech occurs on a variety of soils; it is regarded as a climax, and although it has been so sadly reduced in area and quality, in the absence of Man it would recapture all but the highest slopes. In fact, the upper mountain forest has been under continuous attack from transhumant flocks and it has been widely replaced by pastures, constantly overgrazed and rarely worth cutting for hay. The hardy shrubs and stunted trees, which are the pioneer fringe of the Alpine forests, are almost entirely absent in the Apennines.

## STRUCTURE

The geographer's interest in structure, a term which will be very liberally interpreted, lies mainly in its profound influence on Man's physical environment. Since the relationship between this environment and the human response to it is often best discussed in its regional setting, only the broader structural aspects will be treated here.

Ancient shields and their associated fold mountain systems are the basic elements of Europe's anatomy. Unless there is justification for the view, now less generally accepted, that a foundered crustal block underlies the Tyrrhenian, the former have no part in the build of Italy, but at least three mountain-building systems are represented. Of the Caledonian folding the main evidence lies in the Cambrian beds of Iglesiente, but sizeable fragments of the Hercynian system are exposed within the Italian Alps, notably in the massifs of Argentera, Mt Blanc and Monte Rosa, as well as in the Carnic Alps; they have their counterparts beyond the frontier in the Mt Pelvoux, Belledonne and Aar-St Gotthard massifs. It was against and over these Hercynian Palaeo-Alps that the Alpine folds proper were later to be thrust. The Hercynian movements were accompanied by intrusions of granite and extrusions of lava, the latter being best represented in the porphyries of Besimauda (Ligurian Alps), Valsèsia, Lugano and the upper Adige. Outside the Alps the crystalline blocks of Corsica–Sardinia and Calabria–Peloritani massifs are also regarded as Hercynian.

But the most important contribution to the build of Italy was made by the Alpine orogenesis which reached its greatest intensity during the Eocene and Oligocene when vast thicknesses of sediments, accumulated in the Tethys Sea from the Carboniferous onwards, were thrust northwards over the Hercynian barrier. In the huge mass of material so formed a number of *nappe* systems have been identified. Of these the lowest, the Helvetic, is restricted in Italy to the Val Ferret (Valle d'Aosta). Much more widely represented are the Pennine nappes which occupy the great sweep of the western Italian Alps from the Riviera di Ponente to the Bernina group. They include a great variety of rock types but are particularly notable for their mica schists (*schistes lustrés*) and calcareous schists which were derived from sediments laid down in the deeper parts of Tethys and are associated with the extreme plasticity and extensive tangential displacement of the Pennine nappes. Markedly different in character are the Austrid nappes which are represented in Italy in the Alpi Atesine; their constituent sediments, which are presumed to have originated in the southern continental shelf of Tethys, exhibit severe thrusting in contrast to the recumbent overfolding of the Pennine nappes. The latter are thought to have been overlain in the western Alps by the Austrides which have since been removed by erosion. This assumption is supported by the exposure of the Pennine nappes through the Austrides in the Hohe Tauern; a small part of this 'window' falls within the Italian frontier to the east of the Brenner.

In contrast to the Alpine nappes proper (the Pennides and Austrides as far as Italy is concerned) which are mainly composed of crystalline rocks, the Dinarides flanking them to the south are overwhelmingly calcareous. This contrast between the crystalline Alpine core and the calcareous southern flank is fundamental. The Dinarides, which continue south-eastwards into the Balkans, are best represented in the Pre-Alps of Lombardy and Veneto as well as in the Dolomites and the Brenta group. The lack of a true Pre-Alpine zone to the west of Lake Maggiore is attributable to the absence of the Dinarid zone here, at least on the surface; it may well have collapsed or been down-thrust and later covered by the alluvial deposits of the plain. In the eastern Alps the Dinarid nappes have been under-thrust so that the rock sheets, severely faulted and dislocated, are falling back to the south like a series of roof tiles. In consequence, massive flexures, inclined 'slabs' and isolated blocks are common features of the area's relief.

Earth-movements on the scale experienced in the Alps were inevitably accompanied by extensive metamorphism and vulcanicity. During the first rumblings of the earth-storm in the Mesozoic, the preliminary disturbance of the Tethys sediments favoured the injection and extrusion of magma now recognizable as the *pietre verdi* of the Piedmontese Alps and the northern Apennines. During the main folding numerous granitic masses were intruded, later to be exposed in the Alto Adige, the Cima d'Asta range (north of the Val Sugana), the Adamello group and the Biellese, while in the Monti Lessini, Monti Berici and Monte Baldo extrusions of basaltic lava occurred.

Folding on a less intensive scale continued into the Miocene but thereafter earth-movements in the Alps were radial rather than tangential in character. In the meantime, in the Oligocene, thrusting from the west had brought the Apennines into existence. As in the Alps this thrusting produced nappes; the lowest of these, which is exposed in the metamorphosed limestones of the Apuan Alps and more extensively in the Mesozoic limestones of the Abruzzi, is auto-chthonous, while the overlying Tuscan nappe, which constitutes much of the northern Apennines, has been extensively displaced. The uppermost nappe, the Ligurian, which has suffered similarly, is represented somewhat fragmentarily in the Anti-Apennines, notably in Monte Pisano, Montagnola, the Colline Metal-lifere and Elba, and it is frequently associated with metamorphism and mineralization.

To the geographer the main significance of the Apennine nappe structure seems to be that it represents a vast accumulation of folded and faulted material which constitutes the foundation of the peninsula; that it determined the arc-like trend of the peninsula and created on its eastern flank a continuous foretrench, stretching from the Valle Padana, through the Marche to the Bradano depression, in which vigorous sedimentation continued through the Miocene and Pliocene; and finally that, with the help of rapid denudation, it offered a varied pattern of surface rocks, mainly clays and sandstones in the north, limestones in the centre and igneous rocks in the south, each with its peculiar landforms and scenery, its human problems and opportunities. The nappes themselves help very little towards an appreciation of the modern relief but subsequent faulting has been of great significance.

As a result of radial movements in the Pliocene the sea regained something of its former dominance and the land area of 'Italy' during most of this period consisted of the Alps; a narrow Apennine peninsula running from Liguria to the Abruzzi and so as an island arc through Campania and Calabria to Sicily; Sardinia and Corsica; a cluster of islands in 'Tuscany' to the west of the main peninsula; and the islands of Gargano and the Murge isolated to the south-east of it. The relentless demolition of the land surface, which had begun as soon as the first folds showed themselves above the waves in the Oligocene so that new deposits (*flysch*) interpenetrated the folds even as they rose, was now directed towards the deposition of a wide variety of sediments in the shallow waters offshore. In the post-Pliocene these sediments, mostly clays, sands, conglomerates and marls, with some limestones, were uplifted without serious disturbance; they are now revealed on either flank of the peninsula, sometimes as high as 800m above sea level, overlying the older folded rocks of the Apennine basement. They are most characteristically exemplified in the strip of deeply dissected hill country which extends from Monferrato down the eastern flank of the Apen-nines (the Adriatic Sub-Apennines) through the Marche into Basilicata. Where the sea has come to rest against these deposits the coastline is unindented with few natural harbours. Elsewhere the uplift of the former sea bed has revealed a more fragmentary distribution of the Pliocene deposits; they are found widely in southern Sicily, while in Calabria they floor the Crati lowlands and flank the Sila plateau on the south and the Serra Bruno on the west. In the Campanian Apennines they occupy several transverse gaps where faulting and collapse had earlier allowed the Pliocene sea to penetrate.

Compared with its Adriatic counterpart the geological history of the Tyrrhenian flank has been much more complex. In the intermontane basins and on the former sea bed of the Tuscan archipelago the Pliocene sediments were revealed but the drainage of these areas was impeded by the active deposition of fluvial debris, by the construction of coastal spits and by repeated local earth-movements. A further complication, with which these movements were often associated, was provided by outbreaks of volcanic activity. The earliest manifestations, beginning in the late Miocene, were in the Colline Metallifere, Elba, Giglio, Capraia and the Monti della Tolfa, while the volcanoes of Lazio (Monti Volsini, Cimini, and Sabatini and Monte Albano) date from the Quaternary. In some areas this activity and the earth-movements associated with it also served further to impede the development of a satisfactory system of drainage – a legacy which has survived into modern times. The Quaternary also witnessed the emergence of the extensive volcanic complexes of Campania and eastern Sicily.

The post-Pliocene uplift might almost be said to have brought Italy into existence. Apart from the contemporary volcanic activity which has given a special character to so many areas, it traced the rudimentary outline of the peninsula and raised the Po syncline, thus facilitating the 'filling-in' process, a task henceforth assigned to the Alpine and Apennine rivers. Furthermore, the uplift rejuvenated the rivers so that they have since etched themselves deeply into the uplands; this is well illustrated on the Adriatic Apennine slope and in the longitudinal valleys and intermontane basins within and to the west of the range.

By the time the glaciers began to expand in the Alps the demolition of the range by rivers repeatedly rejuvenated was already far advanced. Now the glaciers, covering all but the highest peaks, which emerged as *nunataks*, set their peculiar mark on the morphology of the range and there are few areas in the higher Italian Alps which have not their *cirques*, hanging valleys, U-trenches, truncated spurs and moraines to witness to this period. Down almost all the major valleys leading from the mountains the glaciers trespassed on to the plain which was revealed by successive falls in sea level; they overdeepened their valleys to enlarge, if not create, the great Italian lakes, damming them with morainic arcs while their melt waters spread vast fans of coarse gravel, sand and alluvium over the plain. In the Apennines true glaciers were confined to a few very high and exposed areas, for example the Apuan Alps, Monte Cimone and Gran Sasso, but they never descended far into the valleys below. Although the drop in the snowline and the wider incidence of frost no doubt accelerated erosion in the Apennines the relative unimportance of glacial modelling provides one of the major morphological contrasts between this range and the Alps.

With this brief summary of the salient events of the geological history of Italy in mind it may be useful to consider some of the more important groups of rocks represented, in particular as they influence the natural landscape and the human environment.

THE CRYSTALLINE AREAS. Under this somewhat unsatisfactory heading we are concerned mainly with the older deep-seated igneous rocks and with the metamorphic rocks with which they are often associated (vulcanicity in general will be treated below). The three main crystalline areas in Italy are to be found in the western Alps and in the inner zone of the central and eastern Alps, in Sardinia, and in the Calabrian–Peloritani massifs. The Alpine area is distinguished from the other two by its greater height, its arc-like form, its actively mountainous relief and by the imprint of glaciation.

The structure and morphological history of the Alps are of such complexity that generalizations about the relationship between relief on the one hand and the rock type (or structure) on the other are of limited value; scarcely any topographical feature is the monopoly of one type of rock or one structural pattern. Even so the granites, syenites, quartz-diorites (tonalite) and gneisses have shown remarkable resistance and they do constitute much of the highest and most rugged relief, notably in the Argentera, Mt Blanc, Monte Rosa, Bernina and Adamello groups as well as in the Graian and Lepontine Alps. The mica schists with their scaly texture are less resistant and steep slopes developed on them may become very unstable. This is even more true of the calcareous schists which constitute a large part of the arc of weaker rocks lying between the interior Hercynian massifs (mostly outside Italy) and the chain of resistant bastions immediately overlooking the Piedmont plain. The presence of this zone has encouraged the penetration of the Dora Riparia, Chisone and Dora Baltea towards the main watershed and has facilitated the development of longitudinal valleys in their headwaters (Val Veni, Val Ferret, upper Dora Riparia). There is no lack of very active relief but on the whole the rocks in this zone have allowed the forces of erosion to produce gentler slopes, more open valleys (frequently encumbered by masses of debris) and lower cols (Moncenisio, Fréjus, Little St Bernard). The dolomites and limestones with which the calcareous schists are often associated, provide more rugged relief, but they lie mainly over the French frontier. The schists generally have a deservedly bad reputation for landslips.

Although lithologically Sardinia and Calabria have much in common with the western Alps (granites, gneisses and mica schists, for example, are widely exposed) they offer a very different selection of landscapes. They are, of course, lower, and the contribution of tectonic movements, as revealed in rift valleys (Campidano, Crati valley), steep-sided blocks and faulted coastlines is more obvious. Furthermore, in the higher areas there is none of the morphological asperity bequeathed by glaciers; instead, rolling plateaus, locally meriting the status of mountains, occupy large areas. This is particularly true of the Sila plateau and of east-central Sardinia where rock-strewn rounded summits fall away to wide, debris-filled valleys. Under the higher temperature conditions experienced here the granite weathers to much greater depths than in northern Europe, producing a coarse sand which is easily transported by the winter torrents. In Gallura the lower relief is largely composed of such detritus, in contrast to the irregularly weathered masses of 'solid' granite which emerge from it. The greater erodibility of the schists contributes to the gullied slopes of the Catena Costiera and to the deeply etched network of the Flumendosa. Peneplanation has also played its part in producing the plateau-like outlines of the Calabrian and Sardinian horsts; erosion surfaces forming a series of wide terraces, once thought to be marine abrasion platforms, are particularly well exemplified on the western side of the Serra. From the point of view of human occupation the most significant aspect of the crystalline rocks is their hydrology – a matter deserving fuller treatment in its regional context.

THE VOLCANIC ZONES. Italy is a classic area for vulcanicity which has provided us not only with a vocabulary but also with the longest historical records on the subject. Areas which have been involved in the accident of vulcanicity bear a family resemblance but each has its own personality; in Italy differences in the age, composition and mode of occurrence of the material concerned, as well as its response to the forces of erosion, make for a great variety of landscape – the splendid active cones of Campania and Sicily, the wasted giants of Lazio with their flooded craters, the sharp hills of the Sub-Alpine fringe of Veneto, the chaotic relief of the Monte Ferru complex, and the tabular masses of the Campidano and Lugodoro. From the point of view of early settlement the volcanic areas had much to offer – easily workable soils, often of exceptional fertility, defensible sites, structures favourable to a regular supply of ground water, and a wide variety of building stones and minerals.

The earliest evidence of vulcanicity in Italy, which was associated with the Hercynian orogenesis, is to be found in the western Alps, south-east Sardinia and Calabria–Peloritani massifs. The lava flows which produced the porphyries of Lugano, Valsèsia, the Ligurian Alps and the Bolzano plateau are Triassic in age and some, the last-named for example, were of submarine origin. But the great volcanic era in Italy arrived with the Tertiary, that is with the Alpine upheaval. Basalt flows of Eocene age, sometimes intercalated with contemporary sediments, occur over sizeable areas in the Monti Lessini, in the Sub-Alpine foothills between Thiene and Bassano, and along the eastern flank of Monte Baldo. In the nearby Berici hills basaltic explosive material predominates, while the core of the Euganei hills is of trachyte lava.

The Sardinian block was not immune from the shock of the Alpine movements and volcanic activity associated with fracturing continued at intervals into the Quaternary. On the eastern side of the Campidano rift trachytic and basaltic lava welled up in contrast to the more explosive activity on the western side.

75

Near Orosei vulcanicity has left its mark in basaltic lava flows whereas in the islands of S. Pietro and S. Antioco trachytic lava and tuffs prevail. Volcanic rocks cover more than half of the north-western quarter of the island; trachytic tuffs and lava predominate in Anglona and Lugodoro and basaltic lavas in the Monte Ferru complex, which remained active into the Quaternary.

But the best known volcanic areas in the country are associated with the zone of chronic instability which flanks the Tyrrhenian Sea. In the Tuscan plateau magmatic intrusions, some dating back beyond the Mesozoic, have resulted in widespread contact metamorphism and mineralization. This activity also involved the relatively shallow platform on which the Tuscan archipelago now stands; western Elba, Montecristo and Giglio are of granite while Capraia is of trachyte lava. The actual exposure of intrusive rocks in Tuscany is quite limited but the minerals with which they are associated, notably the iron and copper of Elba and the Colline Metallifere and the tin of Monte Amiata, gave Etruria a particular significance in the ancient world. Iron, pyrites, mercury and marble are still economically important.

From Monte Amiata southwards into Campania the landscape is increasingly dominated by the aftermath of vulcanicity. Monte Amiata itself, a trachyte cone rising from a base of *argille scagliose* and Eocene clays, was active from the Pliocene into the Quaternary; it is somewhat younger than the similar extrusions of the Monti della Tolfa which erosion has reduced to insignificance. The volcanic plateau of Lazio, continuing beyond the Tiber in the Colli Albani and the Colli Laziali, lies mainly on a platform of Pliocene sediments and is Quaternary in age. Its undulating surface, formed mainly of basaltic tuffs, is punctuated by gently rising cones which only become obvious when the crater rim is reached to reveal a lake below (Bolsena, Vico, Bracciano, Nemi).

The Campanian volcanic zone, whose active life spans the Quaternary into the present, consists of four main elements. The first, Roccamonfina, is composed chiefly of basaltic lava and tuffs and has been inactive since prehistoric times. The second, Vesuvius, is well known for its long quiet periods punctuated by violent paroxysms, a type of activity to which the mountain gives its name; the last major outburst was in 1944. The inner cone is built mainly of loose ash but from time to time lava flows have breached the circular outer rim left by the violent explosion of AD 69. The third element, the Campi Flegrei (Phlegraean Fields), is a volcanic wreck in which a number of small, partially demolished cones crowd together to form a chaotically hilly relief. The area is well known for its volcanic curiosities associated with the decadent stage of volcanic activity to which the shallow crater of Solfatara, with its gaseous exhalations and boiling muddy vents, has given its name. Lake Averno, the mouth of Hell according to ancient pagan tradition, is an obvious crater lake. Nearby stands Monte Nuovo (140m) a well-documented ash volcano which first appeared in 1538. The fourth volcanic element in Campania is provided by the trachytic islands of Procida, Ischia, Ventotene and Ponza, survivors of a much more extensive submarine volcanic complex. Wide areas of Campania have been repeatedly showered with ash from Vesuvius, and at one time from Roccamonfina, to their great advantage agriculturally. The Vulture complex, although administratively part of Basilicata, may be considered an annex of the Campanian volcanic region; it is also composed of basalt lava and tuff.

Volcanic activity in and around Sicily seems to have occurred along three main zones of structural weakness. The first, roughly parallel to the northern coast, is marked by Ustica and the Lipari group, which includes Vulcano and Stromboli. The latter, emitting gases and hurling out cinders, most of which fortunately fall back into the crater, is ceaselessly but rarely dangerously active and gives its name to this particular type of volcanic behaviour. The second line of weakness runs southwards from the Lipari islands, roughly along the 15th meridian, and is associated with the lava flows on the northern flank of the Monti Iblei and with the imposing mass of Etna (3263m). Both areas are predominantly basaltic and date back to the Pliocene. Etna has been repeatedly active in historical times and in 1669 one of its lava flows destroyed most of Catania. A third volcanic zone occupies much of the Sicilian channel where ash volcanoes have erupted frequently in recent centuries only to be demolished by the waves. The best known occasion was in 1831 when in two months an ash cone rose some 200m from the sea bed to create an island nearly 4 km in circumference. It now appears on the charts as the shallow submarine platform known as the Graham bank. Further south Pantelleria and Linosa are also of volcanic origin.

Minor manifestations of volcanic activity, representing various stages of decadence, are widespread in Italy, especially in the north and centre of the peninsula and in Sicily. They include *solfataras*, typically exemplified at Pozzuoli, which emit steam and acid gases, particularly sulphuretted hydrogen; *mofettes*, for example the Grotta del Cane (Lago d'Agnano in the Campi Flegrei), discharging carbon dioxide; and geysers (*soffloni*) ejecting steam and boiling water and providing borax as a useful by-product. The geysers of Lardarello (Tuscany) have been harnessed to generate thermal electricity. In the Tusco-Emilian Apennines mud volcanoes occur as well as emissions of methane. Italy has also a long list of spas based on thermal springs (Valdieri in the Argentera massif, Abano in the Euganei hills, Lucca, Bagnoli, Tivoli, Castellammare) which have catered for the ailing rich since classical times.

EARTHQUAKES. With such a turbulent geological history since the Eocene, Italy's long record of seismic instability is readily understandable. As a rule shocks associated with volcanic activity have an epicentre at no great depth (often less than a kilometre); the Vesuvius eruption of AD 79 which separated Pompeii from the sea falls into this category. More disastrous are the tectonic shocks which have their origin deep in the earth's crust, as much as 10 km down in the case of the Apennines and several times that distance in the Alps. The principal zones of instability in Italy are located along the main Apennine ridge from the upper Tiber down through Aquila, Campobasso, Benevento, Potenza, Cosenza and Messina. The faulted blocks of the central Apennine calcareous zone and the crystalline horsts of the Calabria–Peloritani massifs have a particularly bad reputation; the earthquakes of Messina (1908), Avezzano (1915) and Irpinia (1930) all reached disaster proportions. Other vulnerable areas are the Riviera di Ponente, Forli and Ferrara, the Pre-Alpine foothills eastwards of Bergamo, Gargano and south-east Sicily. Sardinia and Corsica seem to be relatively immune.

Very different are the barely perceptible readjustments taking place along most of the Italian coastline. Sections of the Calabrian and Sicilian coast on either side of the Messina straits are slowly collapsing; the same is true of the Ligurian Riviera where the drowned river channels are traceable in the sea bed. On the other hand parts of the Apulian and west Sicilian littorals are tending to rise. Coasts near actively volcanic zones are understandably unstable because of the shift of magma below; the behaviour of the Pozzuoli coast (Temple of Serapis) is well known in this respect.

THE LIMESTONE AREAS. Over large areas of Italy the human geography is a reflection of Man's response to the rather special environment presented by various types of limestone terrain. This is the case in much of the eastern Alps, the Pre-Alps, the central and southern Apennines, Sicily and Apulia. In age the rocks concerned are mainly Triassic, Jurassic and Cretaceous, but they may be as old as the Carboniferous or as young as the Pliocene. Their lithological character is as diverse as their age – metamorphosed limestones in Tuscany (Apuan Alps, Montagnola); dolomites in the western Alps and in the Pre-Alps as well as in the type area; massive, well-jointed beds of immense thickness in Veneto; and chalks and marls, Cretaceous in age in the Pre-Alps and Miocene in the peninsula. When to this lithological variety, a great diversity in the structure and morphological history are added, the result is a wide range of natural landscape. The low platforms of Gargano and the Murge are easily classified; less so the mountainous areas. In the Alps and Gran Sasso the glaciers have left their mark; in the eastern Alps a greater rigidity has favoured the block, the faulted trench and the massive scarp, whereas in the western Alps the limestones are more intimately involved in the plasticity of the folding. In the Dolomites the isolated massifs of the principal dolomite share the landscape with the underlying, less resistant marls. In much of the Abruzzi the limestones dominate absolutely, while further south the calcareous mountain blocks form islands of relief (Monte Taburno, Cervialto, Volturno, Pollino, etc.), their flanks lapped by younger and softer rocks. The coastal limestone blocks (Argentario, Monte Circeo, Monti Latteri, Monte Pellegrino) constitute yet another group.

In most of the massive Mesozoic limestones caverns and underground drainage are common enough, but well-developed karstic features on the surface, as exemplified in the small section of the Carso left to Italy, the Norcia plateau, the Gran Sasso and the Sette Comuni, are rarer than one would expect. To judge from the dryness of the caves in many areas (e.g. the Murge and the Sette Comuni) subterranean erosion is not proceeding very actively at present; similarly many of the surface features, for example the dry valleys (*gravine*) of the Murge, the deep gorges of the Astico and Cismon, and the dolines of Cima Dodici, must be attributed to conditions no longer obtaining – a fossil landscape in fact. On the other hand the marls and chalks show clearly the scars of contemporary surface erosion.

With their meagre soils (see p. 88) the limestone massifs are usually of little agricultural value and wide expanses are abandoned to pasture and forest. The profitable areas are the tectonic depressions which are frequently floored with fertile upper Tertiary and Quaternary lacustrine deposits (Rieti, Aquila, Sulmona). Water supplies are a major problem with an obvious bearing on the distribution of settlement. In fact, the main beneficiaries of limestone zones are often neighbouring areas at a lower level, which enjoy the water supplies stored in the calcareous massifs; the basins of the lower Tiber, Pescara and Volturno are favoured in this way.

THE TERTIARY SEDIMENTS. Structurally (as noted above) there is a distinction between the folded Tertiaries (Eocene, Oligocene and Miocene), which form the Apennine foundation, and the Pliocene sediments (*molasse*) which frequently overlie them and which were uplifted in the post-Pliocene without serious disturbance. Resistant rocks do occur in the Tertiaries, the Oligocene sandstone of the northern Apennines for example, but as a group their main characteristics are their instability and their susceptibility to erosion, weaknesses which are the more readily exploited because of the torrential nature of the rainfall and the considerable altitudes at which the rocks occur. To an English eye the ferocity of erosion revealed in the landscape is often shocking. On quite moderate slopes the Eocene and Pliocene clays and the *argille scagliose* slump down repeatedly when saturated, leaving a shallow depression uphill and a lumpy mass of debris below; such landslips are known as *frane*. Where the slopes are less vigorous the clays and marls tend to erode into a monotonously undulating surface, but locally a chaotic relief of fretted domes and mud-choked depressions may result; this is the case in the badlands of the Crete Senesi. Elsewhere the clays may be scarred by a maze of steep gullies (*calanchi*) so that settlement and communications must seek the temporary stability of the crests. When weakly consolidated sandstones cap a succession of sands and clays, as is often the case in the Pliocene sediments, the tabular surface is deeply etched by the dendritic drainage pattern and the plateau edges fall away in steep, fretted scarps which give way to *calanchi* as the torrents reach the clays; this is classically exemplified at Volterra (pl. xia).

In short, the Tertiaries, overwhelmingly soft and impermeable, are being wasted rapidly by erosion and the demolition of the uplands has its counterpart in the disastrous silting of the lowlands. To the farmer they give little satisfaction; the sands drain too quickly while the clays bake out in summer and become sticky and unworkable in winter. On such lands the original topsoil has long since disappeared and the farmer is working the parent rock.

THE PLAINS. In Italy these are overwhelmingly plains of alluviation, their constituent sediments rarely dating back further than the Quaternary. It may be objected that the Valle Padana owes much to glaciation, but its morainic fringe is more hill than plain, and the spreads of pebbly gravels, sands and alluvium which fall away to the Po are the work of rivers, albeit rivers swollen by ice-melt and stimulated by rejuvenation. Perhaps the Tavoliere di Puglie, Italy's second largest plain, should be put in a different category since its alluvial covering is a fairly thin veneer overlying the Quaternary sea bed. This contrasts strongly with the Valle Padana where, at least in Lombardy and Veneto, some hundreds of metres of fluvial deposits cover the marine sediments proper.

Their very differing population densities and levels of economic development invite a distinction between the Northern Plain on the one hand and the coastal plains of the peninsula on the other. In fact, the latter with their violent silt-laden floods, their marshes and malaria have proved a difficult environment which only now is yielding to new enterprise and new techniques. The Valle Padana too has its problems, but for various reasons, historical and social as well as physical, Man's mastery of the hydrology, which is the key to the development of all the Italian plains, has been more successful here than further south. The problem of water supplies and water control is a basic theme in Italian geography which will receive further treatment in its regional context.

## SEAS AND COASTS

THE SEAS. As might be expected in an area which has so recently experienced earth-movements on a majestic scale, vast expanses of the sea bed surrounding Italy fall away to great depths and the continental shelf (roughly above 200m) is poorly represented. The Tyrrhenian, for example, reaches nearly 4000m to the northwest of Stromboli and the rim of its basin is particularly steep along the coasts of Calabria and the Corsica–Sardinian block. Its relief is complicated by a number of east–west submarine ridges of volcanic origin, two of which break the surface in the islands of Campania (Ponza, Ventotene, Ischia) and Sicily (Ustica, Lipari islands). Northwards of 41°N the Tyrrhenian shallows irregularly and communicates with the Ligurian Sea over a relatively shallow shelf from which rises the Tuscan archipelago. Even here the Corsican straits exceed 200m while the other main exit from the sea, south of Sardinia, is never less than 1000m deep. In the straits of Bonifacio, however, the Corsica–Sardinia block is barely submerged.

The Ligurian Sea exceeds 2000m in the west but shallows towards the Tuscan coast where Gorgona and Capraia stand on the edge of one of the wider expanses of continental shelf. Along the unstable Riviera coast the submarine slope is steep and the continuation of the rivers across it is regarded as evidence of recent collapse.

The Mediterranean reaches its greatest depth in the Ionian Sea (4115m some 170 km east of Malta). Its basin climbs sharply to the Sicilian coast from 2000m, and 40 km to the south of Cape Spartivento depths of over 3000m have been plumbed. Along the eastern coast of Calabria the fall-away to 1000m is still rapid but off the western Salentine coast a limited continental shelf appears.

The Adriatic is divided into two basins by a wide sill on which stands the island of Pelagoza. The southern basin descends to over 1200m whereas the northern one is nowhere below 243m and shallows towards the Venetian shore to form one of the few extensive continental shelves in the Mediterranean. It may be regarded as the submarine extension of the Valle Padana whose rivers continued across it when sea level fluctuations associated with the ice age exposed much of what is now the sea bed.

The relief of the Sicilian narrows is much more complex. In the south a wide continental shelf extends from the gulf of Hammamet to include the volcanic islands of Lampedusa and Linosa; in the north the Miocene platform of south-east Sicily continues southwards to emerge in Malta and Gozo. Towards Pantelleria the shallowness and irregularity of the sea bed are attributable to accumulations of volcanic ash, much of it very recent; Graham bank, Pantelleria bank and Talbot bank are all shallower than 20m. Pantelleria itself rises steeply from one of the deepest sectors of the Sicilian channel.

The configuration of the seas surrounding Italy is not without its influence on the geography of the peninsula itself. The deeper Ligurian and Tyrrhenian seas, with their correspondingly thicker homothermal layer, contribute towards the greater mildness of the western flank of the peninsula in winter; at that season the surface water at 13°C in the Ligurian Sea is four degrees warmer than in the shallower gulf of Venice, while in summer there is little to choose between them (25°C). The submarine relief is also of obvious importance to the fishing industry. The dominance of the warm homothermal layer below 200m and the consequent absence of those cold up-wellings which stimulate plankton growth elsewhere, the great depth, the high salinity and the poor contribution of organic matter made by rivers together serve to reduce the value of the Mediterranean as a fishing ground. Catches are varied but usually very meagre in quantity. In these circumstances the limited continental shelves, especially that of the upper Adriatic, have a particular importance, favoured as they are by the greater penetration of light to the sea bed, by the organic contribution of the Po and other rivers, and by seasonal changes in salinity and temperature.

Round most of the Italian coasts tidal movements are so weak that they can be ignored. The Venetian coast at the shallow end of the Adriatic cul-de-sac is exceptional in having a spring tidal range of nearly a metre, a movement which helps to scour the lagoons of unwanted silt. When a spring high tide coincides with the *scirocco* the Venetian squares may be flooded. Elsewhere significant tidal movements are restricted to narrow straits, notably the Straits of Messina.

The anticlockwise circulation of surface water in the western Mediterranean basin and the Adriatic encourages a northerly drift off the west coast of Italy and a southerly drift off the east coast.

THE COASTS. Since the rudimentary outline of 'Italy' emerged in the post-Pliocene its coastline has been subjected to continuous modification. Glacial fluctuations in sea level, local crustal warping, uplift and collapse, the massive accumulations of rivers and of waves and volcanoes have all made their peculiar contributions. Although the local coastal morphology may often be complex in origin, certain broad types may be identified.

The first is the faulted coast, falling away steeply to great depths and fairly regular in outline. The east coast of Sardinia south of Cape Comino, the Catena Costiera of Calabria and the Ligurian littoral are typical; the eastern edge of the Peloritani massif and the eastern half of the north Sicilian coast might also be included although the latter could be classified as longitudinal. In places along the Calabrian coast the mass of detritus provided by a succession of torrents has been so great that the steepness of the profile has been modified by wave-built features. Along the Riviera di Ponente faulting parallel to the coast and accompanied by drowning has introduced some of the features of a longitudinal coast.

Another type includes those coasts where the sea has come to rest against a well-defined, homogeneous block, in fact usually linestone. Such are the coasts of Cilento, eastern Gargano, Monte Conero and the Murge. The cliffs may be high or quite modest (as in the Murge) but the fall-away below sea level is more gradual than in the case of the faulted coast and there is usually a noticeable wave-cut bench. In outline such shorelines have few major indentations but rather a succession of rocky coves sometimes difficult of access because of reefs. In limestone areas the few good natural harbours are often the drowned mouths of fossil valleys (Brindisi, Otranto). Inland the plateau-like surface may be broken by marine abrasion platforms. Along the Tyrrhenian shore there are many small headlands which might be regarded as miniature representatives of the block type, for example Monte Argentario, the Sorrento peninsula and Monte Pellegrino.

The best examples of the ria coast in the Mediterranean are to be found in Corsica but the type is also represented in Gallura whose deep bays and island-enclosed anchorages were highly regarded by Nelson.

One of the elementary facts of Italian geography is the contrast between the uniformity of the Adriatic coast and the diversity of the Tyrrhenian (and incidentally of the Dalmatian). Between the rivers Conca and Fortore the sea rests against roughly horizontal Pliocene beds to produce a monotonously straight coastline broken at intervals by the shallow mouths of a succession of rivers; apart from the shelter given by Monte Conero these are the only natural harbours available. At best there is only a very narrow coastal plain where river debris has been distributed laterally; sizeable cliffs are rare and the long beaches continue gently below sea level.

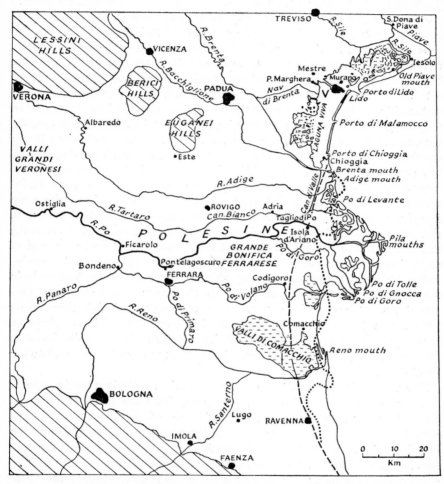

*Fig. 17.* The Po delta zone. Broken line – coastline *c.* 500 BC; dotted line – coastline 1500 AD. Most of the 'fossil' deltas referred to in the text lie between these two lines

During the glacial and post-glacial phases the alluvial coast which now stretches from Rimini to Duino fluctuated extensively; in fact, its history has been one of continuous change, much of it well documented. The coastline at any one time represents a balance of forces – the deposition of rivers, the constructive,

distributive and locally destructive action of waves working over a gently inclined sea bed, the subtle drift of tides and currents, local collapse in overloaded
deltaic areas, and finally the influence of Man, who with ant-like persistence, has
tried to manipulate these forces, often very effectively, for his own ends.

From Chioggia northwards lies the classical lido coast. Except where the
Tagliamento and Isonzo have succeeded in building their deltas, the smooth
coastline is edged with sandspits (*lidi*) and lagoons (*lagune*). Most of the latter
have been reduced by silting to mere remnants of their former selves but two
have managed to survive, one, the Marano-Grado lagoon, because the rivers
entering it are short and carry little silt, and the other, the Venetian lagoon,
because the Venetians have always been at pains to preserve it. On the landward
side of the Venetian lagoon lies the *laguna morta*, a jigsaw puzzle of flat islands
and muddy creeks (*valli*) where the tide rarely penetrates; its inhabitants lead an
amphibious existence shared between horticulture and fishing. The rest of the
lagoon, the *laguna viva*, owes its survival to the imperceptible scouring of
the tide and anything likely to check this process, for example floating mills in
the more active channels, was forbidden by the Republic. The hydrology of the
*laguna viva* is complex. Shallow muddy ridges separate it into three basins
whose waters tend to behave independently. Each basin is associated with a gap
(*porto*) through the *lidi*, and at these exits breakwaters have been built in modern
times to encourage scouring as well as to assist shipping (pl. VII). Between the
active stretches of the lagoon muddy islands have emerged with the aid of
vegetation and it was on such that the refugees from the Huns and other invaders built their settlements, among which Venice assumed the leadership in
the ninth century. Throughout its history the Republic was constantly pre-
occupied with the protection of the *lidi* from wave action and of the lagoon from
silting. To this end the Brenta and the Piave were diverted in the sixteenth
century, and by means of a cut at Portoviro (1604), the Po, whose distributaries
were threatening Chioggia, was persuaded to empty more of its waters into the
Po di Goro.

From Chioggia southwards, almost to Comacchio, the Po delta barely manages
to rise above sea level and its seawards slope slides gently below the Adriatic.
The bulge of the modern delta, the latest of a series of seven since classical times
according to Marinelli, is the work of the last five centuries, and half of it has
been built since 1900. The speed of accretion has rarely been constant for long;
very little was added in the first half of the nineteenth century, but the considerable growth since then probably reflects the pace of deforestation in the Apennines and the increasing confinement of the river by means of levees. The
localization of accretion along the distributaries produces a finger-like pattern;
the intervening 'dead' areas (*sacchi*) silt up more slowly with the aid of vegetation, and at a later stage, although still easily identifiable, are sealed off from the
sea by the lateral drift of material from the 'fingers'. Similarly, when a channel
becomes inactive, wave action gets the upper hand and the deltaic bulge is

84

flattened to form a fringe of frontal spits. Largely as a result of human inter-ference the delta north of the Po Grande is moribund (at least at the moment) and half its surface is occupied by imperfectly filled *sacchi* which are ignored by the two weary distributaries 'draining' this part of the delta (Po di Levante, Po di Maestra). Some 80% of the river's discharge, which has been calculated to include a detritus load of 40 million tons per annum, passes through the Pila and Tolle mouths; most of the rest uses the Gnocca and Goro channels. The negligible gradient of the distributaries makes land drainage by gravity almost impossible and reclamation by poldering has had to contend with the further lowering of the surface by shrinkage. Furthermore, apart from the hazards of autumn flooding, this area, like most deltas, is sinking under its own increasing weight and in recent years the pace of collapse has quickened. It is feared that this acceleration may be connected with the extraction of methane; one zone fell 70 cm between 1951 and 1956.

South of the modern delta, in Emilia, a somewhat different type of alluvial coast may be recognized. It consists very largely of fossil deltas (classical and medieval in age) whose seawards edges, never sharply prominent, have been redistributed by waves and wind into a more or less continuous sweep of sand-spits and dunes. In classical times the most active distributaries of the Po, each with its rather flat delta, were what are now the upper Po di Goro, Po di Volano and Po di Primaro (which passes Ferrara and wanders into the Valli di Comac-chio). The famous break at Ficarolo (1152) robbed the Po di Volano of most of its share of the Po waters, and the discharge of the other Emilian rivers flowing directly into the sea is quite small. Lines of fossil dunes and sandspits (*dossi*) sweeping round from Ravenna towards Chioggia mark stages in the development of the classical and medieval deltas; they can be easily identified in the two large expanses of shallow brackish water sealed off from the sea by coastal drift, the Valli di Comacchio and the Valli di Codigoro. The meandering causeways in these sheets of water (they cannot properly be called lakes or lagoons) are the levees of former distributaries. Ravenna, which stood on the southern side of the entrance to a commodious bay, and was Rome's main naval base in these waters, survived the insidious threat of silting until the Byzantine era. The diversion of the Reno round the Valli di Comacchio, which was planned in the eighteenth century was only satisfactorily achieved in the 1920s. In this area the heavy burden of silt in the rivers has favoured *colmate naturali*[1] rather than poldering as a means of reclaiming land.

From Carrara to Cilento the Italian coast is characterized by a series of shallow sickle-shaped bays looped between headlands (Monte Massoncello, Argentario, Circeo, etc.) many of which were formerly islands. The smooth shoreline of the bays is mainly the work of waves which from the Quaternary onwards have built off-shore bars and spits; the headlands and islands provided convenient anchors for these constructive features. The extensive areas of water sealed off

[1] See page 40.

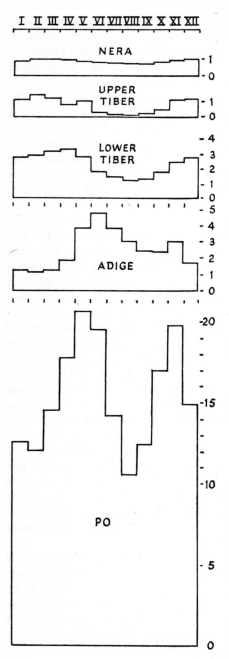

behind these *cordons* have been largely filled in by the erratic and silt-laden rivers of the hinterland, but remnants survive in the lagoons of Orbetello, Sabaudia and Fondi. Few rivers are powerful enough to prevail against the lateral distribution of detritus by wave action so that even the deltas of the Arno, Ombrone and Tiber are flattened. The failure of many rivers to find a satisfactory outlet through the coastal spits and dunes has added to the difficulty of draining these coastal lowlands which for centuries were almost uninhabitable because of malaria.

## RIVER REGIMES

For whatever use it is destined – power, agriculture, industry or domestic supplies – there are few things more precious in Italy than water. A river regime owes its character to a multitude of influences – the size, shape and climatic diversity of the basin, its lithology, vegetation cover and land-use – but in Italy the influence of climate is paramount.

In the peninsula and islands the limited area of many catchment basins, the absence of natural lakes, the steep profiles and the impermeability of so much of the surface combine with the seasonal and erratic rainfall to produce a torrential regime. In summer rivers may be completely dry or at best a series of tenuously connected pools; in winter they fluctuate wildly with the

*Fig. 18.* Regimes of the Nera at Macchia-grossa, the Tiber at Biaschi and Rome, the Adige at Boara and the Po at Pontelagoscuro in cubic metres per second

vagaries of the weather. The larger rivers may survive the drought and high evaporation of the summer more successfully, but their behaviour is a clear reflection of the rainfall regime of their basins. Most fortunate are those rivers whose watershed encloses a large area of permeable rock; such are the Pescara, Velino and Nera whose flow is maintained by the limestone springs of the Abruzzi. Without the contribution of the Nera, Velino and Aniene, the flow of the Tiber at Rome in summer would be as meagre as that of the Arno at Florence. In Campania, the Volturno and the Sele (source of the Apulian aqueduct) are similarly privileged. To a less degree the volcanic rocks, for example the permeable tuffs of the Lazio plateau, also help to even out the discharge.

The regimes of Italy's Alpine rivers show clearly the effect of melting ice and snow. The former's contribution lasts from spring till autumn while that of snowmelt is concentrated in April and May. In consequence Alpine rivers experience a spring and early summer maximum, maintain a fair level in summer and autumn (both seasons of considerable rainfall in the Alps), then drop to a minimum in winter. When the larger Alpine rivers reach the Northern Lowlands the seasonal peculiarities of the rainfall there begin to make themselves felt. In general the spring peak is reinforced and the winter minimum is maintained, but the heavy autumn rains in the Pre-Alps and in the plain produce a second peak at that period. The Po itself (at Pontelagoscuro) is normally highest in late spring (May–June) and in autumn (October–November), and lowest in winter and summer. The Apennine tributaries which reinforce its spring and autumn peaks, make only a modest contribution to the Po. Their seasonal fluctuations are liable to be suddenly interrupted by severe flooding, a tendency increased by the absence of lakes in their courses and by the impermeability of their catchment basins. The loss of material per square kilometre on the Apennine slope is many times greater than on the Alpine slope.

## SOILS

Although much work remains to be done before a definitive classification of the soils of Italy can be made, they are, no less than those of other areas, the outcome of the subtle inter-relationship of parent rock, climate, vegetation and other biotic factors. The character of the parent rock deserves special attention, not only because it determines the mineral content and texture and affects the behaviour of water on the surface and in the subsoil, but because over vast areas the natural evolution of the soil has been cut short by the replacement of the natural vegetation by farmland. In fact, in many parts of the peninsula, particularly on the Tertiary clays, the farmer is cultivating the parent rock, and although here and there the original profiles may have survived along with the vegetation, to classify a zone as a whole on the basis of such remnants would be unrealistic. The recognition of a regosol group, covering much of the area underlain by *argille scagliose* and Eocene and Pliocene clays, is therefore fully justified (see fig. 19). In general these clay-based soils are far from amenable to cultivation; apart from their surface instability, they tend to become water-logged and cold in winter, to the detriment of autumn-sown cereals, while in summer they bake out and become as unworkable as in winter. Locally they may be so profoundly fissured by shrinkage in summer that tree crops are eliminated altogether.

Another broad group clearly related to the parent rock is the alluvial soils. Their agricultural value depends very largely on the mineral composition and texture of their constituent sediments and on the behaviour of water within them. For example in the Piedmont plain the alluvium derived from the *pietre verdi* is much less valuable than that from the lime-rich calcareous schists, and in the Northern Plain in general the coarser deposits of the upper plain are less fertile and less suited to irrigation (because of their permeability) than the fine alluvium of the lower plain. On the whole, at least compared with north Germany, the Italian alluvia are sufficiently recent not to have been excessively leached, al-though in the coarser fluvio-glacial terraces chemical alteration associated with this process has encouraged the development of an impervious clayey pan (*ferretto*) which may inhibit the drainage. The hydrology is also of obvious impor-tance in those low-lying sectors of the plain which have only recently been re-claimed. The soils, in such zones, although rich in organic matter, are only cultivable after expensive hydraulic systematization. They are sometimes re-ferred to as hydromorphic soils.

Soils derived from volcanic rocks, which are perhaps too uncritically equated with fertility, are of such diversity as to be best classified by other criteria than the accident of their origin. For example, recent lava flows (Etna) and pyroclastic accumulations (Vesuvius), although no doubt potentially valuable, are from a practical viewpoint best classified as lithosols. Similarly the well-drained gritty loam evolved on the tuffs of the Lazio volcanic plateau owes much to the mild, humid climate experienced there and to the former oak forest cover, and so it is best fitted into the zonal scheme; Mancini classes most of it as a brown forest soil. Of course there is no denying that the fertility of many areas is closely related to the chemical composition of weathered volcanic rock rich in mineral plant foods. The basaltic lavas of Etna, rich in sodium, potassium and calcium, and the widespread basaltic and trachyte ash of Vesuvius, much of which has been redistributed by water, are obvious cases.

Except in the Alps where the terrain inevitably includes large areas of scree and bare rock, lithosols occur most extensively where limestones outcrop. From the farmer's point of view at least, large areas of the calcareous massifs of the Abruzzi, Campania and Basilicata, as well as parts of the Apulian tablelands, carry no continuous soil cover; what little soil there is is often concentrated in joints, fissures and karstic depressions. Deforestation and excessive grazing are blamed for much of this desolation, but it is probable that many of the high areas were never much better. The improvement of such areas is retarded by the expense and practical difficulty of re-afforesting almost bare rock and by the slowness of topsoil accumulation on a surface where the weathering is largely chemical. Fortunately extensive areas of residual soil have survived on the lime-

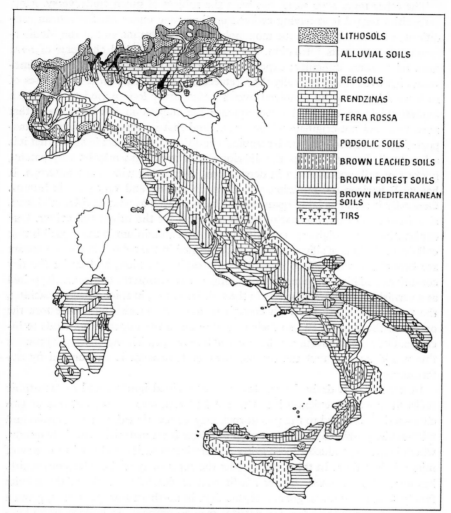

*Fig. 19.* Distribution of soil types (after F. Mancini)

stones, although few of them are without their threadbare patches and rocky scars. Two main types are recognizable, each of which has evolved in response to a different climatic and vegetational environment. The rendzinas are character-ized by a dark brown, loamy A-horizon, rich in humus and resting directly on the parent rock; fragments of limestone are usually embedded in the topsoil but there is no true B-horizon. This type is widely represented in the Pre-Alps and the higher calcareous massifs of the peninsula where the climate favours the beech.

The other type, *terra rossa*, has been the subject of much controversy. Most authorities regard it as having evolved on limestone under Mediterranean conditions, but some question the monopoly of both limestone and of the Mediterranean climate in its formation. Even the assumed residual character of *terra rossa* raises some difficulty; experiments with the soluble content of the limestones involved (most typically the Cretaceous) suggest that great thicknesses of rock would have to be dissolved over an excessively long period to produce a modest thickness of soil. In consequence the suggestion has been made that *terra rossa* did not originate wholly *in situ* and that it represents material transported by water and wind under tropical conditions in the past; in short, that it is a fossil soil. In a given area the distribution of *terra rossa* may be very patchy, pockets of soil, accumulated in depressions, alternating with rocky outcrops. It has no B-horizon (cf. rendzinas), is clayey in texture and very poor in humus. Generally it contains large quantities of bases as well as sesquioxides of silicon, aluminium and iron, the last of which accounts for the bright red colour. One explanation of the high concentration of iron and aluminium in the topsoil is that colloidal solutions of silica and iron oxide formed in the subsoil in the wet season are brought to the surface in summer by capillary action, and under the dry conditions and high temperatures obtaining at that season the oxides are deposited as a varnish around fine particles in the soil. In winter, in spite of heavy leaching, the temperatures are not high enough to free this varnish and so restore the oxides to the subsoil, and so their contribution to the upper layers tends to increase. Only the application of humus will free the varnish and check the process; this would suggest that the development of *terra rossa* is encouraged by deforestation.

In general soils derived from the coarser-grained igneous and metamorphic rocks fit most conveniently into the zonal pattern (see below) but one or two characteristics related to the parent rock may be mentioned. Granite, gneiss and mica-schist provide a high proportion of coarse inert material, especially quartz, which helps to produce a loose gritty texture but contributes little in the way of mineral plant food. In this latter respect the superiority of the calcareous schists has already been noted. Under Mediterranean conditions rocks of the granite family weather to much greater depths than in northern Europe so that, given a suitable terrain, a thick layer of detritus may accumulate. In hollows or on low-lying ground this may become waterlogged but elsewhere it may serve as a valuable subsoil reservoir which can be tapped for irrigation. On the whole the granite soils are not the worst in the Mediterranean area.

The attention so far given to the parent rock should not be allowed to obscure the paramount importance of climate in soil formation. The relationship between precipitation and evaporation, as revealed in soil profiles, is particularly significant, and there is an unmistakable similarity between the distribution of soil associations on the one hand and that of rainfall and vegetation on the other.

In the high areas of the Alps where the rainfall is very heavy the characteristic soils are the podsols (pH 4–5), whose distribution coincides roughly with that of the coniferous forest zone. Except where drainage is bad the typical ash grey horizon is usually present. On impermeable marls and clays where the forest has been cleared and the slopes are often less steep (e.g. on the high plateaus of the Dolomites) the podsols may be replaced by a peaty accumulation carpeted with spongy turf. The brown podsolic soils differ from the podsols in degree rather than kind; they occur at a somewhat lower altitude where the rainfall is less heavy but they are still very acid (pH 5·5). They are extensively represented in the Alps but elsewhere they occur only on the very high areas of the northern Apennines and of the Calabrian plateaus. They are best used for forestry and hay pasture. A third type of very acid soil (the brown leached soils) occurs on the moraines and coarse fluvio-glacial soils along the Sub-Alpine margin of the Northern Plain where the higher temperatures are offset by the extreme porosity of the surface.

The brown forest soils correspond roughly to those areas which are mild enough and humid enough to support (or to have supported in the past) large expanses of deciduous oak and beech. Geographically this includes the lowest slopes of the deep valleys penetrating the Alps (Adige, Piave, Valtellina, etc.), the Pre-Alpine foothills where non-calcareous, and much of the Ligurian Alps, as well as large expanses of the Apennines and the higher Anti-Apennines where the parent rock is not limestone. These soils, which tend to be slightly acid, have been cultivated extensively for a very long time so that the soil profile, in which at best the B-horizon is poorly represented, is often incomplete.

Just as, when the vegetation cover was complete, the deciduous woodlands shaded off into the evergreen woodlands below, so the brown forest soils give way to the brown Mediterranean soils as one descends to the drier low hill country near the coast. Large sections of Sicily, Sardinia and the Tyrrhenian littoral are occupied by this latter type of soil which has suffered extensively as a result of over 2000 years of continuous cultivation. Where the B-horizon has survived it is better developed than in the brown forest soils; this is attributed to longer periods of mild, wet weather in spring and autumn which favour soil-forming activity (for example, the leaching down of clay and humus).

Where the climatic conditions are suited to a more xerophylous Mediterranean vegetation, for example on the Tavoliere di Puglie, a neutral soil evolves in which the available raw humus is poorly assimilated. The satisfactory utilization of these soils, which may be slightly alkaline locally, requires irrigation.

In a few flat and poorly drained sections of the Apulian littoral, where the rainfall is low and unreliable, a soil similar to the *tirs* of Morocco occurs. It is characterized by a thick, dark topsoil directly overlying the parent rock, which in most cases is alluvium or recent marine silt. The dark colour is only partially explained by the rich organic content, a legacy of a steppe or coastal marsh vegetation. Until recently the *tirs* were used almost exclusively for extensive cereals and sheep grazing.

The following is a summary of the soil types referred to above (adapted from Mancini):

| Type | Parent rock | Associated vegetation |
|------|-------------|----------------------|
| **Azonal** | | |
| Lithosols | Scree, bare limestone, etc. | |
| Alluvial soils | Alluvium | |
| **Intrazonal** | | |
| Regosols | Clay, marls, etc. | |
| Rendzinas | Limestone | Deciduous forest (beech) |
| *Terra rossa* | Limestone | Mediterranean evergreen forest |
| **Zonal** | | |
| Podsols | | Coniferous forest |
| Brown podsolic soils | | Coniferous and mixed forest |
| Brown leached soils | Moraine | mixed forest |
| Brown forest soils | | Oak, beech, chestnut |
| Brown Mediterranean soils | Non-calcareous | Mediterranean evergreen forest |
| *Tirs* | | Mediterranean coastal steppe |

# PART III

# Regional Geography

# REGIONAL GEOGRAPHY

The regional treatment of a country is largely a matter of convenience and a too rigid application of purely physical criteria is apt to result in distortion. On the basis of structure and relief the Italian Alps form one major region, but plain and mountain are so closely connected by their common interests in Alpine routeways and in water and hydro-electric supplies that it might be argued that the central Alps and the adjoining Lombardy plain should be treated together rather than separately as parts of the Alpine and Padane major regions. Similarly, if climate is taken as the criterion of regional division, Liguria falls within the Mediterranean zone, but its industrial and commercial associations link it firmly with the North. Furthermore, the history of Italy as a political unit is so recent that feeling for the traditional historical divisions cannot be ignored. People still tend to think of themselves (and others) as Piedmontese, Calabrians, Venetians or Sicilians, and this is understandable in a country where the majority rarely leaves its home district and where the industrial development has still not yet brought about the internal mobility experienced in England over the last hundred years. The present administrative system recognizes this fact by bracketing the provinces (roughly the size of French departments and named after the principal town) into regions which correspond broadly with ancient historical divisions. Indeed the 1948 constitution granted autonomous status to Sicily, Sardinia, the Valle d'Aosta and the Trentino–Alto Adige, and although elsewhere the *regione* has little administrative force, there is a strong current of opinion in favour of further regional devolution, and a beginning has been made recently with Friuli–Venezia Giulia. Except where there is a clearly recognizable minority whose interests are in need of protection, the wisdom of this departure may be questioned; but for the geographer in search of a satisfactory regional division there is much to be said for tempering devotion to the conventional criteria of regional delimitation (relief, structure, climate, etc.) with a respect for ancient associations and traditional sentiments, even though the units which emerge may lack a satisfactory peripheral definition in terms of physical features. Indeed, this weakness is almost unavoidable in a country where the urban traditions are so strong that the historical region is often the projection of the dominating influence of an ancient city into its immediate surroundings; Florence and Milan, Venice and Naples are among the more obvious examples.

The customary division of the mainland into three major regions, the North, the Centre, and the South, will be adopted here. The North is given unity by the sweep of the Alps and the great plain they enclose; by its close continental connections with central and western Europe; by the productivity of its agriculture and industry which furnish, by Italian standards, a high standard of living; and by the consciousness of its people of being Northerners. For reasons mentioned above the broad climatic unity of the area is violated by the inclusion of Liguria.

The North will be further divided into:

I. The Alps.                    (a) The western Alps
                                (b) The central Alps
                                (c) The eastern Alps

*Fig. 20.* The regional divisions of Italy adopted in the text

II. The Northern Lowlands.   (*a*) The lowlands of Piedmont
                                (*b*) The lowlands of Lombardy
                                (*c*) The lowlands of Veneto and Friuli–Venezia Giulia
                                (*d*) The plain of Emilia–Romagna

III. Liguria.

The Centre is essentially peninsular and Mediterranean, and although it contains two large cities whose contribution to western civilization has been incalculably great, it is still predominantly agricultural. Its component parts, which include the former Grand Duchy of Tuscany and the Papal States (outside the Valle Padana), have many common problems, notably the need for water control in all its aspects and the absence of industrial advantages. The Centre may be further divided into:

*a*. The northern Apennines
*b*. The Marche and the central Adriatic flank
*c*. Umbria

*d*. Tuscany
*e*. Lazio
*f*. The Abruzzi highlands

The South, although it differs from many sections of the Centre only in degree, constitutes a special region because of its poverty and backwardness, in part the legacy of centuries of maladministration and neglect, in part the consequence of its geographical endowment. Furthermore, the people are conscious, and are made conscious, of being Southerners. The region will be treated in the following subdivisions:

*a*. Campania
*b*. Molise
*c*. Apulia

*d*. Basilicata
*e*. Calabria

There can be little dispute over treating Sicily and Sardinia as separate major areas. Their physical isolation has been reinforced by a racial inheritance and by a political and social history different from the rest of the peninsula so that regional consciousness is strongly developed.

# THE NORTH

## I THE ALPS

**I [a]** *The Western Alps*
The range so named, all of which falls within the administrative regions of Piedmont and the Valle d'Aosta, will be regarded as that sector of the Alps lying between the rivers Tanaro and Strona (Lake Orta); the orientation of the Val

d'Ossola towards Milan rather than Turin associates it more closely with the central than with the western Alps.

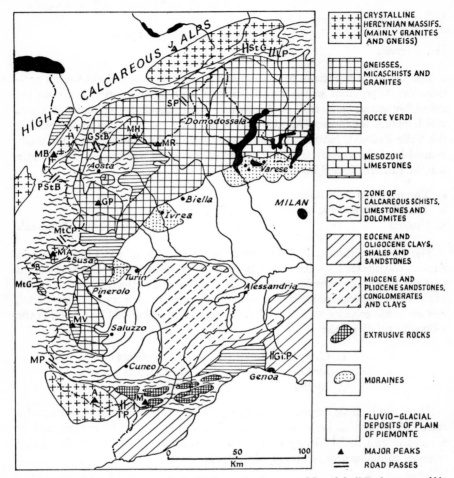

*Fig. 21.* The Western Alps, geological. The peaks shown are Mongioie (M), Argentera (A), Monviso (MV), Rocca d'Ambin (MA), Gran Paradiso (GP), Mt Blanc (MB), Matterhorn (MH), Monte Rosa (MR), Jungfrau (J); the passes shown are the Giovi, Tenda, Maddalena (Col de Larche), Moncenisio (Mt Cenis), Mongenivra (Mt Genèvre), Petit St Bernard, Grand St Bernard, Sempione (Simplon), St Gotthard and Lukmanier

Except where the break is interrupted by morainic hills, the western Alps rise sharply from the plain to reach the watershed in a surprisingly short distance; where the mountain belt is widest Mt Blanc is less than 90 km from the plain and further south, opposite M. Viso (3841m) and Argentera (3297m), the gap falls to 20 km. The narrowness of the Italian flank of the western Alps is in part explained by the absence of a Pre-Alpine zone which is such a marked feature further east. For most of its length the frontier coincides with the watershed and this principle was strengthened by the award of the largely French-speaking Tende-Brigue (Tenda-Briga) area to France in 1947. Oddly enough the same settlement brought the French frontier over the watershed in two small sectors to include the final approach to the Mt. Cenis (Moncenisio) pass and the village of Mont-Genèvre (Monginevro). As in so many sectors of the Alps the linguistic boundary does not always coincide with the watershed; French survives in a few of the valleys of the Cottian Alps and is the principal language of the Valle d'Aosta.

The structure of the western Italian Alps which is associated mainly with the Pennine nappes, is extremely complex. Those features of special interest to the geographer run along the 'grain' of the arc. Immediately above the plain and swinging round from the Maira river into the central Alps, a zone of very resistant crystalline rocks may be identified. In the south this zone rarely penetrates westwards more than 20 km, but north of the Stura, where it incorporates the so-called Canavese root zone, it widens to include the massifs of Gran Paradiso and Monte Rosa. Throughout most of this area granites, gneisses and mica-schists predominate, but in the M. Viso district, in the middle Valle d'Aosta, and between the Stura and Dora Riparia wide expanses of *pietre verdi* (serpentines and other metamorphosed basic rocks) are exposed (fig. 21). To the rear of this zone of crystalline bastions lies an arc of less resistant rocks on which the slopes tend to be gentler, the valleys wider and the cols lower. Roughly in the form of a crescent, this belt runs longitudinally between the Piedmontese crystalline bastions and the Hercynian blocks further west, most of them beyond the French frontier. It narrows to the east of the Mt Blanc massif, where its weakness has been exploited by the headwaters of the Dora Baltea (Val Veni, Val Ferret), and again to the north of the Argentera massif; it is widest in the latitude of the Dora Riparia. On the Italian side of the frontier the most widely distributed rocks are the calcareous schists which are locally associated with partially metamorphosed Triassic limestones, for example between the Maira and the Stura di Demonte. Here and there, notably in M. Ambin, the gneiss and mica-schists penetrate the calcareous schists, while in the upper Valle d'Aosta a narrow belt of metamorphosed Carboniferous sediments passes from France, where it is extensive, through Thuile and Morgex, into Switzerland. Anthracite is worked in small quantities at Thuile. Carboniferous rocks also occur alongside calcareous schists in the Cogne valley. In the Maritime Alps, east of the Tenda routeway, the structure is complicated by extensive exposures of porphyry which share the relief with Triassic limestones and calcareous schists.

Except in the south where the Stura di Demonte conforms to the 'grain' of the structure, the rivers of the western Alps cut across the mountain arc like the spokes of a wheel. Most of them are short and steep but two, the Dora Riparia and the Dora Baltea, have penetrated deeply into the less resistant interior zone to provide important low-level routeways. In contrast to the central and eastern

Alps, longitudinal valleys are poorly developed so that movement from one sector of the arc to another involves a descent to the plain, where Turin is the obvious focus. The Dora Baltea, Dora Riparia and Stura di Demonte divide the range into four recognizable sectors, namely, the Pennine Alps, to which the Mt Blanc massif may be annexed, the Graian Alps, the Cottian Alps and the Maritime Alps. The whole range has undergone severe glaciation but a combination of latitude and increasing altitude has served to imprint its characteristic features most deeply on the landscape of the northern sector. Although they are more extensive beyond the frontier, a number of small glaciers survive on the Italian side of the Pennine Alps (notably on the flanks of Monte Rosa and M. Gelé) and in the Mt Blanc massif from which two tongues descend into the Val Veni and another into the upper Val Ferret. In the Gran Paradiso massif there are several small glaciers on the range's northern face, but further south, even on such peaks as M. Ambin and M. Viso, the largest occupy no more than a square kilometre. The snowline follows a similar pattern; in the Valle d'Aosta it varies between 2800 and 3100m, according to aspect, while in the Maritime Alps, except on M. Argentera (3297m), only isolated north-facing patches of snow survive the summer.

As far as communications are concerned most valleys in the western Alps are culs-de-sac, but the deep penetrating trenches of the Dora Baltea and Dora Riparia are obvious exceptions which have been exploited since classical times. Aosta (Roman Augusta), whose street plan still retains the imprint of its founders, was established to ensure Rome's communications with Gaul through the Grand St Bernard (2472m) and Petit St Bernard (2412m) passes. Until the opening of the road tunnel under the Grand St Bernard in 1963, the valley was isolated from France and Switzerland for seven months; with the completion of the longer but lower road tunnel under Mt Blanc (from Entrèves to Pèlerins) the Dora Baltea is likely to surpass the Dora Riparia as the busiest routeway through the western Alps and the proposed extension of the autostrada from Aosta will become a necessity. In view of the convenient orientation of the valley towards north-west Europe, it seems odd that it was not chosen to carry the first trans-Alpine railway in preference to the Dora Riparia. The explanation usually given is that, at a time when Piedmont had recently surrendered Savoy, Cavour was reluctant to encourage closer communications between France and the French-speaking Valle d'Aosta. Proposals for a railway tunnel have been revived recently.

In the Dora Riparia, Susa had a similar origin and has a similar function to Aosta. The Mt Cenis (2084m), leading down the Arc valley to Chambery, is an easy pass but it is closed from November to April and a road tunnel (cf. Grand St Bernard) is under construction. Since 1947 the approaches to the col on both sides have been in French territory. Further up the Dora Riparia the Mt Genèvre pass (1760m), which like the Mt Cenis and the St Bernard passes was first opened to wheeled traffic by Napoleon's engineers, gives access to the Durance valley. The railway tunnel between Modane and Bardonecchia which carries the main line from Paris to Turin (and so to Genoa and Rome), although called the Mt Cenis route, actually underlies the Fréjus Pass.

Busy as they are in the tourist season, the two routes converging on Cuneo are of less importance internationally. One, the Maddalena (Col de Larche, 1996m), joins the Ubaye (a tributary of the Durance) and the Stura di Demonte, while the other, the Tenda (Tende, 1908m) connects Cuneo and Nice along the valleys of the Vermenagna and Roya. The Maddalena is often blocked in winter, but the Tenda, whose summit is avoided by a tunnel, is only closed occasionally. Despite repeated agitations for its reopening, the railway from Cuneo to Nice is still out of service as a result of wartime destruction, so that in fact only one railway pierces the western Alps.

Only 6% of the area under consideration is cultivated; the rest is classed as forest (32%), pasture (44%) and waste. On the fluvial and glacial deposits flooring the two deep trenches the cultivation retains something of the character of the adjoining plain with maize, fodder and hard fruits occupying much of the cultivated land. There are also numerous vineyards on the south-facing lower slopes. In the higher and narrower valleys the typical farm unit consists of three elements; near the hamlet on the valley bottom or lower slopes, a patchwork of tiny fields produces hay, rye and potatoes with occasionally a few vines. On the middle slopes, often on a sunny shoulder, a few rudimentary structures mark the temporary halting place of the spring and autumn animal migrations to the high pastures; even at this height, frequently 1700m, suitable slopes are used for potatoes and rye as well as hay. Further up are the high pastures where cattle are grazed, mainly on communal land, in the care of a few professional cowherds. With so many Piedmontese valleys trending east–west aspect is particularly important in the location of settlement and cultivation, but the nature of the rock is also relevant. For example, the calcareous schists provide more workable terrain and better soils than the *pietre verdi*, so that in the Val Maira cultivation is pushed up to over 1800m, some 300m higher than in the upper Po Valley.

Throughout the western Alps the pressure of population on the agricultural resources is excessive and deforestation for arable and pasture has far exceeded the desirable limits; the peasant usually owns the land he works but his holding rarely exceeds two or three hectares. Although there is always something melancholy about the sight of abandoned farmsteads, the drift from the land which has been accelerating over the last fifty years, is inevitable and desirable. Emigration is traditional both overseas (mainly to Argentina) and to France, where Piedmontese have widely established themselves on land abandoned by local farmers. The industries of the plain of Piedmont have absorbed their share of mountaineers and in recent decades their capacity to do so has increased notably. The movement of population in the western Alps is not just a simple exodus, however; the development of tourism has helped to check the drift and there is a small counter-current of seasonal workers into the resorts. Furthermore, constructional projects and industry are opening up new employment opportunities which have even attracted an influx from other parts of Italy, sufficiently great in the case of the Valle d'Aosta for traditional sentiment there to be disturbed for the special character of the region.

The industrial resources of the western Alps are not outstanding. The only minerals of note are the anthracite of Thuile (40,000 tons per annum) and the magnetite of the Cogne valley. Water and hydro-electric power are the principal assets; unfortunately the power has tended to benefit the plain rather than the mountains and production, which is mostly from modest-sized units because of the small size of the catchment basins, cannot be developed much further. The output of Piedmont and the Valle d'Aosta exceeded 8200 million kWh in 1964, roughly 18% of Italy's hydro-electric total. Even so the landscape of the two main valleys is becoming increasingly industrialized. The Dora Riparia as far as Susa has become a spill-over area for Turin with factories producing light engineering goods, special steels, cotton textiles and other consumer goods, notably at Susa and Bussoleno. In the Valle d'Aosta the outstanding industries are rayon at Chatillon and steel at Aosta itself. The latter, with a production of about 120,000 tons, is based on Cogne magnetite; pig is produced both in blast furnaces, for which coke has to be imported, and in electric furnaces.

The tourist industry is so far less developed than in the central and eastern Alps and caters mainly for Italians, but there are many winter and summer resorts of international repute, among them Sestriere, Claviere, Bardonecchia, Limone, St Vincent and Courmayeur. In this respect the new accessibility of the Valle d'Aosta to north-west Europe will doubtless prove to be a great asset.

## I [b] *The Central Alps*

This region lies between the Val d'Ossola and a line passing from the Stelvio, through the crests of the Ortles and Adamello groups and so along the Chiese river southwards from Tiene. This somewhat arbitrarily defined area includes a small part of Piedmont but otherwise it falls almost entirely within the administrative region of Lombardy, whose capital provides a common focus.

Perhaps more than in any other sector, the summer traveller descending from the passes here cannot fail to be aware that he has arrived in Italy, culturally if not politically. The chill and mists of the high Alps are left behind, the sun suddenly feels unusually strong, and the light has an unaccustomed intensity. Stone and tile have replaced wood and shingles in the domestic architecture; the type of cultivation in the valley bottoms is unmistakably Italian; and the northern eye glimpses exotic touches in the vegetation. In fact, the frontier coincides neither with the watershed nor with the linguistic boundary. The Poschievo salient and the canton of Ticino, both lying to the south of the watershed, are culturally Italian, but politically they are undeniably Swiss; there is no question of irredentist sentiment here. The detached fragment of Italian territory centred on Campione (whose economy depends on the casino) adds to the complexities of the frontier in the Lugano area. With the exception of the Splügen, the summits of all the main passes lie within Swiss territory; on the other hand two very small sectors of Italy are drained northwards, one (the Lei valley) to the Hinter Rhein, the other (the Spöl valley) to the Inn.

From the Northern Plain to the crests of the Bernina and Lepontine Alps, the mountain zone varies in width from 60 to 100 km. It is penetrated by a number of deep low-level valleys, both transverse and longitudinal, which favoured the spread of the Italian type of settlement as far as the watershed. The occurrence of longitudinal valleys, notably the Valtellina, Val Brega, Val Vigezzo and the middle Ticino (between Locarno and Bellinzona), is in marked contrast to the western Alps. The numerous transverse valleys, of which the Val d'Ossola, Val Levantina, Val Mesocco, the Liro–Mera valley and the Val Camonica are the most important, offer a wide choice of trans-Alpine passes. All the major valleys, most of them following fault zones, have been overdeepened by glaciers which were thick enough in places to have scored the valley sides to a height of 1500m. Lakes Maggiore (Verbano), Como (Lario) and Iseo have been gouged out to reach depths of 372, 410 and 251m respectively; this means that at their deepest points their beds are well below sea level. The higher valleys, many of which are notched with a post-glacial V, are impeded with moraines and occasionally graded into valley steps (Val Mesocco). The lower valleys on the other hand, although steep-sided, are floored by a ribbon of alluvium with here and there the shallow remnants of once more extensive lakes. Well-drained detritus cones provide useful cultivable land and favourite sites for settlement.

Structurally one of the main contrasts between the central and the western Alps is the presence in the latter of a Pre-Alpine zone. As in all the Pre-Alps this sector is predominantly calcareous, as opposed to the crystalline Alpine core. The junction between the two zones lies somewhat southwards of the major fault zone, known as the Tonale or Insubrica line, which runs from Domodossola through Locarno, Sondrio, and the Tonale col and so along the Val di Sole to Cles. Throughout much of its length this line of weakness has been exploited by the Adda, Oglio and Noce to provide an easy longitudinal routeway (fig. 22). Between Lake Maggiore and the Lecco arm of Como the Pre-Alpine zone is much dissected by steep glaciated valleys, some of them occupied by deep ribbon lakes, and the dominance of the Jurassic limestones is broken by the exposure of Permian porphyries south of Lugano. From Como to the Oglio valley (Val Camonica) the Pre-Alps constitute a massive block through which there is no satisfactory pass to the Valtellina. Here within a short distance of the plain the rounded, rather soft Cretaceous and Jurassic limestones are replaced by Triassic rocks, mainly tough limestones and dolomites with some marls. The dolomites produce the highest and most rugged relief in the Bergamasque Pre-Alps, for example le Grigne, Pizzo Arera and Pizzo di Presolana, all of them over 2400m. The Brembo and the Serio, with their tributaries, cut through the Triassic limestones in deep steep-sided valleys, but where the marls occur the relief is less

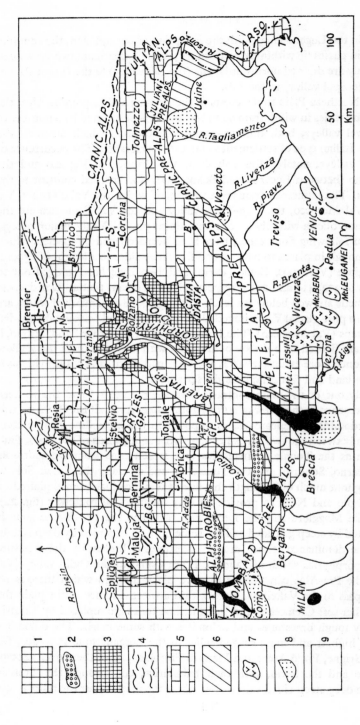

*Fig. 22.* The Eastern and Central Alps – geological. 1 – resistant crystalline rocks, mainly granite, gneiss and mica-schist. 2 – Permian conglomerate. 3 – The Porphyry plateau. 4 – Calcareous schists and limestones. 5 – Massive Mesozoic limestones. 6 – Eocene sediments. 7 – Volcanic ash and lava. 8 – Moraines. 9 – Fluvio-glacial deposits and alluvium. BG – Bernina group; AP – Adamello-Presanello group

rugged and the valleys, though often steep, are less restricted; most of the cols connecting the Val Seriana and the Val Brembana are also developed on marls. The limestones, on whose surface karst phenomena frequently occur, are extensively forested while the marls are used for hay and hardy crops. The main ridge of the Alpi Orobie, topping 3000m in Pizzo di Coca, is carved in gneisses, mica-schists and Permian conglomerates; the same rocks extend over wide areas to the north of the Brescian Pre-Alps, which are structurally a continuation of the Bergamasque Pre-Alps (fig. 22).

The crystalline zone of the Alpine core is deeply trenched by the Tonale fault line into which numerous transverse valleys from the main watershed find their way. Prolonged denudation punctuated by rejuvenation has produced a complex drainage pattern with several captures; thus the upper Oglio once flowed into the Adda through the Aprica col but was captured by the Oglio as it cut back northwards. The commonest rocks exposed are gneisses, mica-schists and granites with occasional outcrops of *pietre verdi*; any tendency towards differential erosion is usually reduced to insignificance by the overwhelming ferocity of glacial action. The Adula and Bernina (4055m) groups on the main watershed and the Ortles (3763m) and Adamello–Presanella groups to the south of it are high enough to support extensively permanent snowfields and a number of small glaciers.

In the case of the western Alps a distinction was made between the agriculture of the deep, low-level valleys and that of the higher valleys; this distinction is equally valid for the central Alps. In the Valtellina, for example, fodder, cereals and fruit, often grown with the assistance of irrigation, cover much of the alluvial valley floor; on the lower *solatío* slopes the chestnut zone has been widely replaced by terraced vineyards whose names and reputations are well known in the industry. Further up, the slopes are shared between chestnut woodlands and small peasant holdings created and maintained at immense pains; such units, many of which are now being abandoned, clearly reflect the population pressures of the recent past. Except on the lowest slopes, where hardy crops and hay are cultivated, the *ombría* side of the Valtellina is clothed with coniferous forests broken here and there by high pastures. Outside the main valleys and the lake shores (where delicate tree crops assume a modest importance) the rural economy depends on forestry and animal rearing. Transhumance is on the decline generally and is now in the hands of professional cowherds.

The main industrial resources of the area lie in its water and in its hydro-electric power (21% of Italy's output in 1964). Both have been fully exploited, although the Alps themselves get less than their fair share of the benefits. The traditional extractive industries are still of some importance in the Pre-Alps; the cement industry is served by a number of large quarries, and lead and fluorspar are mined in the Val Brembana and the Val Trompia. Metal working has been a traditional activity in Brescia province since the Middle Ages and there are still a number of small iron works in operation using local ore. The most productive mining zone is in the Val di Scalve and the biggest iron and steel plant is sited at

Lovere. Textiles are another long-established activity; both cottons and woollens are manufactured in the Val Seriana and the Val Brembana. The beauty of the lakes and mountains of the central Alps have long held a particular fascination for the trans-Alpine visitor and this easily accessible area is well equipped to accommodate tourists in winter and summer.

Despite their hazards, the passes leading through the central Alps from France, Switzerland and southern Germany and focusing almost inevitably on Milan, have always been of the greatest importance militarily and commercially, but the popularity of individual passes has varied considerably. Thus the Simplon (Sempione 2009m) was relatively unfrequented until Napoleon completed the carriageway in 1806, while the San Bernardino (2063m), less well known until the recent construction of a road tunnel under its summit (1965), has been of great military significance since Roman times.

The function of the Simplon route has always been to link north-west Europe with northern Italy and until the opening of the Grand St Bernard road tunnel it was the obvious north-western gateway into Italy for motor traffic. Two tunnels, some 18 km long, the first completed in 1906 and the second in 1921, link the upper Rhône with the Val d'Ossola and carry the main line from Paris to Milan and Rome. Just before the northern entrance, at Brig, this route is joined by a line from Bern which pierces the Bernese Oberland through the Lötschberg tunnel (1912).

Three passes, the St Gotthard (2112m), the Lukmanier and the San Bernardino, all of them within Swiss territory, lead down to Bellinzona. The first, linking the Reuss and the Ticino valleys, gives access to the Rhineland by way of Zurich. Mule traffic on it was first systematically organized in the twelfth century but the roadway was not completed till 1859. The rail tunnel, 15 km long and opened in 1882, normally carries some 40% of all trans-Alpine rail traffic and the construction of another tunnel to relieve congestion is under study; the proposed route, from Amsteg to Biasca, will be lower but much longer (32 km). The building of a road tunnel 15 km long has also been recommended. The Lukmanier (1919m) and the San Bernardino roads wind over to the Vorder and Hinter Rheins respectively; once much used by pilgrims and by Imperialist armies, they both descend to Chur, like the Splügen and Julier passes further east.

Chiavenna has much the same function in relation to the Splügen and Maloja as Bellinzona has in relation to the passes leading into the Valle Levantina. The Splügen, which carries the ENI pipeline from Rho to Ingolstadt, crosses the narrow watershed between the Hinter Rhein and the Liro-Mera valley. It provides one of the most direct routes between Milan and the Rhineland and it seems strange that it has not been exploited for rail traffic; a line to relieve pressure on the St Gotthard is in fact under discussion. The Maloja (1815m) gives access to the Engadine and from there by means of the Julier Pass (a favourite with the Romans) to the Vorder Rhein at Chur.

The upper Adda provides the approach to two passes into the Swiss Engadine;

one, the Bernina (2330m) is exploited by a road and a most spectacular light railway; the other, the Giogo di S. Maria (2502m), carries only an indifferent road. The Adda valley also forms part of two longitudinal routes, one leading over the Stelvio pass (2756m) into the Val Venosta and so to Merano, the other along the Tonale fault line to Cles, a journey which involves the negotiation of the Aprica and Tonale passes, one leading into the Oglio basin and the other climbing out of it into the Vale di Sole. To reach Bolzano the Mendola Pass must be crossed.

The Stelvio and all the trans-Alpine passes mentioned above are closed from November till April, if not for a longer period, and although this problem can be solved by using car-train services through the Simplon and St Gotthard tunnels, the central Alps so far lack an all-season motor route. The new San Bernardino road tunnel, due to come into service in 1966, should help materially in this respect.

## I [c] *The Eastern Alps*

Roughly 160 km at their widest and 240 km from west to east, the eastern Alps constitute one of the most extensive tracts of high mountain country in western Europe. The external foci provided by Turin and Milan for the much narrower western and central Alpine sectors have no counterpart here; Venice, at least modern Venice, lacks the necessary dynamism for this rôle. Fortunately the massive bulk of the eastern Alps is fragmented by a network of easily accessible valleys so that, except along the frontier, which for much of its length follows the main Alpine watershed, isolated mountain groups are more typical than continuous ranges. Although clearly exploited by rivers and glaciers, many of the major valleys are of tectonic origin. Such are the faulted trenches occupied by the Adige (south of Rovereto), the lower Sarca, and the Chiese (north of Lake Idro); in the latter case a massive downthrow brings the Mesozoic limestones and dolomites in contact with the crystalline basement. The upper Brenta and Piave (above Pieve di Cadore) exploit fractures of similar magnitude.

Within the complex structure of the eastern Alps four main zones may be identified each distinguishable by the broad similarity of rock type and landforms found within it. The first zone includes the Alpi Atesine (or Tridentine) along the frontier, the Ortles group and the Adamello–Presanella group (fig. 22). The latter is composed of quartz–diorite (tonalite or Adamello 'granite') and represents a massive intrusion. The rest of the area is almost monopolized by the mica-schists of the Grisonid and Tirolid nappes which have undergone severe thrusting. The relief frequently exceeds 3400m (Cevedale 3764m, Presanella 3558m) and its morphology is typical of high glaciated areas; small glaciers have survived in the Ortles group and they are more numerous and extensive along the frontier. Despite their detritus cones and morainic debris, the deep and ample valleys of the upper Adige (Val Venosta) and Rienza (Val Pusteria) provide easy longitudinal routeways, the first for traffic from the Valtellina and the Engadine over the Stelvio and Resia passes respectively, the second for traffic heading for the Brenner from the upper Drau and the upper Piave. Similarly the Val di Sole presents little difficulty along the most direct route from Milan to Bolzano, but from the latter northwards to the Brenner the building of the road and railway through the Isarco gorge was difficult and expensive. The crystalline rocks exposed in this zone underlie both the quartz-porphyry plateau and the high calcareous zone; they are exposed again in the Cima d'Asta range where they are also associated with granitic intrusions.

The quartz-porphyry plateau, Permian in age and submarine in origin, has its share of rugged and rock-strewn slopes but it is considerably lower than the crystalline zone identified above. The immense thickness of the flow is revealed as one ascends the Avisio valley or the gorge of the Ega river into the heart of the Dolomites. The exposure of the red porphyry on one side of the Rolle Pass opposite the white dolomite on the other presents a striking scenic and morphological contrast.

For much of its extent the high calcareous zone rests on the porphyry plateau and it varies in age from Permian to Cretaceous. The sequence varies laterally but in general the Permian and lower Triassic rocks consist of marls, clays, sandstones and soft limestones; they are succeeded by more clays and sandstones interbedded with compact limestones and dolomite. The middle Triassic is represented by a variety of marine sediments but especially by the resistant unstratified reef dolomite known as the *dolomia ladinica*. Higher still comes the principal or Noric dolomite, upper Triassic in age, very permeable, extensively fractured and massively stratified. Here and there the Triassic series is capped by remnants of Jurassic and Cretaceous limestone, giving an indication of the extent of the demolition to which the area has been subjected.

The general pattern of relief and the characteristic morphology of the Dolomites have their origin in the near-horizontal arrangement of the Triassic beds and in their lithological diversity. There are two fundamental elements: the first is an immensely thick platform composed mainly of marls, favouring gentle rounded forms, but interrupted at intervals by more resistant strata to produce steeper slopes and broad undulating terraces. This platform which provides many perfect ski slopes, is deeply incised by valleys, wider or narrower according to the nature of the horizon involved, and littered with the debris of glaciation. To reach these valleys the traveller may have to follow the narrower, steeper-sided courses of rivers cutting through the porphyry plateau, but the climb to the platform, brilliantly green with hayfields and pinewoods and dotted with farmsteads, usually offers little difficulty. Once on the platform a widening panorama unfolds in which the second element in the landscape is revealed; it consists of a number of distinct massifs rising above the gentler pasture-covered slopes of marl or drift and the steeper wooded scars of limestone to a crown of gleaming, waterless dolomite. Where the bedding is compact and massive the summit may be tabular in form, its rugged surface chaotically sculpted by glaciers and strewn with debris, its precipitous sides edged with aprons of scree resting precariously on narrow terraces (Sella group, Cima di Groste, Monte Sciliaro). Where the dolomite has been severely fractured during the orogenesis it responds to erosion by taking the form of towers, bastions and pinnacles emerging from massive screes (Gruppo delle Pale, Sassolungo, Cima Brenta). A few small glaciers survive, the biggest of them on the northern face of Marmolada, and the origin of the irregular spreads of drift on the plateaus and of the cirques and U-valleys of the higher massifs is unmistakable, but on the whole the rôle of

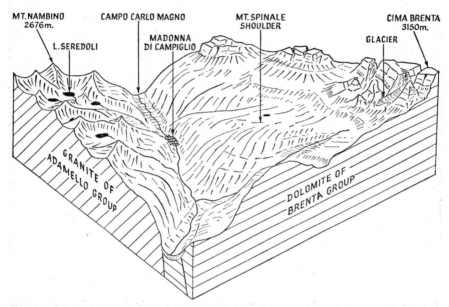

*Fig. 23*. Block diagram of the Madonna di Campiglio area illustrating the contrasting morphologies of the Brenta and Adamello groups

glaciation in the morphology of the Dolomites has been a secondary one compared with that of the structure and the lithology. This is well illustrated on either side of the Campiglio valley along which a fault has brought the crystalline rocks of the Adamello group face to face with the dolomites of the Brenta group. Both areas were glaciated (and in both small glaciers persist) and yet in the homogeneous crystalline zone to the west the sharp arêtes, lake-filled cirques and hanging valleys of M. Nambino and M. Ritorto illustrate the classic glaciated landscape, while in the Brenta group the structure and lithology assert their dominance in the form of a succession of shelves crowned by the bastions of Cima Brenta, Torre di Brenta and Cima Tosa (fig. 23 and pl. 11b).

Even in the Dolomites the proportion of true dolomite among the calcareous rocks is quite modest; in the rest of the high calcareous zone, notably to the north of Garda and Feltre, Cretaceous and Jurassic limestones predominate. The continuity of the limestone sheets, which are often severely dislocated, and the rarity of softer beds, such as those widely exposed in the Dolomites, produces a landscape of steep mountains and karstic plateaus whose barrenness is only partially hidden by scrubby woodlands. The infrequent rivers are often incised in gorges (R. Cismon); elsewhere the deep valleys may be impeded by gigantic landslips (near Dro in the Sarca valley).

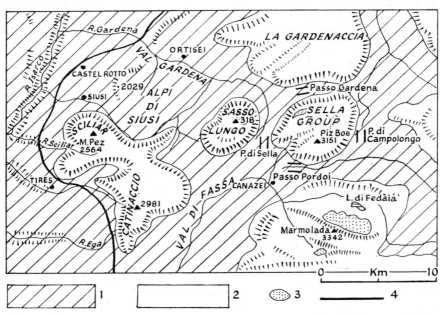

*Fig. 24.* The western Dolomites. 1 – the high plateaus mainly developed on the under-lying, less resistant marls and limestones and widely used for hay and grazing. 2 – the high rugged dolomitic massifs. 3 – glaciers. 4 – the eastern boundary of the crystalline rocks (porphyry plateau)

The northern boundary of the Pre-Alps will be taken, somewhat arbitrarily, as following the Belluno basin and the Val Sugana and thence through Rovereto to Riva. Almost everywhere they fall abruptly to the plain dwarfing the sharp volcanic hills (west of Bassano), down-faulted remnants and minor folds half buried in fluvio-glacial sediments, which complicate locally the junction of mountain and lowland. Basalt lava flows and tuffs outcrop extensively in the Monti Lessini behind Vicenza and on the eastern flank of M. Baldo, but elsewhere the Pre-Alps are overwhelmingly calcareous. Even so their structure and lithology are sufficiently varied to present a diversity of relief and landform.

The deep trenches occupied by Lake Garda and the major rivers escaping from the Alps divide the Pre-Alps into a number of easily identifiable blocks. M.

Baldo (2218m) is essentially an anticline of Jurassic limestones denuded at its summit to expose Triassic rocks; the barren slabs of its western limb form the shore of Garda. The lake itself occupies a tectonic depression which was over-deepened by the Adige glacier whose main tongue abandoned the valley of that river for the Sarca some distance north of Trento; hence the great size of the Garda moraine compared with that of the Adige. The glacier is also responsible

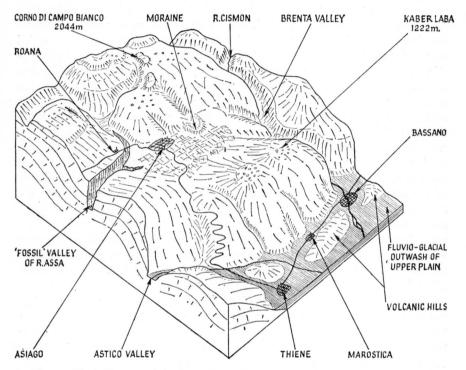

*Fig. 25.* Block diagram of the Asiago area in the Venetian Pre-Alps (see pp. 111–12)

for the hanging valleys and the precipitous face of the western Garda shore along which a road (the Gardesana) was blasted only in the 1930s.

To the east of the Adige trench lie the Monti Lessini from which a dozen pleasant valleys, all of them culs-de-sac, fan out southwards. The exposure of Triassic limestones in the Monti Lessini themselves and in the Pasubio group (2235m) have earned for the area the title of the Piccole Dolomiti. The road from Schio to Roverto forces a passage through them, not without difficulty.

The Asiago plateau, clearly defined by the Val Sugana, the deep Astico valley and the Brenta gorge illustrates a number of characteristics common to the Venetian Pre-Alps generally. Structurally it consists of a syncline of Jurassic and

Triassic limestone the northern limb of which sweeps up to form a high scarp (Cima Dodici 2341m) overlooking the Val Sugana fault. The southern limb rises to 1400m then dips sharply to the plain where a few volcanic hills seem to be breaking in vain against the formidable wall of the Pre-Alps. The waterless surface of the limestone is pitted with dolines and deeply incised with a system of gorge-like valleys, now completely dry, which once drained into the Astico. The only permanent settlements are a few *malghe* where cattle, because of the absence of springs, must be watered from clay-lined ponds filled with rain water. The higher northern zone is a karstic desolation where no creature stirs; elsewhere the limestone surface has been planted with conifers to replace the more varied woodlands razed in the First World War. Fortunately, in the centre of the syncline the Jurassic rocks are overlain by a marly Cretaceous chalk on which rye, potatoes and fodder, but no tree crops, are cultivated; the farm units are small as elsewhere in the Pre-Alps. The population is shared between half a dozen villages and the pleasant town of Asiago, which was rebuilt after its complete destruction in 1916 and is now developing as a summer resort and winter sports centre. Its main development problem is that of satisfying the demand for water. In the past the inaccessibility of the plateau recommended it to refuge groups, and although there is little evidence to support the contention, a remnant of the Cimbri is said to have settled here after their defeat by the Romans; certainly many of the older place-names are non-Italian (e.g. M. Kaberlaba) and the local Germanic dialect was in common use a century ago. Another interesting by-product of the area's inaccessibility was the immunity it gave from the repeated disturbances to which the neighbouring plain was subjected. In the Middle Ages the seven communes of the plateau combined to oppose the ruthless tyranny of Romano d'Ezzelino and thereafter as the Sette Comuni managed to preserve a large measure of autonomy, even under the Venetians, until the Napoleonic reorganization of Italy. The tortuous roads which now penetrate the area were built at a time when the Austrian frontier lay along the northern rim of the plateau and in the minds of older Italians the Altopiano d'Asiago will always be associated with the desperate and bloody battles of the war of '15.

Monte Grappa, which has a history no less tragic, is an anticline involving rocks aged from the Triassic to the Miocene. Its crest forms an undulating whaleback but the softer limestones of the precipitous southern flank are scarred by torrents. It is of little value agriculturally and its sterile surface is now being decently clothed with forests.

The Venetian Pre-Alps east of the Piave Gap are very similar to Monte Grappa. Karstic phenomena are well developed in the Cansiglio plateau where Lake S. Croce is of karstic origin. Like all the Pre-Alps this sector receives a heavy rainfall but its benefits, in the form of springs, are chiefly enjoyed by the plain; the Livenza is the biggest of several streams fed in this way.

The ample Belluno basin is a syncline in which Eocene and Miocene clays have been preserved. It was completely occupied by the Piave glacier which forced its way to the plain mainly through the S. Croce gap to deposit a sizeable moraine at Vittorio Veneto. The basin itself is floored with drift across which flow the braided channels of the Piave.

In the economy of Italy as a whole the eastern Alps are mainly important for their timber, hydro-electric power and tourism. The area is easily Italy's most important source of softwood timber (mainly red fir, white fir and larch); about 50% of the provinces of Bolzano, Trento and Belluno are classed as forested and planting is being widely extended. The hydro-electric resources have been thoroughly exploited and the area is now responsible for about one-third of the country's output from that source. Among the larger schemes are the Resia dam, the S. Giustina dam (R. Noce), the Cardano sull' Isarco dam, the Fedaia dam (just north of Marmolada), the Barcis dam (R. Cellina), and the ill-fated Voiont dam.

The variety of scenery and climate the eastern Alps can offer is probably unique in Europe, and there can be few places better equipped to transport, accommodate and divert the tourist. Cortina alone has over sixty hotels, four cable railways and seven chairlifts. The penetration of the area by an excellent network of roads, most of them built originally for military purposes, and its accessibility from the plain and from central Europe are invaluable assets. The main axis of communication is of course the Adige trench leading up to the Brenner (1375m), a pass rarely closed by snow and much easier of access since the construction of the Europa Brücke beyond the Austrian frontier. On this axis, along which a motorway will soon be added to the existing road and railway, the main foci are Bolzano and Trento. The latter attracts routes from Belluno and Venice along the Val Sugana, from Verona and Bologna along the Adige trench, and from Brescia both along the Valli Giudicarie and along the shores of Garda. The other north–south axis carrying both road and railway follows the Piave to Cortina and so to the junction of Dobbiaco; once known as the German road, this route was much favoured by the Venetians in their trade with south Germany and the Danube basin. Although much of the labour force comes from other parts of Italy, as does much of the capital invested, tourism is, directly or indirectly, the mainstay of the area's economy.

Agriculture in the eastern Alps falls broadly into two categories, that of the lower valleys (especially the Adige trench, the lower Sarca, and the Belluno basin) and that of the higher valleys and plateaus. In general the first type has the advantage of alluvial soils, a long warm growing season with mild winters, and water for irrigation in summer. A great variety of crops is grown including maize, fodder and vegetables, but in the Adige valley from Trento to Merano and in the lower Sarca valley fruit, especially stone fruits, apples, pears and vines, assume a particular importance. Viticulture, relying traditionally on the German market, monopolizes the flat valley floor on either side of Mezzacorona (p. 111a). The cultivation of the olive and the lemon on the shores of Garda is of more interest climatically than commercially.

The second form of agriculture, as typically illustrated in the Val di Sole, Val di Fiemme, upper Piave and Valli Giudicarie, centres on cattle rearing and fodder production; other crops are grown but mainly for subsistence or the local market. In most areas the utilization of the high pastures for grazing between June and September, and of the intermediate pastures for hay making, is essential to the economy. The seasonal migrations of animals no longer involve more than a small fraction of the community; usually professional herdsmen are employed and in some areas the mowing, which reduces the broad shoulders of the Dolomites to the texture of a golf-course fairway, is done by hired labour. Part of the hay may be shifted to the valley but where the cattle remain on the plateaus, permanently or semi-permanently, it is stored in barns. The centre of operations is the *malga*, on average located at 1500m; it consists of a more or less permanent habitation for the herdsmen and a very long byre used to shelter the cattle and process the cheese. Traditionally the herdsmen accept part of their dues in kind, as do the communes to which most of the pastures belong. The enclosed arable areas lower down are usually worked by their owners and, as elsewhere in the Alps, are too small to be viable. In the German-speaking areas there is a strong tradition whereby the farm unit (*hof*) is not divided on the death of the owner but passes intact to the eldest son; other members of the family may remain but in a subordinate capacity. This system, while doing little to solve the fundamental problem of rural overpopulation, at least has the virtue of preventing the proliferation of non-viable units. In fact emigration from the eastern Alpine provinces, seasonally into Austria and Germany and permanently overseas, has been an established tradition for over a century.

Except along the Adige trench from Merano to Trento, industry in the eastern Alps is on modest scale. The processing of wood and food is common enough but despite the variety of minerals represented (for example, iron, lead, zinc and pyrites in the Cordevole valley) mining is of little importance; the biggest extractive industry is limestone quarrying for cement. After tourism and agriculture the construction industry is the biggest employer of labour. Among the towns Merano (Meran), Bolzano (Bozen, 92,000) and Trento (82,000) are exceptional in having a notable industrial function; Bolzano in particular, once a quiet spa, has important electro-metallurgical, electro-chemical and engineering works which were established in the inter-war years. At Pieve di Cadore an interesting speciality is the manufacture of spectacles.

The north-eastern frontiers of Italy where the Germanic, Latin and Slav worlds meet has been a zone of conflict for centuries. The post-war settlements with Yugoslavia (1946 and 1954) left no sizeable Slav element within the Italian frontiers, but the confirmation of the 1919 frontier with Austria has meant the retention of a large German-speaking minority in Bolzano province. The linguistic and cultural division of the upper Adige basin, an area known to Italians as the Trentino–Alto Adige and to the Austrians as the Süd-Tirol, dates from the early Middle Ages when the Alto Adige (roughly the province of Bolzano) was occupied by Bavarian settlers while the Trentino (roughly the province of Trento) came under Lombard control and so retained its Latin speech and culture. In 1363 the whole area came under Habsburg rule and except for a short period (1805–1814) it remained Austrian until 1918. With the emergence of an independent Italy the demand grew for the recovery of the Trentino, where irredentist sentiment was increasingly suppressed by the Austrian authorities, and the 'redemption' of the area was one of Italy's main war aims in 1915. In 1918 the Italians successfully demanded the 'strategic' Brenner frontier and by the treaty of St Germain (1919) Italy was awarded not only the Trentino, of whose Italian character there has never been any doubt, but also the rest of the former Süd–Tirol where German-speakers and Ladins were overwhelmingly in the majority; the Austrian census of 1910 recorded 216,000 German-speakers against 23,000 Italian and Ladin-speakers.

With the transfer of the territory to Italy the inevitable bureaucratic influx swelled the Italian total, but with the rise of the fascists to power a much more serious threat to the Germanic character of the Alto Adige appeared in the form of a large immigration of Italian workers attracted by the new industries based on the development of hydro-electric power. Although this officially inspired movement was bound to cause resentment among the South Tyrolese (i.e. the German-speakers), it could perhaps have been excused on economic grounds had it not been accompanied by a crude and wrong-headed campaign of Italianization which revealed its true purpose. In an attempt to remove the embarrassment caused by the South Tyrol problem to their alliance, Hitler and Mussolini concluded the 1939 agreement whereby the Brenner frontier was confirmed and the South Tyrolese were given the choice either of becoming German citizens and migrating to the Reich or of confirming their Italian citizenship, a decision which might well involve their transfer to a less vulnerable part of Italy. At that time there were some 230,000 South Tyrolese in the Alto Adige (Bolzano province from 1927) as opposed to about 80,000 Italians; the agreement also applied to about 24,000 German-speakers in Trento province, 6000 in Udine province and 7000 in Belluno province. In all nearly 267,000 South Tyrolese opted to become citizens of the Reich and by 1943, when the agreement became inoperative, some 80,000 had emigrated. With the military collapse of Italy in that year the provinces of Trento, Bolzano and Belluno were brought directly under the administration of the Germans who mounted a ruthless campaign of Germanization.

In 1946 the Italian frontier was once more confirmed at the Brenner but in the same year under the Gruber–De Gasperi agreement the South Tyrolese were guaranteed equal rights with other citizens including the use of their mother tongue in official business and in particular as a means of instruction in the schools. Subject to certain safeguards against undesirables, the South Tyrolese who had opted for the Reich in 1939 were to be allowed to return, and in fact the majority of those who had survived the upheavals in Germany in 1944–5 had returned by 1953. Furthermore, under the 1948 constitution, the Trentino–Alto

Adige, in addition to its normal representation in Rome, was granted autonomous status with a regional assembly sitting alternately at Bolzano and Trento. Although this gives the South Tyrolese a strong voice in regional affairs they cannot hope to control a majority in a Diet jointly representing both the Trentino and the Alto Adige. Unfortunately the happier relations introduced by the Gruber–De Gasperi agreement were soon menaced, on one side by the renewed influx of migrants from the poorer parts of Italy, on the other by a revival of Austrian claims after the re-establishment of Austrian independence in 1954.

By 1961, by which time Italian immigration had almost ceased, out of a total population of 383,000 in the Alto Adige, approximately 33% spoke Italian as their mother tongue, 64% German and 3% Ladin. The Italians are overwhelmingly concentrated in the towns of Bolzano, Merano and Bressanone (Brixen) and are engaged mainly in industry, tourism and administration. The South Tyrolese and Ladins, whose birth rate is notably higher than that of the Italians, own and work the land and are heavily represented among the hôteliers and shopkeepers. The Ladins, who resisted Italianization before the war almost as much as the South Tyrolese, are concentrated mainly in the high valleys of the Dolomites. Their ancient language, which is akin to the Romansch of Grisons and is similarly a Latin tongue preserved in isolation, seems doomed to disappear.

On the whole the Italian claim to have implemented the Gruber–De Gasperi agreement is justified, particularly as regards educational matters; inevitably the agreement was a compromise which while falling short of the aspirations of the South Tyrolese at least assured them of continued existence in their own valleys – a privilege shared by no other German-speaking minority unfortunate enough to become involved in the Pan-Germanic ambitions of the Third Reich. Whether the Trentino–Alto Adige continues to enjoy its modest but real prosperity or is to be thrown into the pit of communal strife depends largely on whether the moderate majorities on both sides within the area are allowed to continue working within the present framework, eliminating step by step whatever can be shown to be a genuine grievance. In the present atmosphere, any too strident demand for a revision of the *status quo*, especially if supported by Pan-Germanic propaganda and terrorism, is likely to confirm Italian fears that the real aim is outright annexation.

That remote and somewhat desolate sector of the eastern Alps occupying the northern third of the Friuli autonomous region and generally known as Carnia merits separate recognition. It is bounded on the north by the long ridge of the Carnic Alps along which the frontier runs with exemplary simplicity; on the south by the Tertiary hills fringing the Friuli plain; on the west by the eastern watershed of the Piave; and on the east by the western watershed of the Isonzo. The outstanding feature of its relief, which is markedly lower than that of the Dolomites, is a rectangular pattern of deeply incised longitudinal and transverse valleys (*canali*), most of which feed eventually into the Tagliamento system. In the Alps proper, bounded on the south by the longitudinal courses of the Tagliamento and Fella, two main ranges may be distinguished; the inner one, the Carnic Alps, is easily identified; the other, known in the west as the Tolmezzo Alps and further east as the Giulian Alps, lies further south and is broken into a succession of mountain groups by the transverse tributaries of the Tagliamento. The two ranges are separated by a longitudinal trench drained by the Gailitz and several minor streams whose waters find their way eventually into the Tagliamento. This trench is exploited as a routeway, particularly between Pontebba and Tarvisio. The Carnic Alps form part of the Hercynian system; they present a formidable wall of unstable argillaceous schists through which dolomite masses emerge as teeth penetrate the gums. The range tolerates only one major pass (the Plöcken Pass or Passo di M. Croce Carnico, 1362m), which has been chosen to carry the Trans-Alpine Pipeline from Trieste through Lienz to Ingolstadt, but it is outflanked where tributaries of the Danube (Gailitz and Drau) cut back into Italy. The valleys of these two rivers, which now accommodate roads and railways into Austria from Dobbiaco to Lienz and from Tarvisio to Villach, have provided a favourite routeway into Italy for invading tribes and armies since prehistoric times.

The Tolmezzo and Giulian Alps, rising eastwards to Triglav across the frontier, are composed of Triassic dolomite, limestone and marls similar to those already encountered in the Dolomites themselves; indeed, the landscape here, though harsher and less rich in verdant uplands, has much in common with that area.

The Friulian Pre-Alps, conventionally divided into the Carnic Pre-Alps to the west of the Tagliamento and the Giulian Pre-Alps to the east of it, are also overwhelmingly composed of Mesozoic limestones and dolomites. They include some very rugged massifs as well as some grassy karstic plateaus.

Carnia with only about 60,000 inhabitants presents a difficult, almost forbidding environment. The rainfall is excessive, exceeding 1500 mm in all but the valleys, and rising to 2000 mm in the Pre-Alps which feel the full force of depressions passing across or originating over the head of the Adriatic. Winters are long compared with other parts of the southern Alpine flank and thanks to the effectiveness of the Pre-Alpine barrier, they are often severely continental. Because of their deeply incised character, aspect is of particular significance in those valleys trending east–west. The unfavourable climatic conditions generally are confirmed by the vegetation zones which on average are some 400m lower than further west. The beech zone begins at about 500m and thereafter the forest, which rarely penetrates beyond 1800m, is monopolized by conifers. The resistant black pine is the favourite tree for re-afforestation. Except for hay cut on the summer pastures, cultivation is restricted to the lower valley slopes, where detritus fans provide some of the most rewarding land. Hay, rye, potatoes and, locally, maize are the main crops; vines fail above 350m. The economy of this sparsely populated region is based on forestry and animal rearing. Transhumance is still commonly practised; significantly enough the highest *malghe* are some hundreds of metres lower than in the Dolomites. Forestry supports the manufactures of the area,

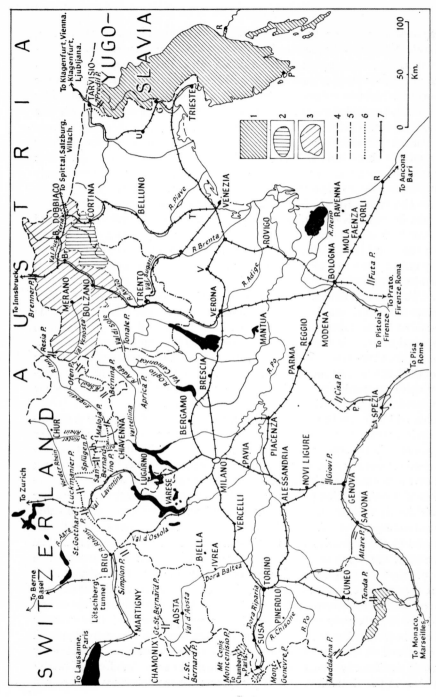

*Figure 26.* The frontiers and rail communications of northern Italy. 1 – Territory lost to France or Yugoslavia as a result of the post-war settlements. 2 – The main Ladin speaking area. 3 – The area where German speakers are in the majority. 4 – Present national frontiers. 5 – Boundaries of the autonomous regions of the Val d'Aosta and the Trentino-Alto Adige. 6 – The main Alpine watershed when not coincident with 4. 7 – The main railway lines

namely paper at Tolmezzo and furniture at Sutrio. Small quantities of coal are mined at Oraro and lead-zinc at Cave del Predil. The development of hydro-electric power notably at Barcis, Sauris and Cavazzo, has done little to provide permanent employment, and emigration, much of it temporary, is an old-established practice. There are several very small German-speaking communities in Carnia (Sauris, Sappada); tradition has it that they settled here as miners in the Middle Ages.

## II THE NORTHERN LOWLANDS

The dominance of the North Italian Lowlands in the economy of the country is one of the commonplaces of Italian geography; it was already apparent in classical times, reasserted itself strongly in the Middle Ages, and has become increasingly obvious ever since, particularly over the last hundred years. In large measure the relative superiority of the area can be explained in terms of its natural endowment, especially the character of its relief, soils, climate and water supplies; other advantages have been its easy access to the Mediterranean and its pivotal position in relation to central and western Europe which have favoured not only commerce but the introduction of new ideas and enterprising attitudes, whether they had their source in the classical and medieval Mediterranean world or in modern industrialized northern Europe. But there was nothing automatic about the plain's climb to dominance; in fact its history is studded with setbacks, most obviously during the long night following the eclipse of Rome and during the stagnation which attended Spanish political control. The opportunities had to be recognized and exploited and in no aspect is this more apparent than in the control of water, which has always been fundamental to the continued development of the area and whose achievement represents the patient labour of a hundred generations.

The Valle Padana is essentially the work of rivers and it provides convincing evidence of the extent to which the forces of erosion have succeeded in demolishing the Alps and the Apennines.[1] In Pliocene times the Po syncline was occupied by a continuation of the Adriatic which communicated with the Ligurian Sea through several narrow channels in what are now the Ligurian Apennines. Although the Pliocene deposits are mainly marine their immense thickness is none the less a reflexion of the activity of the Alpine and Apennine rivers; beneath Vercelli they extend from −2191m to −680m; in the Lomellina the corresponding depths are −3000 and −1100 while at Codigoro they are reached at −2345m (Gabert). With the passing of the Pliocene the syncline shared in the uplift of the mountains on either side and the rivers, their energies renewed, continued the work of filling in even though their load was now increasingly spread over the former sea bed; the Quaternary sediments in Lomellina exceed 1200m

[1] See P. Gabert: 'Une tentative d'évaluation du travail d'érosion sur les massifs montagneux qui dominent la plaine du Pô', *Revue de Géographie Alpine*, 1960.

and thicken to over 2000m in the delta. The post-Pliocene uplift of the syncline was far from uniform; the sea bed seems to have emerged most steadily on the Alpine hinter-zone (i.e. that part of the syncline structurally associated with the Alps) while in the Padane foretrench (associated structurally with the Apennines) the uplift of the southern margin was partially offset by a severe sagging further north. In fact, although the uplift increasingly revealed a strip of Pliocene deposits along the foot of the Apennines, an area of sea survived for a very long time along the Padane foretrench so that here marine deposits often occur at quite modest depths. This sagging movement is sometimes invoked to explain the absence in Piedmont of a calcareous Pre-Alpine zone which it is thought may be buried below the Quaternary sediments.

Along the margins of the plain, where the force of the rivers was checked, detritus cones and alluvial fans spread out into the Po depression until they formed a continuous belt in which the material was naturally graded from large pebbles upstream to very fine silt downstream. At any one place the character of sedimentation rarely remained uniform for long; the erratic behaviour of the rivers, the unevenness of the uplift and the fluctuating climatic conditions favoured rapid changes in the nature of successive deposits. Because of their more northerly situation, greater height and more abundant precipitation, the Alps were much more severely glaciated than the Apennines; the latter carried only a very few small glaciers, none of them large enough to impinge on the plain, but from the Stura to the Tagliamento several massive valley glaciers succeeded in reaching it to form morainic arcs which now serve to raise the level of the major Alpine lakes. To the south of these arcs the melt waters from the glaciers spread vast outwash fans of gravel, sand and silt which merge into a continuous east–west belt. These surfaces were not left undisturbed for long; indeed, they were radically modified as the behaviour of the rivers varied with successive glacial and interglacial phases and with the fluctuations in sea level and shoreline associated with them. The net result has been the creation, southwards of the moraines, of a series of gently inclined, low fluvio-glacial platforms forming the interfluves between the modern floodplains of the Po's left-bank tributaries. The presence of these platforms and their associated moraines provides one of the main contrasts between the Valle Padana north of the Po and that to the south of it. In the latter zone the surface deposits are of post-glacial alluvium; their texture becomes increasingly fine northwards but really coarse sediments are restricted to the detritus cones on the Apennine margin; elsewhere the fluvio-glacial platforms, so typical of the trans-Padane sector of the plain, are so poorly developed as to be imperceptible.

Above Piacenza the Po hugs the edge of the Apennines and their structural continuation in the hills of Monferrato; downstream it flows at an increasingly greater distance from the Apennines. In part this pattern may reflect the fundamental structure of the syncline and in particular the persistence of collapse in the Padane foretrench, but the relative load-carrying capacities of the Alpine and

Apennines feeders have certainly helped to determine the course of the main artery. Above Piacenza the heavily charged Alpine tributaries pin the Po against the Apennine margin; downstream the Alpine feeders, despite their greater discharge, cannot compete with the enormous load of the Apennine rivers. This contrast owes much to the absence of lakes in the courses of the Apennine rivers and the extremely erodible nature of their catchment basins.

A notable feature of the Po's Alpine feeders is the tendency they exhibit to turn eastwards in their lower courses. A possible explanation is that they were diverted by the very heavy load of silt brought down by the Po itself at a time when its course was unconfined by levees; in much the same way the Adige is still obliged to find an independent outlet to the sea to the north of the modern delta zone. It is perhaps significant that the easterly trend of the tributaries becomes more marked downstream from a point where the heavily charged Apennine rivers begin to make their contribution to the Po.

It will already be apparent that the seeming uniformity of the plain masks a great diversity of relief, structure and hydrology. This diversity may not be obvious to the casual observer but its influence on the pattern of cultivation and settlement is extremely important. In an attempt to simplify what is in fact very complex, the following physiographical zones may be recognized (fig. 27):

I THE HILL ZONE OF THE ALPINE MARGIN. This varies greatly in width, relief and composition. To the south of lakes Maggiore, Lugano, Como, Iseo and Garda, and where the Dora Riparia, Dora Baltea, Adige and Tagliamento reach the plain, this zone is mainly developed on morainic arcs. As far as it has been possible to distinguish the contributions of successive glacial phases, the Gunz deposits are exposed only where the major rivers have incised themselves deeply. The Mindel moraines, however, are extensively revealed and enclose within their arcs the fresher debris of the last two glacial phases. The characteristic terrain is usually one of low irregular hills but occasionally more continuous arcs and ridges are recognizable; the most obvious example is the Serra d'Ivrea. In general the moraines are excessively permeable but in places, usually on the older surfaces, a chemical alteration associated with leaching has produced a clayey impermeable pan known as *ferretto*. The soils on the moraines are always acid but this tendency is particularly marked on the *ferretto* where, under natural conditions, the associated vegetation is a sterile heath (*brughiere*). In depressions among the morainic debris, where the water table reaches the surface or where glacial clays discourage seepage, peat bogs and lakes were a common feature of the post-glacial landscape; most of the peat bogs (*torbiere*) have been drained but a sprinkling of lakes survives within the Dora Baltea moraine (Viverone) and between the Ticino and the Adda (Varese, Comabbio).

Elsewhere the hill country is developed on 'solid' structures. In Lombardy and Piedmont these usually take the form of isolated spurs or down-faulted fragments of the Alpine or Pre-Alpine margin (Saluzzo spur, Rocca di Cavour); in Veneto

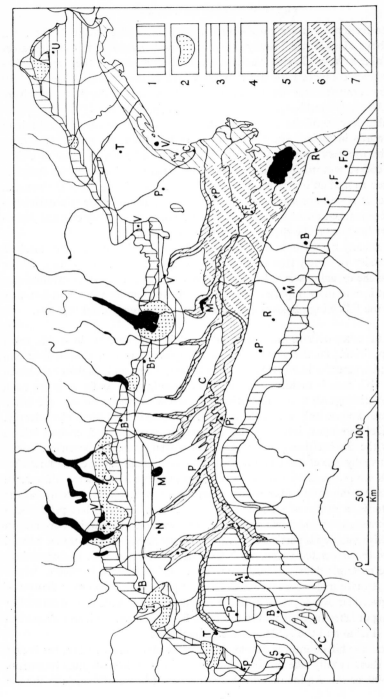

*Fig. 27.* The physiographical regions of the Northern Lowlands. 1 – The Pre-Alpine and Apennine hilly margins including Monferrato and Le Langhe. 2 – Moraines of the Pre-Alpine hilly margin. 3 – Upper plain of coarse fluvio-glacial deposits. 4 – Lower plain of fine fluvio-glacial deposits and alluvium. 5 – Floodplains of the major rivers. 6 – Fen zone of *bonfiche.* 7 – Deltas, lagoons and spits

they appear as volcanic rocks and the folds of upper Tertiary sediments. The volcanic exposures are best exemplified in the basaltic tuffs and lavas to the west of Vicenza and between Bassano and Thiene; the Berici and Euganei hills may be regarded as detached fragments of this zone although the former also include Oligocene clays and the latter are mainly trachytic. From Bassano to beyond Vittorio Veneto the hill zone is underlain by Tertiary sediments folded against the Pre-Alpine margin; the gentle swelling of Montello immediately to the south is a low dome of Miocene limestone.

2 THE APENNINE HILLY MARGIN. Stretching from Novi Ligure to Pesaro this zone consists of a narrow strip of *molasse*, repeatedly incised by the rivers and torrents of the Apennines and edged with detritus cones. Between the Po and the Ligurian Apennines the hill country of the Langhe and Monferrato is developed on gently folded Tertiary sediments; this area will receive attention below (p. 128).

3 THE UPPER PLAIN (ALTA PIANURA). The junction between the moraines and the fluvio-glacial deposits of the upper plain is rarely obvious. The latter is divided into a succession of isolated platforms by the incised floodplains of the major Alpine rivers; the imperceptible southerly slope of these platforms is occasionally interrupted by a shallow step marking the position of former shorelines. The surface deposits of the plain are graded southwards, not always regularly, from pebbles embedded in gravel to coarse sands. Where the coarser deposits have been converted into a conglomerate the rivers are sometimes confined in shallow gorges; at Paderno sull' Adda one of these was exploited for Italy's first hydro-electric station. Although favourable to easy clearance and communications, the permeability and altitude of the fluvio-glacial platforms hindered the development of irrigation; serious progress in this field had to await the successful diversion of water from the Alpine rivers on to the interfluves. Locally the impermeable character of the surface is interrupted by *ferretto*.

4 THE FONTANILI ZONE. Where the coarser deposits of the *alta pianura* fall away to the finer sediments of the lower plain the alternating exposure of impermeable beds and permeable aquifers gives rise to a host of springs (*fontanili*). They are best developed in Lombardy which has over 2000 of them; they are less well represented in the upper Po basin (south of Turin) where the fluvioglacial platforms are more fragmentary; in Veneto the zone is interrupted by the Berici–Euganei hills. Although affected by fluctuations of the Alpine rivers, the discharge of the fontanili is remarkably constant and since the streams to which they give life are never deeply incised, their waters can be easily distributed. Even in January they maintain a temperature of at least 10°C, a circumstance which helps to promote continuous growth in the water-meadows (*marcite*).

They have been exploited for at least eight hundred years and even today they water over one-third of Lombardy's irrigated area.

**5** THE LOWER PLAIN (BASSA PIANURA). The northern margin of this zone of fine, only slightly permeable fluvio-glacial deposits lies at about 100m in Lombardy and at about 50m in Veneto; it shades off without an obvious break into the floodplains of the Po and its feeders. The water table is high and although this part of the plain lends itself to irrigation, its development must be preceded by the establishment of satisfactory drainage, especially where *ferretto* occurs, as in the Vercellese.

**6** THE FLOODPLAINS OF THE PO AND ITS ALPINE TRIBUTARIES. Both along the Po and its major left-bank feeders the fall-away from the interfluvial platforms to the modern floodplains is more marked upstream. The interfluves have been reduced by lateral corrasion and although the process has been checked by dyking, the floodplains have been repeatedly worked over by migrating meanders; while these may now be drained and cultivated, the outlines of abandoned meanders (*mortizze*) are obvious from the air. The reclamation of the tributary floodplains, at least upstream, was a comparatively simple matter; part of the river's flow was diverted along the foot of the interfluve and allowed to drain back by gravity through minor drainage and irrigation channels to the river bed. The application of this method to the Po floodplain was ruled out by the scale of operations required and by the imperceptible gradient. Below the junction with the Oglio the difficulty of drainage by gravity increases; except in summer the water table of the barely inclined recent alluvium, much of it derived from the Apennines, is almost at the surface and the movement of water laterally is impeded by slightly upraised fossil river beds and by *lidi* left from former shorelines. From the sixteenth century onwards attempts were made to drain this fenny zone by straightening and banking the rivers and by cutting a network of gravity-flow channels. These efforts were frequently defeated by exceptional floods and by the lowering of the surface through shrinkage, but where they met with success these areas are known as the *terre vecchie*. Elsewhere reclamation had to await the application of efficient pumping machinery in the later nineteenth century, a development which has won large tracts of Rovigo and Ferrara provinces for cultivation. Unfortunately the history of the Po fenlands is too repetitively catastrophic to encourage rash prophecies as to the permanent security of the recent *bonifiche*. In Ravenna province a method of reclamation known as *colmate naturali* has been successfully employed; essentially it is the diversion of the heavily charged flood waters of the Apennine rivers on to an enclosed area until the accumulation of silt raises the surface to the required level.

**7** THE COASTAL LAGOONS AND DELTAS. In a different context this area has already received attention (p. 83).

**8** THE EMILIAN PLAIN. This forms a triangle with its base roughly along the Via Emilia (from Piacenza to Cesena) and its apex at Ferrara. Except for a narrow belt of coarse detritus along its southern margin the plain is composed of compact alluvium which slopes imperceptibly to the fen zone along the Po. The fluvio-glacial platforms of Lombardy have no counterpart here and although springs are common enough, they are niggardly in discharge and do not constitute a continuous *fontanili* zone. Locally the alternation of beds of varying permeability provides conditions suitable for Artesian wells; known here as *pozzi modenesi*, they have been used for domestic and irrigation purposes since the Middle Ages. The Apennine rivers whose annual average discharge compares very unfavourably with that of their Alpine counterparts are torrential in regime. As far as the *bonifiche* of the floodplains are concerned this presents a twofold problem, namely drainage and flood control in winter, and the lack of topsoil moisture in the summer.

## II [a] *The Lowlands of Piedmont*

The generalized physiographical pattern of the Northern Lowlands outlined above needs some qualification in the case of Piedmont. Firstly between the Ligurian Apennines and the Po (downstream from Turin) there lies an expanse of hilly country whose structure, relief, hydrology and land-use distinguish it from the rest of the lowland. Secondly, at the exits to the Valle di Susa and the Valle d'Aosta, the crescent-shaped sweep of the plain proper is interrupted by two particularly extensive morainic complexes. Thirdly, in the south of the crescent, especially where it is drained to the Tanaro, the upper plain is incised into a number of elongated platforms from whose base a multitude of small springs emerge; this fragmentation of relief and the hydrology associated with it frustrate any attempt to delimit any continuous fontanili zone comparable with that of Lombardy.

From the point of view of land-use, four main sub-regions emerge, namely, the Alpine hill country including the moraines, the plain eastwards of the Dora Baltea moraine, the plain to the south of it, and finally the Tertiary hill country of Monferrato.

Morainic debris encumbering the entrance to the Valle di Susa protrudes on to the plain almost to the edge of the Monferrato plateau leaving a narrow gap over which Turin has watched since Augustus's day. Outliers of the Alpine margin which served to guide and obstruct the glacier, lie half buried among the chaos of morainic hills. In the Dora Baltea moraine, however, the characteristic amphitheatre is well developed although even here it seems likely that the loftiest part of the arc, the Serra d'Ivrea, is underlain by a 'solid' base similar to the diorite masses which emerge from the lakes, drift and former bogs of the intra-morainic depressions. Much of the surface of the moraines is occupied by heath and by woodlands in which the chestnut is the most profitable member; elsewhere, particularly on the drained peaty soils of the intra-morainic depressions, a patchwork

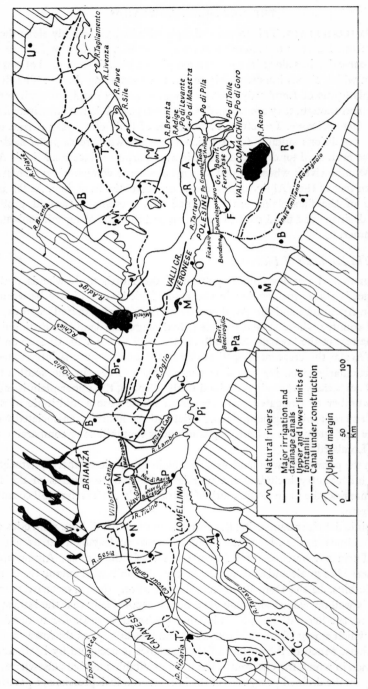

*Fig. 28.* The hydrology of the Northern Lowlands; rivers, canals and spring lines

of small fields and strips produce fodder crops, cereals, potatoes, mulberries, hard fruits and vines. As in other areas of ancient settlement the pressure of population is reflected in the small size and fragmentation of property; most of the farms are owner-worked but they rarely exceed three or four hectares. Quite often the younger members of the household are employed in factories and only contribute to the work of the farm in their spare time. The small mixed farm economy also dominates the non-morainic sectors of the Alpine hill zone although locally one crop, for example vines on the granitic Gattinara hills, may assume a special rôle. Settlement is often dispersed or in small hamlets, and the residential element is becoming increasingly marked near large towns, especially Turin.

The 'typical' succession from hilly margin, through the upper and lower fluvio-glacial platforms to the modern floodplain is best exemplified in the provinces of Vercelli and Novara. On the higher terraces of the *alta pianura* large tracts of heath, here known as *baragge*, are left uncultivated either because of excessive permeability or because of the presence of *ferretto*. Elsewhere the upper plain is dominated by cereals and fodder crops. *Fontanili* were exploited as early as the thirteenth century and by the sixteenth century the Dora Baltea and Elvo had been tapped for irrigation, but the transformation of the economy and landscape of the lower plain dates from the completion of the Cavour Canal in 1863. Fed from the Po and its Alpine tributaries its flow of 120 mc/sec irrigates some 500,000 hectares devoted overwhelmingly to the production of rice and fodder crops. The rice zone, centred on Vercelli, presents a mournful landscape of vast, imperceptibly terraced fields, glinting with water and bordered by screens of poplar, elm and willow. Massive brick-built farms, usually arranged round one or more courtyards and often surrounded by high walls, stand like fortresses in an apparently deserted countryside. These buildings house the families of the owner and his permanent work force and they also include vast grain stores and machinery sheds whose lofts may be temporarily converted into dormitories for seasonal workers. The large villages studding the plain were built to accommodate the workers who were attracted into the area with the development of irrigation; from the first the seasonal character of the work available was a source of hardship and increased mechanization has forced many to seek alternative employment. Normally about 70% of the Vercellese is under rice which thrives on what is naturally quite mediocre soil, often underlain by *ferretto*. Most of the cultivation is now done by machine, but if the present high yields (frequently 12 tons per hectare) are to be maintained, the planting must still be done by hand, a task traditionally performed by teams of women from outside the area who find temporary accommodation on the farms. High yields demand the liberal use of fertilizers and after several years under rice a field is put under grass, clover and cereals. Although the Vercellese is still a monocultural area, there is a growing tendency towards diversification, especially in the direction of milk production. In the neighbouring district of the Novarese this type of economy predominates over risiculture, and the specialized cultivation of rotation fodder and of irrigated water meadows, which reaches perfection in Lombardy, is widely practised here. The exploitation of the lower plain made possible by the Cavour Canal demanded capital and large-scale organization; in consequence the farm units, whether rented or owner-worked, are compact and rarely less than 50 hectares. It is still true that the very special physical and economic conditions of the lower plain do not favour the small producer and the replacement of the existing sizeable units by a multitude of smaller ones would certainly result in a loss of productivity. In fact the land reform authorities have not interfered in this area.

In the extreme south of the Piedmontese plain, the incision of the rivers has produced a succession of elongated fluvio-glacial platforms separated by flood-plains whose floors are laced by braided channels. Except where the Valle di Susa moraine intrudes, the rest of the plain between the Maira and the Orca exhibits more obviously the transition from the *alta* to the *bassa pianura*. On the former the *baragge* of Vercelli have their counterpart in the *vaude* of Turin province. In the plain of Poirino the permeability of the upper terraces condemned the area until recently to an economy based on extensive cereals; between the wars an ex-servicemen's colonization scheme did something to diversify the area. In general the upper plain is dominated by small mixed farms on which the field crops, especially wheat, maize, potatoes, beans and fodder, are lined with tree crops, among them mulberries, apples, pears, plums, cherries and vines; this two-tiered type of cultivation, known as *coltura promiscua*, recommends itself to the small farmer. The mulberry, once planted extensively in support of the silk industry, has no longer any economic importance and it is being eliminated in the interests of mechanization. Towards the lower plain, where irrigation is extensively practised, hay and rotated fodder crops become as important as cereals. Many of the farms exceed 50 hectares and their substantial buildings include byres, machinery sheds, grain silos and barns. On the bluffs of the fluvio-glacial terraces woodland has a stabilizing rôle and the floodplains are commonly devoted to plantations of poplars.

The hill country of Monferrato and Le Langhe is structurally part of the Apennines; from the Ligurian border the Miocene beds dip down to the Tanaro syncline and rise again to present a steep edge overlooking the Po. The centre of the syncline is floored with Pliocene (Astian) marls underlying softish sands. The latter have been eroded into cuestas whose permeable surface is best suited to vines and dry *coltura promiscua*. In the valleys the marls promote a more intensive cultivation of cereals and forage, locally enriched by irrigation. Further north where the Miocene rocks emerge from below the Pliocenes, rolling hills developed on marls and soft sands climb up to the wooded conglomerate capping of the Colline Torinesi whose slopes are being invaded by the residential suburbs of Turin. A patchwork of cereals, lucerne, lupins, beans, fruit trees and vines, relieved by woodland on the steeper sandy outcrops and dotted with little farmsteads and hill-top villages, gives the landscape a civilized air of modest prosperity. In fact the holdings (generally 2 or 3 hectares) are too small and the drift from the land is well advanced. Where the Miocene rocks of Le Langhe form the southern flank of the syncline, the countryside is different only in degree. The tributaries of the Tanaro have incised themselves to produce a succession of north-pointing spurs whose edges are abrupt where the marls are capped by sands and conglomerates. The latter are more extensive and more actively eroded towards the Apennine watershed and the cultivation on the marly hills lower down gives way to deciduous woodlands higher up. Compared with other alluvial plains in Piedmont that of Alessandria is poorly supplied with water and the rural economy is still closely tied to cereal production.

Although the landscape of Monferrato and Le Langhe is attractively varied and counts cherries, hazel nuts, lavender, strawberries, truffles and market garden crops among its specialities, its economy is closely wedded to viticulture. In those vineyards with any pretensions to quality, notably near Asti and Alba, the vines are pruned and staked after the French fashion. The nomenclature of Piedmontese wines is confusing; some, for example Barbera, Grignolino and Dolcetto, indicate the type of grape used, while others, such as Barolo and Barbaresco, are named after villages. At home the best-known variety is the moscato d'Asti, a sweet sparkling wine sold as Asti Spumante; abroad the vermouth of Turin finds a wide market. Viticulture in this part of Piedmont is passing through a difficult period; phylloxera is still active, many of the most skilled vine-tenders have left the land, and marketing abroad suffers from insufficient standardization in the grading and naming of the product, a common Italian failing.

Whether judged by total production, yields, the use of fertilizers or the degree of mechanization, Piedmontese agriculture compares favourably with that of any region in Italy except Lombardy;[1] the water resources have been skilfully exploited (470,000 hectares are irrigated) and, except in the hill country, much of the cultivated area is in medium- or large-sized holdings. In general the opportunities for alternative employment in industry have reduced rural underemployment and increased productivity. But important as agriculture is in the Piedmontese lowlands it is being steadily overshadowed by industry. Until the mid-nineteenth century Piedmont's industry amounted to little more than agricultural processing, brick-making and the small-scale manufacture of silk and woollen goods, but thereafter her rulers, with England's success in mind, gave every encouragement to industrialization. At the time her natural advantages were meagre, in particular most of her raw materials and nearly all her coal had to be imported. The first enterprises, for example the Turin arsenal and the woollen mills of Biella, were heavily dependent on government patronage, but Piedmont's early start proved a great advantage when the market expanded to embrace all Italy. By 1900 Fiat, Lancia, and Olivetti had arrived, and with the

[1] Of Italy's total in 1962 Piedmont produced the following percentages; rice 60%, rye 34%, maize 14%, soft wheat 12%, wine, meat and milk 11%.

stimulus of war and the active development of hydro-electric power and the strategic industries under fascism, Piedmont established herself firmly as one of Italy's major industrial zones.

The processing of agricultural and forest products (wine, pasta, cheese, confectionery and paper) is still one of the region's most important and most widely distributed activities. In the building material sector, an industry whose distribution is clearly related to the occurrence of the raw material, the traditional and widespread manufacture of bricks and tiles has been joined by that of cement (Casale) and sanitary ware (Gattinara). The older branches of the textile industry are represented in the silks of Cuneo and Pinerolo and in the woollens of the Biellese. Turin and Vercelli manufacture synthetic fibres and Alessandria has long been famous for felt hats (Borsalino).

The metallurgical sector, leaning heavily on the hydro-electric power of the Alps and more recently on that of the Po itself is concentrated at Turin, Novi Ligure and Lesegno (steel), and at Borgofranco d'Ivrea (aluminium). Novara and Trecate, the former concerned mainly with nitric acid and fertilizers and the latter with the refining of oil piped from Savona, are Piedmont's main chemical centres. But the region's high ranking in Italian industry depends overwhelmingly on its engineering and in particular on the production of motor vehicles. In this sector Fiat of Turin enjoys a dominating position in the country; in 1965 the company, which employs over 100,000 workers, produced over a million vehicles, mainly at its Mirafiori plant. Fiat is also Italy's foremost producer of railway and marine engines, tractors, precision instruments and electric motors; its other interests range from domestic appliances to autostrade, Alpine tunnels, dam building and nuclear power. Lancia is also a Turin firm although its main plant is now at Chivasso. Most of the other enterprises of Turin (e.g. rubber) and of the neighbouring townships of the province (e.g. ball-bearings at Perosa) are dangerously dependent on vehicle assembly for a market. Outside Turin the most notable engineering centres are at Novara (C.G.E. electricals), Novi Ligure and Ivrea; the last is almost entirely dependent on the fortunes of Olivetti and, like Turin itself, comes near to being a 'company' town.

It will be apparent that industry in the Piedmontese lowlands is localized in one major zone and several lesser ones, notably in the provinces of Vercelli and Novara. Given the widespread availability of water and the flexibility of electric power, many industrialists since the war have sought to avoid the high land prices and congestion near Turin by siting their new factories in the countryside or in those towns whose functions remain principally those of market and administrative centres. An added advantage is that in such areas there is usually a large number of workers anxious to accept employment and there is little competition for their services. In layout and architecture the older centres of Piedmontese towns bear a strong family resemblance; the rectangular street plan, the spacious porticoed squares and the long apartment blocks of almost barrack-like severity seem to be in harmony with the traditional Piedmontese respect for order and discipline. Among such towns are Cuneo (48,000), a provincial capital and route centre with little industry, Asti (62,000) of similar rank but very active in wine processing, and Pinerolo, steeped in military tradition and the focus of the Waldensian valleys. Novara (92,000), on the autostrada and main line from Turin to Milan, is heavily industrialized and its cartographical publishing house (Agostini) should not pass unnoticed. Alessandria (92,000), founded only in 1158, is Piedmont's second biggest town; agricultural processing and textiles are its main industries and it derives importance as a route centre from its position midway between Milan, Turin and Genoa.

Turin was founded by the Romans among the lands of the Taurini on a terrace wedged between the Stura and the Dora Baltea. Its function was to control the passes of the western Alps and the narrow gap between the northern and southern sections of the plain; if modern roads, motorways and railways are substituted for Roman roads its rôle as a communications centre seems to have changed very little. The urban renaissance of the Middle Ages passed it by but once chosen as the capital of Savoy (in the sixteenth century) its importance waxed with the fortunes of a ruling house more French than Italian. French cultural influence remained strong until the mid-nineteenth century by which time, as if in imitation of its founders, the city had assumed the severe, rather grandiose rectangular street plan, which has since been continued into the suburbs. Ironically but inevitably, the unification of Italy obliged Turin to exchange the rôle of a capital for that of a hardworking, enterprising industrial city. Since 1950 its fortunes have soared with the motor vehicle boom and its population (officially 1,050,000 in 1961) has almost doubled. This vulnerable prosperity has brought with it many problems, not least the absorption of 400,000 Southerners whose social outlook could hardly be more different from that of the Piedmontese.

## II [b] *The Lowlands of Lombardy*

Since the most permanent of Italy's Germanic invaders established themselves in the area, Lombardy has rarely managed to survive as a well-defined political or administrative region; in the Middle Ages much of it was incorporated in the Duchy of Milan and indeed that city has always been its essential nucleus. Today that part of the *regione* falling within the Northern Lowlands extends beyond the Ticino (to the Sesia) in Pavia province, and beyond the Mincio and Po in Mantova province; there is even a wedge of Lombardy penetrating into the Apennines.

Geology and relief combine to suggest a threefold division of the area into the hilly zone of the Pre-Alpine margin, the upper plain and the lower plain (fig. 29). Between the Ticino and the Adda the first division presents a chaos of irregular morainic hills interspersed with depressions many of which are occupied by lakes and reclaimed peat bogs. Further east an arc of low morainic hills pens in Lake Garda but elsewhere the moraines are small and isolated and the hill zone consists of little more than the foothills of the Pre-Alps. Southwards the moraines shade gently into the coarse fluvio-glacial deposits of the upper plain into which the major rivers have incised themselves as they leave the hilly margin; the low swellings of the outwash fans reveal themselves clearly in cuttings along the railways and autostrade. Topographically the transition from the upper to the lower plain is imperceptible; the essential change is best reflected in the soil texture and in the hydrology. The upper part of the *bassa* coincides with the *fontanili* zone; towards the Po and its left-bank tributaries the finer diluvial deposits shade without serious break into the modern floodplains.

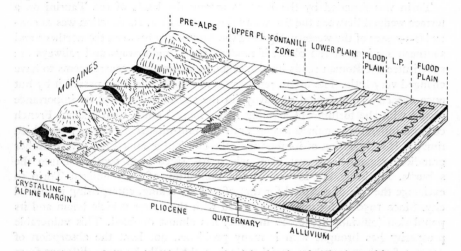

*Fig. 29.* Block diagram of the Lombardy plain showing the physiographic zones

Although technical progress has blurred their outlines, the physiographical zones identified above are still recognizably reflected in the agricultural economy and in the pattern of settlement. As in Piedmont much of the morainic hill zone is occupied by woodland and heath (*brughiere*); the rest is devoted to small-scale mixed farming with cereals, fodder crops and fruit dominant in the land-use. In many households farming is a part-time occupation for the younger members of the family who find employment in local factories. In the non-morainic hilly zone viticulture assumes some importance. On the coarse deposits of the upper plain most of the surface is still not irrigated although east of the Adda, where the upper plain is narrower and the water table is high, there are a large number of local schemes based on minor rivers and wells. At one time the land-use was monopolized by wheat and maize, but potatoes, grass and clover have been widely introduced into the rotations and the production of meat and milk is on the increase. Over 60% of the cultivated area is farmed in units of over 10 hectares and large properties are common. The latter provide one of the characteristic features of the settlement pattern in the *corte*, a group of farm buildings which include the owner's house and accommodation for the permanent workers, arranged round a large rectangular courtyard. Small dispersed farmsteads are also fairly common but the majority of the rural population still lives in villages many of whose inhabitants may be employed in industry. In fact the landscape of the upper plain, dotted with Milan's satellite towns and laced with high-tension wires and autostrade, is becoming increasingly an industrialized zone.

In the northern belt of the lower plain the high water table, the fine texture of the diluvial deposits and the presence of *fontanili*, which are better represented here than in any part of the Northern Lowlands, have encouraged irrigation since the Middle Ages. The economy is geared to the production of milk for cheese (Parmesan and Gorgonzola) and butter; the animals are fed mainly on fodder grown on water meadows (*marcite*) over whose imperceptibly inclined surface trickles a fine film of water tapped from *fontanili* and enriched with treated sewerage. Irrigation is continuous from September till March and the long growing period assisted by the tepid spring waters assures almost unchecked growth; ten cuttings per annum are quite normal. The cows are stall-fed in the *cassina*, a specialized type of *corte*, and are rarely seen in the fields. The milk may be processed on the farm or it may be sent to co-operative dairies.

South of the water-rich *fontanili* zone *marcite* are still a frequent element in the landscape, particularly between the Ticino and Adda, but except in the specialized rice-growing zone of Lomellina, forage crops share the land-use with wheat and maize. Irrigation here is much more intermittent than in the *marcite* but the importance of animal rearing is reflected in the rotations, commonly a seven-year cycle in which four years of cereals, interspersed with grass and clover, are followed by three years of meadow. With the progress of drainage this type of land-use occupies much of the modern floodplains but the massive levees and the extensive poplar plantations on land unsuited to the plough are a reminder of the menace of flooding. On the whole the lower plain is an area of medium (10–25 hecs) and large farms, the latter dominant in the specialized *marcite* and *risaie*. When not farmed or managed by the owner, rents are paid in cash on a long-term tenure; except in the less progressive eastern sector of Lombardy, *mezzadria* is unimportant.

Although often falling short of the most modern standards of productivity the exuberance of its agriculture has earned the admiration of visitors to Lombardy for centuries. The credit for this achievement should be given less to the natural fertility of the area (which has often been exaggerated) than to those who knew how to realize its opportunities. Of these by far the greatest was Lombardy's bountiful water supplies. Although the Romans were active in water control their main object seems to have been to supply the cities with domestic water; hence the diversion of the Olona and Séveso for the benefit of Milan. The most easily exploitable sources for irrigation are the *fontanili*; they have been used since the eleventh century and even today they serve nearly 40% of Lombardy's irrigated surface. The utilization of the major Alpine rivers for the irrigation of the interfluves began in 1177 with the digging of the Ticinello from the Ticino to Abbiategrasso; its continuation to Milan as the Naviglio di Gaggiano (part of the Naviglio Grande) was only completed in 1271 (fig. 28). In the meantime the diversion of the Adda into the Muzza canal had begun (1220); it now irrigates some 42,000 hectares, nearly as much as the Naviglio Grande. Many of the early canals were built with barge traffic as well as irrigation in mind; the Naviglio Grande was used to ferry marble from Lake Maggiore for the construction of Milan cathedral and the Naviglio di Pavia was intended to provide a navigable link with the Po. In fact, this canal, which was not completed until 1819, has never been of any navigational significance. Although canal building was most common near Milan there was considerable activity during the Middle Ages on the upper plain further east. The Naviglio Grande of Brescia, diverted from the Chiese in the thirteenth century, serves a sizeable area to the south of that city, and elsewhere the Adda, the Serio and the Oglio have been put to similar use. Before the Spanish stagnation enveloped the area the Naviglio di Bereguardo and the Martesana were begun (1457). Thereafter progress was slow until the nineteenth century when the Cavour canal and the Villoresi canal (completed 1891 and serving 46,000 hectares) brought much of the upper plain under irrigation. At the moment about 60% of Lombardy's farm land is irrigated; of this about 40% relies on *fontanili* and another 40% on the contributions of the Adda and Ticino. Not all this area can be perennially irrigated; except in the *risaie* and the *marcite* the crops are watered for short periods which may total from one to three weeks. The main 'dry' areas today are to be found on the upper Milan plain and in the provinces of Mantova and Cremona. Further progress will involve greater utilization of the waters of the Alpine lakes. Unlike so many modern schemes the irrigation system of Lombardy has stood the test of time; salinity presents no problem but to prevent waterlogging careful attention has always been given to drainage. The circulation of water in the land may be compared with that of blood in the body; the feeders or arteries (known as *rogge*) provide the water which seeps into the drainage canals leading like veins back to the natural rivers.

Paramount as irrigation has been in the evolution of Lombard agriculture there have been other beneficial influences which deserve passing mention. At a time when most of a city's food had to come from a limited radius the precocious urbanization of Lombardy was a powerful stimulus to intensification and specialization. If the noble was enticed into the city in the hope of commercial gain the merchant was no less disposed to invest in the land; thus the low standards generally associated with feudalism were abandoned in favour of a more commercialized agriculture more ready to adopt new techniques[1] and new crops.[2] In recent times the growth of industry, besides providing a market, has reduced the

[1] For example, in the Middle Ages the use of green manuring and urban sewerage, and more recently rotations, artificial fertilizers and mechanization.
[2] Notably mulberries, rice, maize, potatoes and tomatoes.

burden of rural under-employment and has enabled the farmer to use machinery profitably. Moreover, Lombardy has been more fortunate than most of Italy in its rulers. For example, under the Austrian and French administrations of the late eighteenth and early nineteenth centuries the break-up of the estates of the aristocracy and the distribution of communal land broadened the basis of ownership and further involved the bourgeoisie (the most progressive element in the community) in agriculture.

Lombardy's lead among the regions of Italy in industry is even more marked than in agriculture. In 1961[1] over one-quarter of the country's industrial workers were employed there, a proportion twice that of Piedmont, Lombardy's nearest rival. Furthermore, although there is no shortage of small concerns of the workshop type, Lombardy has the biggest proportion of workers employed in large units; these are the enterprises which pay high wages and often provide lavish fringe benefits and at the same time are efficient and account for a large part of Italy's exports.

Even in the pre-factory era Lombardy had a long-established reputation in commerce and manufacturing, notably in banking, textiles and metal working, but the modern expansion in terms of large-scale industry does not go much further back than the end of the nineteenth century. Agricultural riches, a concentrated market, good communications internally and through the Alps, water supplies, hydro-electric power and later gas – all these played their part in promoting industry, but great weight should also be given to the enterprising spirit of the Lombards and especially of the Milanese. Milan is the spiritual home of the Italian industrial tycoon and the respect accorded to hard work in the pursuit of business is almost as great here as in North America.

The absence of locally produced solid fuels and minerals and the ease of distribution of electric power have tended to favour the growth of industry in or near old-established market and administrative centres enjoying good communications. From its physical nature the upper plain has always been more favourable to the development of communications and urbanization than the lower plain and these advantages are clearly reflected in the industrial distribution, but the distinction is tending to become less valid as manufacturers seek to avoid the congestion and high land prices near Milan and take advantage of uncommitted labour resources in areas formerly dependent on agriculture.

Food processing is one activity in which the lower plain is well represented; Cremona, Lodi and Pavia are noted for their cheese (Gorgonzola, Parmesan) and butter production but much of the large-scale manufacturing, for example of pasta and confectionery (Motta, Allemagna), is none the less concentrated in Milan. The textile industry, much the most important in the country, is located mainly in the upper plain; cottons, the most important sector, are manufactured at Busto Arsizio, Gallarate, Legnano, Monza and Bergamo although Voghera and Vigevano are also notable in this connection. The spinning and weaving of

[1] Industrial census of that year.

silk is found in and around Como while the manufacture of artificial silk, whose expansion dates from the inter-war years, is concentrated mainly in Milan and its immediate satellites (Rho, Varedo). The woollen industry, much less important than the other sectors, is located in the Pre-Alpine valleys of Bergamo province and in the lower plain at Pavia and Manerbio; the lower plain also claims with Milan and Varese a large share of Italy's flax and hemp processing as well as the leather industries of Vigevano.

Although, until the discovery of gas in the lower plain in 1946, Lombardy had no fuels and only a few small iron deposits in the Pre-Alps, the local demand for steel justified the establishment between the wars of furnaces at Sesto S. Giovanni (Falck, Breda), Bergamo (Dalmine), Brescia and Lecco. These plants use mainly scrap smelted in electric furnaces and their output, something under 1 million tons annually, is insufficient for the growing and ever more specialized demands of the engineering industry in which Lombardy's economic strength chiefly lies. In the heavy engineering sector Milan is dominant (Innocenti, Brown-Boveri, Breda) but it is also very active in the electrical (C.G.E., Siemens, Philips) and vehicle sectors (Alfa Romeo, Innocenti, Bianchi). Varese (Macchi) and Brescia (O.M.) also have their share in the vehicle industry. Light engineering, including machine tools, precision instruments and textile machinery, is well represented in Milan and the towns of the upper plain. This very varied sector also includes the manufacture of motor scooters and motor cycles in which Italy has been most successful since the war; Milan (Innocenti), Arcore (Gilera), Gallarate (M.V. Augusta) and Mandello del Lario (Moto Guzzi) are the towns mainly concerned. Rubber goods and cables (Pirelli) are mainly produced in Milan while Pavia should be mentioned for its large stake in sewing-machine manufacture (Necchi).

The chemical industry with its endless ramifications is mainly concentrated in the Milan area where Bovisa (Montecatini) is known for a wide range of products including fertilizers, and Rho for its petro-chemicals based on crude oil piped from Genoa. In view of the limited resources of hydro-electric power as yet undeveloped Lombardy will become increasingly dependent on oil; in the meantime the gas deposits of the lower plain make a useful contribution and support several petro-chemical plants notably at Cremona and the new township of Metanopoli (Milan), the headquarters of the state oil and gas agency. Milan has also a major pharmaceutical industry.

Despite repeated disasters the vitality of its urban civilization has been a recurrent theme in Lombardy's history for two millennia. Many cities can trace their origin back to pre-Roman settlements but it was the Romans who fixed the urban pattern and wove it together with a network of roads. The towns were more numerous and the road network was closer in the upper plain which lent itself more readily to settlement and movement, but Cremona and Piacenza (Emilia), sited like so many towns of the lower plain just clear of the treacherous river, were the first Roman colonies in the Po Valley; their rôle was to guard convenient crossing points on the Po. Como, Bergamo and Brescia also had a strategic purpose where Alpine routeways met the road along the Pre-Alpine foothills. Another group of settlements, among them Milan, marked the junction of the better-drained upper plain and the wetter and more heavily wooded lower plain.

Milan itself (1,600,000) was originally a Celtic settlement whose site seemed to have no particular local advantage. As Roman Mediolanum it grew to rival Rome itself in size and influence; for a time it served as the capital of the Western Empire and later earned great prestige as a centre of ecclesiastical power. After its sack by the Huns (451) and the long winter of the Gothic wars it barely managed to survive and for a time it lost its pre-eminence among the cities of the plain; the Goths preferred Pavia as their capital. The extraordinary revival of city life in the eleventh century brought Milan to the fore once more and in spite of its complete destruction by Barbarossa in 1162 it rose again to enter on a period of great prosperity and growth based on manufacturing, commerce and banking. The long Spanish domination first established in the early sixteenth century brought renewed stagnation; it only began to disperse under the more enlightened administration of the Austrians, interrupted by a stimulating French interlude. From 1801 to 1871 Milan grew steadily to reach over one-quarter of a million inhabitants and with the political unification of Italy and the development of modern communications the city began to assume its present dominance not only of Lombardy but of the whole of the North.

The concentric layout of Milan, so different from that of Turin, reveals the successive stages in its growth. A chaos of narrow streets leading from the Piazza del Dumo and bounded by the line of the Roman and early medieval walls sketches the extent of the medieval city. Further out a ring road follows the fortifications built at the time of the Spanish occupation. Still further out and much more extensive sprawls the contribution of the last hundred years, geometrical in plan and laced with boulevards leading round and out of the city. The Milanese have always been ready to build high and since the war the skyline of the city has become increasingly American, but still the oil stain of development spreads relentlessly into the countryside. The Milanese are no strangers to traffic congestion and in the hope of easing it a beginning has been made on an underground railway system. Although there are many factories within the city most of the big plants are sited on the main arteries leading northwards to the Splügen (via Sesto S. Givanni and Monza), to Como and to the Simplon (via Rho, Legnano and Gallarate). The autostrade have given further encouragement to dispersal. Until very recently the northern flank of the urban area has been the popular side for development because of its better communications and the firmer terrain.

The importance of Milan as the focus of roads, motorways and railways within the plain, to the Ligurian and Venetian coasts, into the peninsula and through the Alps need not be further particularized (fig. 26). It has excellent air communications, second only to Rome, but it lacks an inland waterway system. Projects for a link to the Adriatic, either using the Po or by cutting a canal along the upper plain, are revived from time to time; at present 600-ton barges can get as far as Cremona. The industry of the Milan area has already received some attention; in its scale, diversity and vitality it may perhaps be fairly compared with that of Birmingham. Both cities have attracted large numbers of immigrants (in the case of Milan from the South) and both are having to face up to the difficult social and administrative consequences. It is a measure of Milan's rank that many of its functions are those normally associated with a capital. In commerce, finance and insurance it is indisputably the most important city in Italy and its trade fair is the country's main industrial shop window. Its press and its publishing activities are more important than Rome's and its cultural reputation bears comparison with that of the capital. The Milanese are the 'go-getters' of Italy; the country owes much to their enterprise and energy and they may perhaps be forgiven if their business-like attitude makes them intolerant of the less zealous approach of some of their fellow countrymen.

Turning briefly to the other Lombard towns, most of them, especially in the lower plain, still derive much of their importance from their functions as agricultural market towns and communications centres, and all those named below are provincial capitals. The prosperity of Varese (70,000) depends mainly on a wide variety of manufactures, among them vehicles, machine tools, aluminium goods, aircraft and textiles. Bergamo (120,000), a town built on three levels, is the business centre of the textile mills of the Val Seriana and the Val Brembana; the Dalmine tube works are situated nearby. Brescia (179,000) relies mainly on vehicles, metal working, arms and textiles. In the lower plain the old fortress town of Mantua (64,000) stands among its fens as if on a raft and its impressive brick walls have to be approached by causeways on two sides; its industries include agricultural processing and petro-chemicals, the latter based on oil brought by barge and pipeline from Venice. Pavia's (78,000) main interests lie in textiles and textile machinery.

**II [c]** *The Lowlands of Veneto and Friuli–Venezia Giulia*

Veneto appears first in history with the Veneti who sought safety from their Celtic neighbours in an alliance with the Romans. Under Augustus Venetia (with Histria), by now thoroughly Romanized, was organized as one of the Emperor's administrative regions. Unfortunately the accessibility of the area from the Danube Basin exposed it to repeated barbarian invasions, an important by-product of which was the establishment of refugee settlements in the lagoons. Among these the Republic of St Mark had become pre-eminent by the ninth century but it was not known as Venice till the twelfth century; its main expansion into the *Terra Ferma*, which trespassed well into what is now regarded as Lombardy, did not take place till the fifteenth century. This political projection of Venice into its hinterland, which was destined to last some four centuries, restored Venetia as a territorial unit and gave it a focus. Although Napoleon snuffed out the Republic in 1797 and its territory was occupied by the Austrians until 1866, Venetia's identity was firmly established. The modern *regione* of Veneto, consisting of seven provinces, coincides roughly with what is sometimes referred to as Venezia Euganea.[1] For much of the Middle Ages, Friuli (essentially the province of Udine) was organized as a mark; it now forms part of an autonomous region together with the provinces of Gorizia and Trieste, which are all that remain to Italy of Venezia Giulia (fig. 26).

After the almost North American frenzy of development in Milan and its environs, life in the Venetian plain assumes a more leisurely pace in keeping with its essentially agricultural character. Social attitudes have been less disturbed by industrialization and Veneto, loyal to its conservative and clerical traditions, is still a land of large families; with the exception of the Trentino–Alto Adige it has the highest birth rate north of Rome. Until quite recently industry did little to relieve the heavy pressure of population on the land and emigration is a long-established practice. In the nineteenth century the traditional movement, usually on a temporary basis, was into Austria–Hungary, and in the last decade the trans-Alpine current (now mainly to Germany and Switzerland) has strongly reasserted itself. Within the region urbanization continues steadily; between 1951 and 1961 the total population actually declined to 3,770,000 and yet the total of the provincial centres registered a 10% increase.

To the three zones already identified in Lombardy (the Sub-Alpine hills, the upper plain and the lower plain) two others must be added in the case of Veneto–Friuli, namely, the coastal lagoons and spits and the fen and delta zone between the Po and the Adige. Apart from the Garda arc the moraines are only extensively represented among the Sub-Alpine hills where the Tagliamento reaches the plain; here they seal off the fertile plain of Osoppo, once a glacial lake bed. Much more important are the basalt tuffs and lavas which occur on the hem of the Lessini mountains (notably behind Verona), to the north and south of Valdagno, and between Bassano and Thiene; the Berici and Euganei 'islands' are also volcanic, the former of basalt and the latter of trachyte. These areas have long been known for their thermal springs (Recoaro Terme and Abano Terme). Between the Brenta and the Livenza the Sub-Alpine hills are developed on Tertiary sediments folded parallel to the Pre-Alpine margin; a limestone dome underlies Montello while further north (in the Asolo hills, for example) differential erosion working on a variety of sediments has produced minor cuestas. In general *coltura promiscua*, dominates the land-use. Where the terrain is steep chestnut woodlands persist, everywhere challenged by the thrusting acacia. The main speciality is the production of wines among which Bardolino, Valpolicella and Soave enjoy an international reputation.

[1] Reference is sometimes made to the 'Tre Venezie'; they are Venezia Euganea, Venezia Tridentina (roughly the Trentino–Alto Adige) and Venezia Giulia, most of which was ceded to Yugoslavia in 1946.

The upper plain, whose coarse fluvio-glacial outwash surrounds the Sub-Alpine 'islands', is fairly narrow in Veneto but widens markedly in Friuli (fig. 27). The Alpine rivers flow between low bluffs, their courses braided across wide pebble-filled beds. There is a serious loss by seepage and several streams issuing from the limestone Pre-Alps (the Meduna and Cellina, for example) are lost in the coarse deposits. Such a terrain offers only very localized opportunities for irrigation. In Veneto almost all the zone is under some form of *coltura promiscua*; rows of vines, fruit trees and mulberries line the field crops – usually maize, wheat and leguminous fodder. The mulberry, whose introduction dates from the thirteenth century, was encouraged by the Republic; it does best on the higher terraces safe from fog born of temperature inversion. Early potatoes, peas, cauliflowers and asparagus, in part for export, are a speciality of Vicenza province, as is also tobacco; extensive peach, apple and pear orchards are a feature of the Verona area. In general this is a region of numerous villages and considerable dispersal of settlement; small farms, many of them worked under *mezzadria*, are the rule.

In Friuli, where the upper plain widens to occupy most of the lowland, the countryside has a less prosperous air reflecting the greater permeability of the fluvio-glacial deposits; tree crops are less common and there is greater dependence on maize. Between the Livenza and the Tagliamento the calcareous nature of the glacial debris adds to the aridity of the surface. Large areas, for example the sterile *magredi*, are little better than steppe, and except for occasional 'oases', settlement is concentrated on the northern and southern margin of the plain and along the edge of the Tagliamento valley where water is available.

In Friuli the transition from the upper to the lower plain is fairly well defined; it is marked by a string of villages, roughly along the spring line on the road from Pordenone through Codrolpo to Palmanova. In Veneto the transition, which coincides roughly with the 50m contour, is imperceptible topographically and is not obviously mirrored in the land use. The *fontanili* line is interrupted by the Berici–Euganei hills, and the springs are fewer and less bountiful than those of Lombardy. This has meant that while the opportunities for irrigation are more restricted, the problem of drainage has been less acute. In fact, the lower Venetian plain has been densely settled for two millennia and between Bassano and Treviso the Roman pattern of colonial settlement (centuriation) is still traceable in the chess-board arrangement of fields and roads. Throughout the lower plain an intricate grid of drainage and irrigation channels has been superimposed on a maze of meandering rivers, the more important of which have been dyked and straightened in their lower courses. Venice's main interest in its rivers was directed towards promoting navigation, controlling floods and preventing silting in the lagoons, and although many local schemes date back to the Middle Ages, irrigation was somewhat neglected. In the last half-century the irrigated area has increased steadily but except for one or two rice and meadow zones in Vicenza and Verona provinces, it has promoted little regional specialization. In fact, as regards crops the *bassa* remains a region of great variety, and irrigation water, which is usually only available in modest quantities for limited periods, is regarded mainly as a means of increasing yields of the traditional crops. As in so many areas of ancient settlement *coltura promiscua* is widely practised; maize, soft wheat, fodder, sugar beet and a wide variety of vegetables, fruits and vines are grown, the last 'married' to elms or festooned between other fruit trees. Livestock and poultry rearing reinforce the mixed character of the farming. Maize was introduced into Veneto about 1550 and it gradually replaced millet. For long it has been the region's main crop and at one time its excessive consumption in the form of *pollenta* was responsible for the high incidence of pellagra. Although medium (10–25 hecs) and large units are well represented, the small farm whether rented or owner-worked, predominates in the lower Venetian plain.

In the coastal lagoons the traditional occupations are fishing and horticulture. Chioggia is the main port from which the rich fishing grounds of the upper Adriatic shelf are exploited. A variety of 'fish', including eels, prawns and shrimps, is netted or trapped in the river mouths and in the lagoons. A specialized horticulture, aimed at the Venice market, is practised on the coastal spits where the light soil is enriched by broken shells and algae. The reclamation of the marshy alluvial strip immediately behind the lagoons, which in Friuli is embarrassed by the proximity of the *fontanili* line, is the work of the last seventy years and is still incomplete. Associations of landowners and contractors (*consorzi di bonifica*), each responsible for a very large area, sometimes as much as 30,000 hectares, are in charge of the drainage, settlement and management of the *bonifiche*, which are divided into a monotonously repetitive grid of long rectangles; a number of these are combined to form a compact *podere* worked by a family under a *mezzadria* or cash rent contract. Mechanization is widely and increasingly employed although rural redundancy remains an obstacle to its optimum application. Cereals, beet and fodder are the main crops but as the *bonifiche* mature the unbroken skyline is relieved by fruit trees and poplars. The fast-growing timber, as well as locally grown cane, finds a market in the rayon works of Torviscosa (Sniaviscosa).

From north of the Adige to south of the Reno and upstream beyond Guastella lies a triangle of fen whose base merges into the delta. In Rovigo and Venezia provinces Veneto shares this area with Emilia and Lombardy. The landscape has much in common with that of the hinterland of the lagoons and its reclamation posed similar problems in water control except that here they were writ large because of the vastness of the fen and the catastrophically erratic behaviour of the rivers.[1] Wherever the terrain raises itself a foot or two above the general level of the fen, on a fossil dune perhaps or on an abandoned levee or alluvial fan, Man

---

[1] Before the great floods of 589 the Adige below Albaredo flowed through Este to Chioggia and the Mincio flowed independently to the sea. In the same period the Po, which had its mouth just north of Ravenna, switched into the Po di Volano; later, in 1152, it swung still further north. In November 1957 most of Rovigo province was under water.

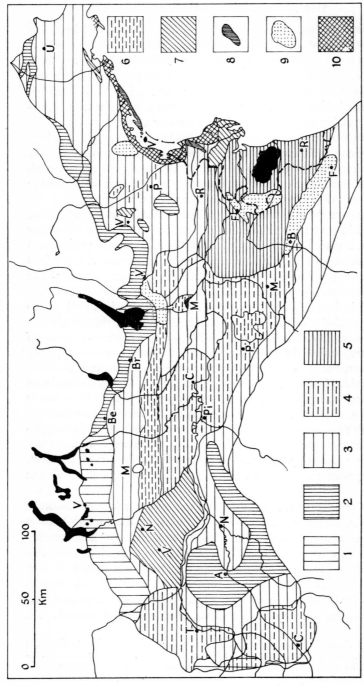

*Fig. 30.* The agricultural regions of the Northern Lowlands combining land-use and farm types. I – Small mixed farms of the Pre-Alpine hilly margin (cereals, fodder crops, cattle and fruit). 2 – Small mixed farms of the Pre-Alpine hilly margin and the Monferrato hills with vines important in the land-use. 3 – Non-irrigated cereals dominant; small and medium-sized units very common. 4 – Cereals and fodder crops, medium-sized units common with *coltura promiscua* in Veneto. 5 – Cereals (including rice) and beet with some hemp; large units predominating. 6 – Irrigated forage crops (*marcite*); mainly large units. 7 – Rice on large units dominant. 8 – Horticulture; small units. 9 – Fruit (apples, pears, peaches) dominant. 10 – Fishing in the lagoons. A horizontal component in the shading indicates that wheat and maize are important in the land-use.

Broken line – limit of the *Ente per la Colonizzazione del Delta Padano*.

(After Sestini, Robertson and the Centro Studi du Geografia Economica) long since seized the opportunity to drain the area by gravity channels. These are the *terre vecchie* so called because their reclamation and settlement may go back as far as the sixteenth century. Elsewhere the stagnant waters defied reclamation until efficient pumps made poldering possible; even then the lowering of the surface by shrinkage often threatened to undo the work. The struggle in these lower areas (*valli*) has been on for over a century; work on the Grandi Valli Veronesi dates from the 1850s and the Isola d'Ariano was not tackled until 1912. The delta itself offered an even more daunting challenge and although most of it has now been won for cultivation, some 100,000 hectares remain untamed. In the past reclamation was in the hands of private *consorzi* but now it is mainly the responsibility of the Ente per la Colonizazzione del Delta Padano. Although with time the contrast fades, the *terre vecchie* are distinguished from the newer *boni-fiche* by the greater variety of their field crops (cereals, beet, fodder, hemp, etc.) and by the more extensive cultivation of tree crops whether planted in lines or in compact orchards. The newer lands present a dismal empty landscape, gridded with ditches, its horizon bounded by massive dykes hiding all but the church towers of distant villages. Except on land recently won by the Ente Delta, the expense of drainage favoured large capitalistic properties many of which have in-evitably received the attention of the land reform authorities,[1] but unless mechanization and other technical improvements are to be permanently impeded redundancy among the labour force must be drastically reduced. In newly re-claimed areas rice is usually the pioneer crop but as the land matures it gives way to cereals, fodder, industrial crops, especially beet and hemp, and fruit.

The cities of Veneto, with few exceptions, stand firm on their Roman founda-tions; Aquileia, once the gateway to Pannonia, never recovered from its sack by the Huns, and Venice (Venezia) must be considered a newcomer, but Padua (Padova) and Vicenza still knot together the routes pioneered by the Romans, and Bassano and Verona still control Claudius's roads up into the Alps. The railway between Verona and Trieste could not do better than follow the route first traced by the Via Postumia. Despite their recent growth the cities of Veneto retain something of the dignified air they acquired when 'La Dominante' held sway, and most of them are still essentially centres of communications and com-merce serving a rich countryside. Apart from agricultural processing which is widely shared, textiles are the most important industrial activity. Silk spinning, based on local materials, has survived at Treviso from the Middle Ages, but the woollen manufactures (including knitwear and knitting wool) of Schio, Thiene, Arzignano, Pieve Rocchete (Rossi), and Valdagno (Marzotto) in northern Vicenza province are much more important. This industry in which Padua and Venice share has also a long tradition. The cottons of Thiene, Montebelluno, Lonigo, Cornegliano and Gorizia, the jute of S. Dona and the rayon of Torvis-cosa are of much more recent date. Apart from small quantities of lignite and

---

[1] By 1959 some 6800 hectares in Polesine had been converted into 1100 poderi with varying success.

anthracite (Valdagno) Veneto is poorly endowed with fuels and the metal-using industries are on a small scale. Maniago has an old-established craft in cutlery, Bassano manufactures bicycles and sanitary ware, Este and Breganze agricultural machines and Schio textile machinery. Verona (230,000) and Padua (206,000), whose nodal positions have been noted, are the biggest inland towns; both are engaged in agricultural processing, textiles, paper-making and light engineering. Padua's university, which at one time was pre-eminent in Europe for its medical studies, is still flourishing.

By far the most important industrial concentrations in Veneto–Friuli–Venezia Giulia are located in or near the two main ports. Venice itself (Venezia, 359,000) may be a museum town but in the evidence of its glorious past it has something unique to offer. The tourist trade, to which the beaches of Lido and Iesolo make a more conventional contribution, supports a variety of craft industries including glass, fine metalware, jewellery and knitwear. On the mainland Mestre and Porto Marghera have been able to devote themselves to industry with fewer inhibitions; the importation of coal, oil and ores supports a heavy industrial complex producing coke, oil derivatives, chemicals, glass, paints, aluminium, lead, zinc, ferro-silicon and steel. A canal links the lagoon with the Po and 600-ton barges can reach Cremona and Mantua. Although less well equipped than Genoa and less favourably placed to serve the heavily industrialized sector of the Valle Padana, Venice and Porto Marghera jointly rank third among Italian ports and handled over 9 million tons, the vast majority incoming, in 1964. The most important regular sailings are to the eastern Mediterranean and the Black Sea. Venice is also a popular point of departure for cruises to the Aegean and a recent development has been the car-ferry service to western Greece.

Few ports have been so much bedevilled by international politics as Trieste (272,000) over the last half-century. Sited on a peninsula between two rocky bays, it was developed in the 1860s to serve as the main port of Austria–Hungary. Despite the competition of Fiume (at that time Hungarian) Trieste built up a flourishing transit and entrepôt trade and developed a variety of industries including steel, shipbuilding and food processing. The disintegration of Austria–Hungary in 1918 left the Italians and Yugoslavs face to face in the disputed marchland of Venezia Giulia. For the time being (until 1945) Italy's claims prevailed and even Fiume (Rijeka) was annexed although the Yugoslavs built up Sušak in competition. Unfortunately the competition of the German ports, the inclusion of most of Trieste's 'natural' hinterland within the successor states of Austria–Hungary, and the atmosphere of economic nationalism prevailing between the wars combined to reduce the transit and entrepôt traffic of the port. In an attempt to maintain its activity Italy encouraged the industrial build-up begun by Austria. In 1945 Yugoslavia annexed Venezia Giulia with the exception of Trieste and its immediate environs, where it was intended to create a Free Territory. This proved impossible because of the rivalry between Italy and Yugoslavia and their associated supporters. In 1954 the Free Territory plan was abandoned and a direct Italo-Yugoslav agreement awarded Italy the present province of Trieste while the rest of the Free Territory remained in Yugoslav hands. Since then the equipment and services of the port, which suffered heavily in the war, have been much improved, and in an attempt to revive the entrepôt trade generous 'free port' facilities have been provided. Quite apart from the difficulties posed by the political situation in central Europe, Trieste has to compete with Fiume (Rijeka) and the German ports for the Austrian trade which accounts for about two-thirds of the transit traffic. If Yugoslav territory is to be avoided the only railway into Austria is the tortuous line through Tarvisio and Villach. The doubling of this line and the completion of the autostrada from Padua should do much to improve communications. In 1964 the port handled 4 million tons, mainly composed of incoming coal, ores and oil. Trieste's industries include food processing, distilling, chemicals, textiles (cotton, jute, flax and rayon), oil refining, iron and steel (Ilva) and shipbuilding (Cantieri Riuniti dell' Adriatico). In this last sector, Trieste, with neighbouring Monfalcone, ranks second to Genoa.

With the annexation to Yugoslavia of almost all Venezia Giulia in 1945 Italy lost about half of her bauxite production, the mercury of Idria and the coal of the Arsa valley. In addition Venetian fishermen found themselves excluded from part of their traditional fishing grounds. Before 1945 Italians were in the majority in the small towns of Istria but the interior was mainly inhabited by Slovenes and Croats.

## II [d] *The plain of Emilia–Romagna*

This region is easily defined; it consists simply of a wedge between the Po, below Piacenza, in the north and the Apennines in the south. Under the Romans, who knew it first as Cispadane Gaul and colonized it thoroughly in the second century BC, it assumed the name of Emilia (Augustus's 8th *regio*) in honour of the builder of its arterial road. With the collapse of the Empire Goths, Lombards and Franks in their turn disputed control with the Byzantine power entrenched at Ravenna. In the Middle Ages Romagna fell to the Papacy which retained it till 1860, but Parma, Modena and Ferrara emerged in the Renaissance as stable elements on the political map; the first two survived as Duchies until the Unification, but Ferrara, for long the seat of the house of Este, succumbed to the Papacy in the seventeenth century. The strong radical and anticlerical traditions of eastern Emilia, which today find expression in loyalty to the political left, are usually attributed to the area's long experience of papal maladministration.

The Sub-Alpine hill zone and the fluvio-glacial platforms of Lombardy have no counterpart in Emilia where the coarser detritus fans shade quickly into a gently inclined alluvial plain. From the point of view of human geography the essential distinction is between the upper and lower plains, the first a zone of small farms, varied cultivation and ancient settlement, the second one of large capitalistic properties growing a limited range of specialized crops. Except for limited *terre vecchie*, for example in Ferrara province, most of the plain north of a line from Piacenza to Ravenna was a wilderness of fen or swampy delta until a century ago. The efforts of Roman administrators, medieval monasteries and Renaissance princes had made little impression on it; only in the mid-nineteenth century did it begin to yield to associations of improvers armed with new techniques and encouraged from time to time by favourable legislation. One of the biggest sectors, the Grande Bonificazione Ferrarese, was tackled in 1872 and between 1880 and 1950 over 400,000 hectares were reclaimed. In their fundamentals these *bonifiche* differ little from those in Veneto described above. Part of the estate is usually entrusted to *mezzadri* and sharecroppers (*comparticipanti*), but the rest is worked with hired labour. The work force originally attracted into the area for reclamation soon proved superfluous to the normal needs of the *bonifiche* most of which employed machinery from the first, and the social unrest smouldering in the dismal villages of this part of Emilia has its principal cause in chronic under-employment. Cereals, hemp and sugar beet are the dominant crops; rice is important between Bologna and Ferrara and wherever land has been newly drained. On the older properties vines and fruit have found their way into the land-use and in the arc to the south of Ferrara peaches, apples and pears are a speciality. Oddly enough these lands, once so poorly drained, need more water than can be expected from rainfall in the summer months; springs, wells and the meagre flow of the Apennine rivers provide intermittent irrigation for about 250,000 hectares but only about 45,000 can be submerged for long periods. Much of this latter area lies on either side of Piacenza where substantial *cassine*, similar to those of Lombardy, specialize in the production of milk and cheese. The Canale Emiliano–Romagnolo (fig. 28), now nearing completion, will irrigate some 150,000 hectares. Most of its water will be drawn from the Po and its distribution will necessitate a number of large pumping stations.

Since 1950 reclamation has been mainly the concern of the Ente Delta (fig. 17) and the new lands, except where suited to specialized rice cultivation, are distributed in family *poderi* which in time will become the peasants' property. Some 45,000 hectares have been appropriated for the accommodation of over 5300 families. Where a reclaimed area is assigned to rice cultivation it becomes the collective responsibility of a group of families.

The upper plain from Fidenza to Rimini has been closely settled since the time of republican Rome whose disciplined system of land development still contributes to the chess-board pattern of roads and fields in the Romagna.[1] It will have become clear already that the older settled parts of the Valle Padana are usually those with a high proportion of small farms and a considerable variety of crops. In the upper Emilian plain the commonest farm unit is the *podere*, a compact property varying in size from 3 to 25 hectares and divided into a number of half-hectare strips. Whether worked by the owner or rented under a *mezzadria*

[1] East of Cesena the grid runs N–S and E–W; in the rest of the Romagna it is orientated parallel to the Via Emilia.

contract it is essentially a family farm and each *podere* has its modest farmhouse and ancillary buildings. Lines of vines and fruit trees separate the strips, some of which are usually reserved for a compact orchard of apples, pears, peaches and other stone fruits. Wheat, maize and lucerne are the basic field crops but they are supplemented by beet and a rich variety of vegetables including peas, beans, potatoes, onions and tomatoes. Cattle and pigs enter into the economy of most farms, the former supported by hay and leguminous fodder crops (enriched where possible by irrigation), and the latter by cereals and skimmed milk. Between Parma and Reggio, a region renowned for its animal products, especially cheese, a sizeable area is under water meadows, while north of Bologna rice still holds a special place in the land-use. The very extensive area in Romagna already devoted to pears, apples and peaches for export is being rapidly extended. Of the four *regioni* of the Valle Padana, Emilia–Romagna is much the weakest industrially. By far the most important activity is food processing whose varied products have contributed to Emilia's high reputation with Italian gourmets. In size the establishments range from the large sugar refineries of Ravenna and Ferrara down through a host of medium-sized and small concerns producing pasta, cheese, butter, sausages, meat and fruit preserves, sauces, essences and wines. Co-operatives have a long tradition and wide ramifications in Emilia and they are well represented in food processing. Textiles are of minor importance and engineering is on a very modest scale. Bologna (456,000) makes railway equipment, electrical goods, precision instruments and agricultural machinery, while Modena (144,000) enjoys a reputation in the world of fast cars (Ferrari, Maserati).

Before the war oil in very small amounts was struck at Fornovo, but since 1946 natural gas has been discovered and developed on a number of sites in the delta and along the northern flank of the Via Emilia (Cortemaggiore, Corregio, Consandolo, Ravenna, Alfonsine). Apart from its significance as a fuel, gas has been responsible for the expansion and diversification of the chemical industry which was previously only represented in Emilia by one or two fertilizer plants (Fidenza). Ravenna is now one of the biggest producers of synthetic rubber and nitrates in Europe and its activities have 'snowballed' to include oil refining and petrochemicals. Emilia is at a disadvantage industrially in lacking a modern port but fortunately oil can be unloaded at Ravenna by pipelines from offshore installations. There are also small refineries at Fornovo, Cortemaggiore and Fiorenzuola.

The siting of all but two of Emilia's large towns along the Via Emilia needs little elaboration. Most of them lean heavily on their food processing and servicing activities as well as on their functions as provincial and marketing centres. Piacenza (91,000) controls the Po crossing and Parma the trans-Apennine railway and road (Cisa Pass) to La Spezia. Bologna gathers traffic by road and rail from Milan, Verona and Padua and passes it on through the Apennines to Florence and Rome. The older roads over the Futa and Porretta passes have been supplemented recently by the *Strada del Sole*, and the original railway to Florence via

Pistoia has been supplemented since the thirties by the Prato route which involves a very long tunnel. Away from the Via Emilia, Ferrara (154,000), once entirely dependent on agriculture, now shares in the chemical industry and Ravenna (116,000), thanks to petro-chemicals, is rising rapidly from its Byzantine tomb; the splendour of its mosaics are a unique attraction for the hosts of tourists on their way to the beaches of Rimini, Riccione and Cattolica.

# III LIGURIA

Along the entire Ligurian coast there is no compromise between the mountains and the sea. 65% of the *regione* is classed as mountainous and 35% as hilly, but very occasionally, as at Albenga and Diano Marina, the mountains fall back to tolerate a narrow lowland, usually where a torrent pauses briefly on an alluvial flat. Communications along the coast have been established only with the greatest difficulty; the railway is punctuated with tunnels, and although a scenic road is now being hacked through the Cinque Terre, the Via Aurelia has to abandon the coast altogether between Sestri Levante and La Spezia. To avoid congestion the autostrada (completed so far only between Savona and Voltri) is being carried along the mountain flank high above the shore. A dozen tortuous roads force their way over the watershed but the vast majority of the traffic inland is channelled into the Altare (459m), Giovi (472m) and Cisa (1039m) passes; all three are exploited by railways and roads, and by autostrade in the case of the first two. A fourth railway line approaches Genoa under the Turchino Pass.

It is the convention to divide the Alps and the Apennines at the Altare Pass. Bearing in mind the strong affinities of the *rocce verdi* between Savona and Genoa with those of the Piedmontese Alps, geologists prefer to make the break at the Giovi, and there is much to be said for treating the Riviera di Ponente separately from the Riviera di Levante. The former exhibits a greater variety of rock type and landform, is drier, milder and more sheltered. Between Tenda, Ventimiglia and Albenga the landscape is developed on erodible Eocene sandstones and marls, and although the terrain is often steep it is hilly rather than mountainous. Inland between Savona and Albenga, where the Maritime Alps reach to 1386m in M. Settipani and to 2630m in Mongioie, the relief is shared by Carboniferous sandstones, Permian limestones and porphyries of similar age; caverns and other underground karstic features are well developed in the limestones. In the 'Alpine' sector of the Ligurian Apennines, where the range is at its narrowest and lowest, the component rocks are gneisses, schists and *rocce verdi*, among which serpentines often emerge as isolated resistant masses (M. Beigua). Here, as in so much of Liguria, short torrents, revived by the post-Pliocene uplift, have cut steep-sided valleys in rocks which are inherently unstable. Soil erosion has been the inevitable consequence of deforestation, and the agricultural land of the lower slopes owes its survival to systems of terraces evolved over the centuries.

If anything the rocks of the Riviera di Levante and its hinterland are even more

148

unstable; besides *rocce verdi* they include Eocene shales, clays and sandstones (*macigno*) as well as treacherous *argille scagliose*. The low longitudinal valleys occupied by the Lavagna and Vara assist communications between Genoa and La Spezia but only the Magra contributes much to the penetration of the wide block of mountainous country which isolates the coast from the Valle Padana.

Sheltered from the north by its mountains, Liguria enjoys a mildness of climate which is not met with again on the Tyrrhenian coast until Campania is reached. Agriculturally this is its greatest asset but it is offset by the steepness of the terrain. 73% of the *regione* is classed as permanent pasture or woodland, 5% is occupied by tree crops and only 6% by field crops. In general the terraced lower slopes are devoted to olives, vines, figs and other elements of Mediterranean polyculture; the olives may straggle on beyond the terraces where remnants of chestnut and ilex woodland thin out in their turn into poor grazing. On favourable land where irrigation is possible citrus fruits and early vegetables are grown, and near San Remo on the 'Riviera dei Fiori' the cultivation of roses and carnations is a speciality. Both in climate and relief the Riviera di Ponente is more favoured than its eastern counterpart; on the exposed and precipitous slopes of the Cinque Terre the only possible cultivation is that of olives and vines. In general holdings are small, often too small to support a family without other sources of income; except in the labour-intensive flower and vegetable zones most of them are owner-worked. Emigration to France and overseas is a traditional practice and with the increasing drift of young people to the coastal cities many of the interior villages are falling into disrepair; in many cases their sites were chosen originally with the danger of surprise attack from the sea in mind.

But agriculture employs less than one-sixth of the *regione*'s active population; over the centuries Liguria has looked to the sea to make up for its deficiencies on land, and today its importance lies in its ports and the industries they have attracted. Sited on an enclosed deep-water bay and controlling the passes over the lowest and narrowest sector of the Apennines, Genoa (Genova; 796,000) flourished first in the Middle Ages when it challenged Venice for supremacy in the Levant and Black Sea trades. By 1500 its influence had shrunk to the western Mediterranean sphere; the convoys to Bruges and Antwerp had long since been suspended and trade with western Europe now came overland or passed through the entrepôt of Cadiz. Thereafter until the nineteenth century Genoa's power lay in finance and banking rather than in commerce. The revival of the port owes much to Cavour who realized that in an age of industrialization Genoa's rôle in a United Italy could be much more than that of a gateway to Piedmont and a link with Sardinia. On his initiative the installations of the port were improved; the western mole, built in the eighteenth century to match the much older eastern breakwater, was renovated and new piers were built into the bay. Above all the railway link with Turin was established in 1853 (supplemented in 1889) and with the opening of the St Gotthard (1882) and the Simplon (1906) Genoa's sphere was extended into Switzerland. By this time Genoa had developed a flourishing entrepôt in grain and coal and the Suez canal had transformed the Mediterranean into a major shipping lane. Between the wars the port was extended westwards outside the bay behind protective moles which have been extended since 1948 to shelter the Cornigliano steel plant and the shipyards and oil jetties of Sestri and Pegli. Genoa has seventeen miles of quays, is equipped to handle any cargo and offers adequate storage facilities for grain, meat, oil, chemicals etc. It is Italy's main passenger port with regular lines to the Americas, northern Europe, South Africa, Australia, the Middle and Far East as well as to other Italian and Mediterranean ports. In 1964 it dealt with 25·0 million tons of merchandise of which 22·8 million were incoming. The principal imports were oil (13·2 million tons, mainly from the Middle East and the USSR), coal (2·0 millions, mainly from the USA), mineral ores, scrap, chemicals, textile fibres, grain and colonial goods. Genoa competes with Marseilles and the north European ports for the supply of oil to south Germany and its pipelines serve the refineries of Aigle and Ingolstadt as well as those of Milan. A large proportion of the raw materials imported, notably oil, ores, oil seeds and chemicals, are processed locally and contribute to the export trade which relies mainly on the wide variety of manufactures produced in the industrial zones of Piedmont and Lombardy. Nearly a quarter of Switzerland's seaborne merchandise passes through the port.

Hampered by the difficult terrain inland, the industrial zone straggles along the coast for ten miles, mainly to the west. There are very important shipyards (Ansaldo) at Sestri and Voltri, and between Pegli and Sampierdarena there are several large engineering works producing marine, electrical and railway equipment. Since the war a large full-cycle steel plant, using west African ore and American coal, has been built on reclaimed land at Cornigliano. Oil refining, non-ferrous metal smelting, chemicals, glass, soap, textiles, machine tools, vehicles, canning and milling are all strongly represented.

Of the other two main Ligurian ports, Savona (73,000) and La Spezia (125,000), the first may be regarded as a miniature Genoa. Its special sphere of influence is Turin to which it has easy access through the Altare pass. Its harbour was first improved in the nineteenth century for the import of English coal, a trade which is less important now than the piping of oil to Trecate; another pipeline is under construction to Turin. The port's other interests include shipbuilding and ship-repairing, coking, foundries, glass, chemicals and leather. Like Genoa it is handicapped by lack of space for development. In this respect La Spezia is better endowed, but the wide tract of difficult country in its rear which, with its excellent harbour, recommended it as a naval base, has been a disadvantage commercially. Napoleon recognized its strategic possibilities but they were not realized until Cavour's time. Apart from those activities connected with a naval arsenal, La Spezia is engaged in oil refining, non-ferrous metal smelting and jute textiles.

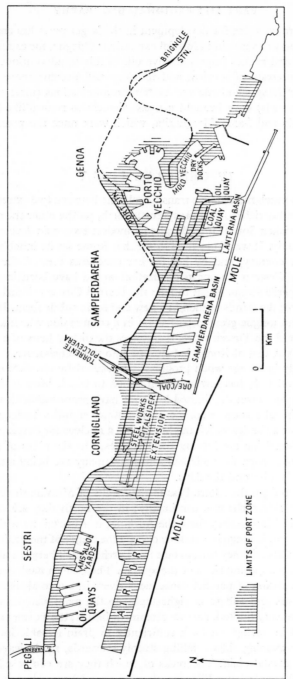

*Fig. 31.* The waterfront of Genoa

The premium on space for development in the larger ports has enabled some of the lesser ports to share in industrial expansion; Oneglia, for example, manufactures pasta and refines imported olive oil. If this trend continues the clash between the interests of tourism and industry will become more difficult to resolve. Rising living standards and better communications (most recently the Alpine road tunnels) have brought a mass clientele to resorts like San Remo, Alassio, Rapallo and Santa Margherita, which were once the preserve of the ailing rich.

## IV CENTRAL ITALY

Central Italy is much more than a transitional zone between two extremes, on the one hand the industrialized and prosperous North, on the other the agricultural and poverty-stricken South; it is, despite its modest economic development, the very heart of Italy. It was from the Centre that Rome set its indelible mark on the rest of the country, and by her further conquests created the conditions without which Western European civilization would have been inconceivable. And when Imperial Rome began to fade the Eternal City continued to exercise its influence over the minds of men in a new and more subtle form. In later centuries the Italian tongue grew to perfection in a countryside which knew Dante and Petrarch, and the Tuscan cities, themselves the distant heirs of a civilization more ancient than that of Rome, led Europe into the Renaissance.

Unfortunately in an age when progress is measured by the pace of industrialization, Central Italy has few assets on which to build. Most of it is mountainous or hilly and even the limited lowlands have proved difficult to develop; its fuel and mineral resources are meagre, its water supplies inadequate, and it lacks a Genoa or a Naples which might provide a nucleus for development. The young and enterprising are leaving their villages, but the cities of the Centre offer only limited scope for their ambitions and many are being attracted into Lombardy or even beyond the Alps.

In their sweep from the Altare Pass to the Straits of Messina the trend of the main Apennine ridges changes continually; in the north they are close to the Ligurian Sea; in Marche they flank the Adriatic; in Abruzzi, by which time all semblance of a simple range is lost, they occupy the centre of the peninsula; from Campania into Calabria they turn to face the Tyrrhenian. There is a marked contrast between the opposing sides of the system. The eastern flank has been dissected by a succession of parallel consequent rivers into a comb-like pattern of steep-sided ridges and valleys at right-angles to the main watershed. Most of these rivers have very limited, narrow catchment basins; the Pescara and Sangro are exceptional in having cut back sufficiently to drain sizeable intermontane basins. The intervening ridges, falling steeply seawards, rarely leave room for even a narrow coastal plain. The rocks of which they are composed (Miocene marls and chalks underlying Pliocene clays and sands) were laid down in the

Apennine foretrench on the flanks of the Apennine nappes. They were exposed without serious disturbance by the post-Pliocene uplift which encouraged the rivers to incise themselves deeply even though their lower courses now may flow over well-developed floodplains. Throughout the whole Sub-Apennine zone from Le Langhe to the Abruzzi a similar structure and a similar erosional experience have produced a basic similarity of landscape.

Along the main Apennine ridge, developed for the most part on the upper Tuscan nappes, there is a gradual change in the lithology and its associated landforms. Between the Giovi and Porretta passes the summits forming the main ridge approach and sometimes exceed 2000m (M. Maggiorasca, M. Cusna, M. Cimone, Corno alle Scale). Occasionally their upper slopes have been steepened by minor glaciers but their crests are usually well rounded and rarely deserve the status of peaks. This is even more characteristic of the range beyond the Porretta Pass where rounded summits, only occasionally surpassing 1000m, alternate with wide shallow cols. The range falls sharply on its southern flank to the longitudinal valleys of the Magra, Serchio, Sieve and upper Arno. In this sector of the Apennines, that is as far as the Bocca Serriola, the most widely exposed rocks are Eocene shales and clays and the somewhat older *argille scagliose* – all of them notoriously unstable. The stronger relief is provided either by serpentines and other *rocce verdi* or by lower Tertiary sandstones (*macigno*). The northern Apennines are sometimes referred to as the sandstone Apennines but the description is brief rather than accurate.

Southwards through the Umbrian Apennines, clays, shales and sandstones still predominate but as Abruzzo is approached the underlying Mesozoic rocks, overwhelmingly calcareous in character, are exposed more frequently in eroded anticlines and begin to provide the higher relief features. Beyond the Nera the effects of severe tectonic disturbance become apparent; massive blocks of Mesozoic limestone, frequently topping 2000m and aligned NW–SE, alternate with longitudinal intermontane basins such as those of Aquila and Sulmona. Towards the Adriatic even the Miocene sediments have been raised up to form mountainous country reaching 2400m in the Monti della Laga.

So much for the main range. To the west of it lies a Sub-Apennine zone, the counterpart of a similar tract on the Adriatic flank but much less easily defined in terms of structure, relief and drainage. For convenience its western limit may be drawn along the Valdarno, the Val di Chiana, the Chiani, the Tiber and the Sacco–Liri. It consists mainly of hills and low mountains, occasionally forming discontinuous ranges or elongated blocks parallel to the general NW–SE trend of the folding (Mti Sabini, Mti Simbruini) but more often independent massifs (Pratomagno, M. Martano, Terminillo). Everywhere it is penetrated by longitudinal valleys, sometimes narrow and steep as in the case of Garfagnana, Mugello and Casentino (respectively the upper Serchio, Sieve and Arno), sometimes widening into extensive intermontane basins such as those of Gubbio, Val Tiberina, Perugia, Terni and Rieti. The western Sub-Apennines are developed on the same nappe system as the Apennines themselves and the lithology of each sector has much in common with that of the main range parallel to it.

Between the Sub-Apennines and the coast are the Anti-Apennines, a term which has little structural significance since they too are underlain by the Apennine nappe system. They exhibit a rich variety of lithology and landform; the Apuan Alps, ruggedly carved in Permian and Triassic limestones, are undeniably mountainous; most of Tuscany between the Arno and the Ombrone is hill and plateau country developed on Tertiary sands and clays; from M. Amiata to the Alban hills the landscape is chiefly the work of Quaternary volcanic eruptions; and between the Pontine Marshes and the Sacco–Liri trench bold Cretaceous limestone blocks form the Lepini, Ausoni and Aurunci mountains. Along the coast discontinuous lowlands accumulated behind sandy spits and interrupted by rocky headlands, penetrate up the larger valleys, especially those of the Arno and Tiber.

In no respect is the contrast between the eastern and western flanks of Central Italy more obvious than in the drainage. The relatively simple comb-like arrangement of rejuvenated consequent streams draining the Emilian–Adriatic slope has already been noted; on the Tyrrhenian side over two-thirds of the surface is drained to the Tiber and Arno whose courses are anything but simple; sometimes they flow longitudinally through intermontane basins, sometimes transversely through narrow gaps or gorges. These two systems owe their complexity, at least in part, to the long history of crustal instability to which the 'inside' of the Apennine system has been subject since the Eocene. Thus during the Pliocene only the higher parts of what are now the Anti-Apennine uplands remained above sea level forming an archipelago off the main western coastline, which ran to the east of the Chiana–Tiber line from just north of Chiusi to a few miles west of Tivoli. The intermontane basins of the Sub-Apennine zone are all of tectonic origin and during the Pliocene some of them were occupied by lakes; the biggest stretched down the Val Tiberina from Sansepolcro through Todi to Terni, with a branch from near Perugia to Spoleto. At the end of the Pliocene the whole peninsula underwent an uplift which eventually raised the Sub-Apennine zone some hundreds of metres and converted the former Anti-Apennine archipelago into a land mass much of which was still penetrated by arms of the sea (e.g. the lower Valdarno); some areas, notably the Val di Chiana, failed to establish a satisfactory drainage system and remained swampy into historical times. The uplift was far from uniform and it was accompanied by local collapse and warping. Thus the Tiber lake, which persisted somewhat diminished into the Quaternary, was obliged by an upwarping to abandon its former course (at that time to the sea) through what is now the Nestone valley and cut a gorge westwards from Todi. Similar movements modified the drainage elsewhere; the Tiber and Terni basins were separated and henceforth the latter was drained exclusively by the Nera through the Narni gorge. It seems likely that the drainage of the Salto into the Liri was reversed by earth-movements to flow into the

Terni lake, remnants of which survive. The upper Arno too once ran southwards into the Val di Chiana but either accumulated debris or warping diverted it into the trench cut by the Sieve. Another major complication was the accumulation of volcanic ash and lava southwards from M. Amiata which obstructed the Tiber

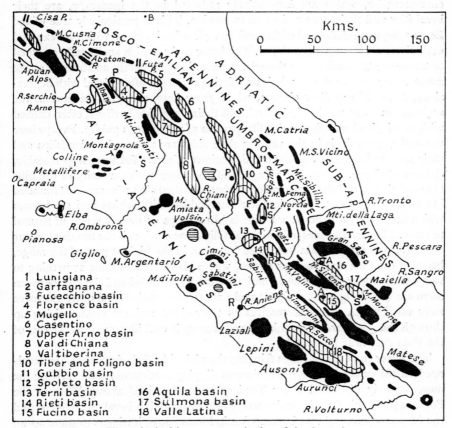

1 Lunigiana
2 Garfagnana
3 Fucecchio basin
4 Florence basin
5 Mugello
6 Casentino
7 Upper Arno basin
8 Val di Chiana
9 Valtiberina
10 Tiber and Foligno basin
11 Gubbio basin
12 Spoleto basin
13 Terni basin
14 Rieti basin
15 Fucino basin
16 Aquila basin
17 Sulmona basin
18 Valle Latina

*Fig. 32.* The principal intermontane basins of the Apennine system

and Nera and obliged their waters to force a tortuous outlet to the sea through the hills of the Campagna. Along the coast, through the many vicissitudes of the Quaternary, rivers and waves combined to choke the shallow inlets and channels between the offshore islands and so build up a series of coastal lowlands, whose seawards edges are fringed with spits festooned between headlands.

## IV[a] *The Northern Apennines*

Convenience and convention suggest the Cisa and Bocca Serriola passes as suitable limits to define this sector of the range, which is sometimes referred to as the Tosco–Emilian Apennines. Although it has a geographical personality of its own, it is essentially a transitional zone between Padane and Mediterranean Italy, and in peace and war it has proved itself less of a barrier than a costly inconvenience.

The range is developed on the upper Tuscan nappes whose component rocks vary in age from the upper Cretaceous to the Oligocene. Their outstanding characteristics, which are impressively reflected in the landscape, are their instability and their poor resistance to erosion. This is particularly true of the Eocene clays and shales and of the *argille scagliose* (scaley clays) which are exposed extensively on the northern slopes. The latter rocks, which are usually assigned to the upper Cretaceous, are thought to have slumped bodily northwards as the range emerged from the sea; their undulating surface is often pitted with depressions, not unlike shallow cirques, where *frane* have occurred. In general the argillaceous rocks are deeply incised, and their steep-sided valleys, often choked with debris, lead back into a fan-like pattern of precipitous gullies. Everywhere the difficult terrain is in the valleys; their sides are menaced by landslips and their narrow floodplains by the erratic regimes of rivers fed from impermeable, deforested slopes. Farms and villages seek the comparative security of the hill-tops and ridges, and the roads toil up to the watershed along the crests of rounded but steep-sided spurs. The clays are interbedded with schists and sandstones which may interrupt the slopes with bold outcrops or form a series of natural terraces. These sandstones, of which the Oligocene *macigno* is the toughest, occur extensively along the main watershed but even in the highest part of the range, between the Cisa and Porretta passes, where glaciation has done something to steepen the upper slopes, the summits are tamely rounded and the cols between them are wide. The most resistant rocks are the serpentines and other extrusive *rocce verdi* which reveal themselves as steep-sided residual masses rising up through the *argille scagliose*; this type of scenery is well illustrated to the east of the Futa Pass near Firenzuola.

The lower tract of the range fringing the plain (the Sub-Apennines) is developed on Miocene and Pliocene sediments dipping northwards and overlying the more severely disturbed lower Tertiary rocks described above. West of the Porretta route this Sub-Apennine strip is very narrow but between the Reno and the Metauro (except for an interruption in Montefeltro) it widens to some 30–40 km because of the more extensive exposure of the Miocenes. These latter, composed mainly of marls and chalks, are interrupted locally by outcrops of more resistant sandstones and limestones, for example in M. Titano on whose scarp stands the fortress of San Marino. In general the marls and chalks form undulating country, more deeply incised along the main consequent rivers; locally the marls are fretted into *calanchi* particularly on south-facing slopes where the more rapid drying out of the surface encourages severe weathering. In the Pliocene zone clays alternate with sands; here too erosion has been very active and the valley floors as they approach the plain are almost entirely occupied with pebbles and gravel.

Over the centuries the northern Apennines have been robbed of their forests in the interests of grazing, charcoal burning and tillage. Vines can be grown up to 650m and wheat to 1100m so that the limit of cultivation is as likely to be imposed by the nature of the terrain as by climate. In most areas the topsoil has long since disappeared and the farmer is often ploughing the parent rock. Although re-afforestation (mainly of conifers) has been widely undertaken, notably in the Abetone district, very few extensive stands of 'natural' forest survive; coppices of stunted oak and beech are much more characteristic. As might be expected the proportion of land effectively cultivated and the degree of intensity increase towards the plain. Below 400m, particularly on the Pliocene sands, a form of mixed cultivation based on wheat and vines predominates. The commonest form of operation is *mezzadria* and there is a fair degree of dispersed settlement on the *poderi* associated with it. Further up on the clays and marls the variety of cultivation is less and cereals tend to monopolize the cultivated area. Holdings, most of them with a proportion of coppice and pasture, are rather larger here, and although peasant proprietors are well represented the rural population is mainly housed in hamlets and villages along the ridges. Towards the main watershed the land is increasingly dominated by coppice and grazing. As a source of hay the pastures are vastly inferior to those of the Alps and they are better suited to sheep than cattle; they often give the impression of having been cultivated at one time and indeed one is rarely out of sight of cultivation altogether.

The rapid fall-away on the southern side of the Tosco–Emilian Apennines to the intermontane basins of Garfagnana, Mugello and Casentino has already been noted (p. 153). These longitudinal basins were formed tectonically, probably towards the end of the Pliocene; they are floored with a varied succession of Pliocene and Quaternary lacustrine sediments into which the Serchio, Sieve and upper Arno, with their tributaries, have incised themselves, sometimes sparing remnants of the former lake beds in the form of terraces (upper Valdarno). These deposits contain lignite which is worked to produce thermal electricity near S. Giovanni Valdarno. The hills on the lower slopes of the basins are devoted to an intensive polyculture into which the olive introduces an unmistakably Mediterranean element. The upper slopes are clothed in chestnuts and coppiced oak and beech. Borgo a Mozzano, the scene of a notable agricultural experiment, lies at the exit of the Garfagnana.

Although the Apuan Alps fall within Tuscany they are perhaps better treated here. They consist of a mass of Permian and Triassic limestone and dolomite, locally metamorphosed into marble, resting on a base of crystalline schists. Structurally they represent a 'window' (cf. the Engadine) through which the lower Apennine nappes are exposed. Although of modest height (nearly 2000m) they are well named; they rise steeply from a narrow coastal plain to peaks of dazzling whiteness whose rugged sculpture owes something to glaciation. The upper slopes are strewn with barren scree in contrast to the chestnut woodlands lower down. The famous marbles of Massa and Carrara, often quarried from wildly inaccessible sites, are the area's main resource.

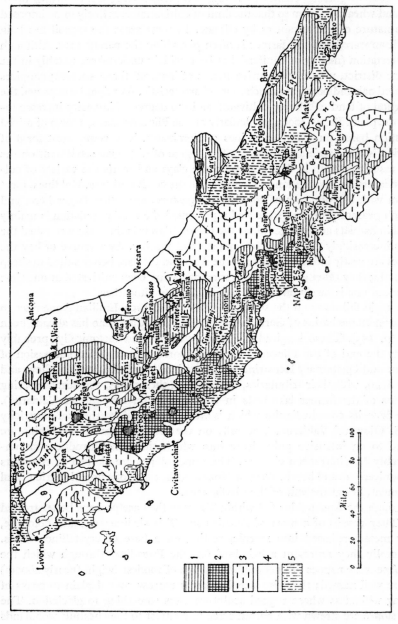

*Fig. 33. The geology of Central Italy simplified.* 1 – Limestones, mainly Mesozoic. 2 – Volcanic rocks. 3 – Eocene rocks including *macigno* and *argille scagliose.* 4 – Miocene-Pliocene sediments. 5 – Quaternary deposits and recent alluvium

In general the northern Apennines are an unrewarding agricultural zone from which population has been draining away for some decades. The communications through them have received attention above.

**IV[b]** *Marche and the central Adriatic flank*

This region whose physical and human geography has much in common with that of the northern Apennines, includes two provinces of Abruzzo (Pescara and Teramo) as well as the four constituent provinces of Marche (Pesaro–Urbino, Ancona, Macerata and Ascoli Piceno); its western boundary runs down the Umbro–Marchigiano Apennines and along the spine of Gran Sasso and M. Morrone to Maiella.

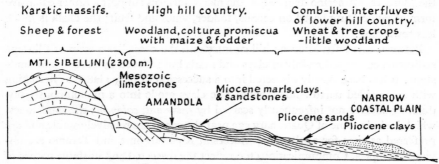

*Fig. 34.* Simplified geological section across the Marche

Immediately north of the Bocca Serriola, in the 'sandstone' Apennines, the main range is low and the cols across it are easily negotiated, but further south the Umbro–Marchigiano Apennines, punctuated by M. Nerone, M. Catria, M. Penna and M. Fema, rise to well over 1500m. This greater elevation coincides with the exposure of an anticlinal ridge of Cretaceous and Jurassic limestones, much complicated by faulting; it emerges from below the arenaceous and argillaceous Tertiary rocks which occur so extensively further north. One consequence of this structural change is that the trans-Apennine routes are rarer and more tortuous; they are sometimes obliged to penetrate difficult gorges like that of the upper Nera (Visso gorge). Further east and parallel to the main range another calcareous anticline reveals itself in the massifs of M. Vicino and the Monti Sibillini. It is incised transversely by the Adriatic consequents and one of them, the Metauro–Candigliano, provides the defile (at Furlo) through which the Via Flaminia penetrates to Fano from Gubbio. Southwards the two chains join to form an assemblage of karstic plateaus and limestone blocks which stretches as far as the Monti Reatini; northwards they enclose a strip of uplifted Miocene sediments in which the rolling hills of the Matelica and Camerino basins have been carved. Miocene deposits, including marls, weak sandstones (*molasse*) and chalk, are also extensively exposed to the east of the limestone ridges. As far south as the Tronto they are carved into a sea of rounded hills through which the tortuous road from Macerata approaches Ascoli. Miocene micaceous sandstones contribute to the ruggedness of the Monti della Laga and cover all but the Mesozoic limestone core of the M. dei Fiori. Gran Sasso is also flanked by Miocene rocks, mainly conglomerates.

Whether developed on Mesozoic limestones or on Miocene sandstones, the Umbro–Marchigiano Apennines are very sparsely populated. Traditionally they are a host region for migrant sheep in summer, and although transhumance is on the decline, most of the surface is occupied by permanent pasture, occasionally interrupted by degraded beech woods. Where the Miocene areas can be classed as hilly rather than mountainous, for example to the north of Gran Sasso or in the Matelica–Camerino depression, the marly surfaces support a rather extensive form of polyculture based on cereals, fodder, vines and fruit; the chalk is much less rewarding.

Between this lofty Miocene hill country and the coast lies a strip of Pliocene sediments composed mainly of clays and marls but relieved by outcrops of sandstone. It has been deeply dissected into a succession of hilly plateaus alternating with steep-sided narrow floodplains. The clays erode into a monotonously undulating surface not infrequently scarred by *frane* and *calanchi*; the sandstones, which include some of Quaternary age near the coast, are relatively stable and are preferred as sites for settlement; Macerata, Ripatransome and Teramo are obvious examples. Communications too reflect the dissected and unstable nature of the terrain; roads penetrating inland use the valleys but keep clear of the floodplains as much as possible. Despite its shortcomings this Pliocene Sub-Apennine strip has been closely occupied for over 2000 years; its forests disappeared long ago and almost all its surface is farmed. The best land is on the floodplains, which besides being the only level areas, have the advantage of a damp subsoil and offer the chance of occasional irrigation. Among the variety of crops cultivated cereals, rotated fodder, sugar beet, tobacco, vines, fruit and mulberries are the most common. On the interfluves the clays and marls tend to be monopolized by cereals and vines but the sands are more intensively occupied by various forms of *coltura promiscua*. Maize and fodder crops are more widely cultivated than might be expected and this is explained by the absence of a severe summer drought; they are used to support oxen and to produce veal for which the breeds of the Marche have a considerable reputation. Most of the area is divided into small *poderi* worked under *mezzadria*, which accounts for the high degree of dispersed settlement. Thanks to repeated fractioning, holdings on the floodplains are often absurdly small.

Taken as a whole the economy of the region is almost exclusively an agricultural one which offers little hope of rapid improvement and has been overmanned for a century. In fact, emigration has a long tradition here and between 1951 and 1961 the population of the six provinces concerned fell by 63,000 to 1,779,000. The region has few industrial assets; its resources of water and water power are meagre, and apart from building materials and small deposits of sulphur in the Miocene chalks, it has no minerals. Agricultural processing, for example of wheat, sugar beet and tobacco, is the best represented activity. Ancona has its modest shipyards and cement and fertilizer plants, and Pescara a small motor cycle factory; otherwise modern industry is scarcely represented. Raw silk production, generally considered an indication of low rural living standards, supports a small textile industry at Ascoli, and Fabriano still makes hand-made rag paper, a handicraft first established there in the twelfth century. Ancona (101,000), sheltered by the limestone block of M. Conero and not too remote from the northern plain, is the Marche's only port; it is also interested in fishing, an activity shared by most of the little settlements along the coast even though they have to content themselves with a shallow river mouth for a harbour. The coastline north of Ancona is being increasingly developed for tourism; for those who tire of the beaches the medieval Republic of San Marino and the Renaissance treasures of Urbino are within easy reach.

### IV[c] *Umbria*

Administratively Umbria consists of the two provinces of Perugia and Terni; in terms of natural features it lies mainly within the Sub-Apennine zone between the Umbro–Marchigiano Apennines and the Tiber–Val di Chiana depression. The discontinuous hill masses which occupy so much of its surface are aligned roughly NW–SE in association with a succession of anticlines. The most widely exposed rocks are the Eocene sandstones and clays whose character has been noted in connection with the northern Apennines; they have been moulded into gentle domes and whalebacks rarely rising to much over 1000m. As one moves south-eastwards the underlying Mesozoic rocks, overwhelmingly calcareous, are increasingly exposed in the cores of the anticlines; they are revealed first in a few hill masses, for example M. Tezio to the north of Perugia and M. Subasio just east of Assisi, but further south and with increasing height they are widely exposed in the highlands surrounding the Narni–Terni basin. In the east of the *regione*, that is roughly beyond the railway joining Terni and Gualdo Tadino, Mesozoic limestones, fractured into blocks and plateau basins, become completely dominant. In fact the geographer, with his passion for regional tidiness, may well feel that this area, so much higher and more rugged than the typical Tertiary hill country of the rest of Umbria, would have been more logically assigned (with Rieti province) to the Abruzzi.

From the point of view of human geography the most important elements in the relief of Umbria are the intermontane basins. The tectonic movements that formed them date from the end of the Pliocene as do the lacustrine sediments (Villefranchian) which partially fill them. These basins, which drain either to the Nera or the Tiber, are at different levels. The highest are those of Norcia and Leonessa but these are more typical of the Abruzzi than Umbria in that they occupy karstic depressions in which lacustrine sediments are not extensively represented. The Gubbio–Gualdo Tadino basin, surrounded by Tertiary 'sandstone' hills and drained superficially by the Chiascio to the Tiber, is also high but is more characteristically Umbrian. The biggest and lowest basin runs from Sansepolcro to Perugia whence one branch sweeps round through Foligno to Spoleto and the other continues to Todi. At one time this western arm of the Tiber lake extended southwards from Todi into what is now the Narni–Terni basin; earth-movements have uplifted this tract and have obliged the Tiber and Nera to escape through the outer ridge of the Sub-Apennines by cutting gorges below Todi and Narni respectively. A rejuvenated Tiber system has etched itself deeply into the lacustrine deposits so that the margins of the basins are characteristically hilly and the flat alluvial floor is comparatively restricted. The rapid alternation of sands, clays and gravels exposed in the hilly margins gives rise to numerous small springs whose modest discharge is used for irrigation lower down; it also promotes erosion and landslips but this has not prevented the peripheral hills and spurs from being occupied by villages and towns whose main concern was once defence (Perugia, Assisi, Spoleto). The extreme west of Umbria trespasses into the low hill country of the Val di Chiana–Tiber depression and even includes part of the Lazio volcanic plateau to the west of Orvieto. Lake Trasimeno is shallow and is shrinking slowly; its waters are seeping through the permeable beds of the Pliocene and Quaternary sediments which form its western rim.

Like almost all Mediterranean Italy, Umbria has been closely settled for over two millennia and except in the higher, bleaker karstic areas to the south and east, the climate is kind enough to have allowed the land-hungry peasant to push cultivation far up the hillsides at the expense of forest. In fact, some 51% of Umbria is under field crops, mainly wheat and fodder, compared with 26% under woodland and 15% under permanent pasture. Except for a few stands of beech most of the 'woodland' is of scrubby oak coppice; the permanent pasture, much of it over-grazed, is found mainly in the limestone highlands where the grazing of migrant sheep is a traditional practice. Umbria's best land lies in the former lake basins, particularly the Tiber basin, where the alluvial floor is intensively occupied by *coltura promiscua*. The tree crops here include olives, almonds, figs, stone fruits, mulberries and vines, these last frequently festooned between elms; the commonest field crops are wheat, beans, lucerne and maize but tomatoes, sugar beet, potatoes and tobacco are also of some importance. Sprinkler irrigation supplied from wells or from watercourses is being increasingly employed to boost the yields of such crops as maize and lucerne. On the hilly margins, where the terrain often demands terracing, olives and other dry tree crops dominate the land-use; further up they may give way to coppice but wherever the slope permits, usually where the lower Tertiary domes present an undulating sweep, the threadbare soil supports wheat and vines up to 1000m. That part of Umbria within the Tiber–Val di Chiana depression is also devoted to wheat, vines and olives, the three basic dry Mediterranean crops.

With such a variety in the quality of the land, the size of holding means very little; in general the best land is farmed in *poderi* under *mezzadria* but peasant proprietors working small properties are also well represented. Really large holdings will usually be found to include a high proportion of woodland or pasture. Cultivation in Umbria has already been pushed well beyond the desirable limits and there is little scope for major improvements, at least while the present rural density persists (frequently over 200 per sq km in the basins). In fact, the drift from the land has already set in and although Perugia and Terni have grown in the last decade, the total population of Umbria has declined by emigration by some 25,000 to 778,000 (1961).

The interior position of Umbria among hilly country has not led to isolation; from early times important routes have led across it, notably the Via Flaminia which crosses the watershed by the Scheggia Pass and was Rome's first link with the Po basin. From the upper Val Tiberina there is a choice of easy passes over the Apennine divide (Bocca Serriola, Bocca Trabaria). Quite often the roads, most of them pioneered by Rome, ignore the river routes and strike out over hilly country instead. For example, there is no road through the Todi gorge, and the Via Flaminia does not follow the Nera up to Narni from Orte as the railway does, but arrives there over the hills by a more direct route from Civita Castellana. To a greater extent than in the Abruzzi, the lack of serious barriers to communication allowed Umbria to share in and make its contribution to Italian Medieval and Renaissance culture. Most Umbrian towns, some of them like Perugia and Orvieto of Etruscan origin, are strategically placed, and, as befits their turbulent story, many of them are built round hill-top fortresses. Their beauty and that of their surroundings attract many tourists, but they are mainly agricultural and administrative in function. Industry, Terni excepted, is poorly developed and what there is falls mainly into the workshop category. The only mineral of note is lignite mined at Pietrafitta (Trasimeno) and near Foligno; it is used mainly for thermal electricity. Perugia (113,000), looking towards Assisi across the Tiber basin, is a provincial centre and a university town but it also manufactures confectionery (Perugina), paper and pottery. Foligno produces woollens and leather goods while Assisi has St Francis to thank for its tourist trade. Terni falls into another category; the waters of the Nera and the Velino have been harnessed to feed the largest power scheme in peninsular Italy. In 1878 Breda, one of the great names in Italian industry, set up an armaments works there; later, with the development of hydro-electric power, Terni became a modest producer of steel, chemicals and engineering goods. Narni shares in this development.

Umbria, like so much of Central Italy, falls between two stools; it lacks the natural advantages and dynamism of the North and yet, although its problems are not fundamentally very different from those of the South, it has little prospect of obtaining comparable aid from the state. Even the Terni industrial area is having difficulty in competing with more fortunately placed centres and it would seem that Umbria is destined to remain an economic backwater.

**IV[d]** *Tuscany*

In every country there are areas which seem destined to remain in the back-waters, while others are always to be found in the turbulent midstream of history; Marche falls into one category and Tuscany into the other. The first highly developed civilization in the Peninsula established itself there, and perhaps the contribution of Tuscany to Italian civilization may be traced in some measure to the racial legacy of the Etruscans.[1] Oddly enough the more important Etruscan towns were in what is now the least productive part, the south, whereas when Tuscany again became significant, in the Middle Ages, the north (and in particular the Arno basin) was the centre of activity. The merchants, sailors and bankers of Pisa and Florence carried with them on their travels the culture of Tuscany, in particular the new-found beauty of its literary language, and gradually the intellectual and artistic superiority of the area was firmly established. In the Middle Ages and Renaissance no area in Europe could boast such a profusion of artistic talent; nor was its genius confined to the arts, for it can claim Vespucci and Machiavelli, and even in its decadence could produce a Galileo. But the expression of regional consciousness in political form was long delayed; the city states ranged in factions were consumed with a burning hate for each other, and yet as Dante converses with those of his countrymen confined to the Inferno it is by their Tuscan speech he recognizes them, and there seems to be present a bond which even their crimes cannot altogether break. Eventually the suicidal hostility of the cities of Tuscany was smothered by the encroaching power of the Medici, and Tuscany assumed the territorial shape which it retained until it was incorporated in the new Italy of 1860. In the three centuries which preceded that event, centuries which were marked elsewhere in Italy by alien tyranny or by native despotism and maladministration, Tuscany was fortunate in both her dynasties; in particular in the nineteenth century there could hardly be a greater contrast than the Tuscany of Leopold II and the Naples of King 'Bomba'. The weight of history sits as lightly on the shoulders of the Tuscan as it does cruelly on that of his compatriot of the former Two Sicilies. Tuscany still enjoys the prestige of her cultural traditions, and it is with good reason that the Tuscan countryman has been called the most civilized peasant in Europe.

In the Tuscan Anti-Apennines only three areas exceed 1000m so that the absence of regular cultivation over very large areas is to be explained more by the thin and unrewarding nature of the soils than by the shortcomings of the climate. In fact vast tracts support little but poor oak coppice, scrub and rough pasture especially where conglomerates, limestones and sandstones are the parent rock; the best stands of woodland, mostly chestnut with beech above, are on the slopes of M. Amiata which is a landmark for twenty miles around. The proportion

---

[1] The very high proportion of blood group B found among modern Tuscans reveals a racial origin different from the other peoples of Italy and Sir Gavin de Beer has suggested that the occurrence of a similar blood group distribution in Asia Minor gives support to the theory of the Eastern origin of the Etruscans.

of cultivated land is highest on the Pliocene sediments among which the sands, as represented in the Era, Elsa and Pesa valleys, support a more intensive form of cultivation than the underlying clays. The basic crops are wheat, rotated with beans and other leguminous fodder crops, vines and olives, but mulberries, pears, figs and stone fruits are often included in the rows of tree crops lining the fields. The vines are commonly 'married' to elms or festooned between them, but there is a growing tendency for both vines and olives to be planted in specialized plots. Strictly speaking Chianti wines should come from vineyards on the western flank of the Chianti hills in the districts of Greve, Radda, Gaile, Castellina and Poggibonsi (in fact mainly on soils derived from limey Eocene clays) but the name has been usurped by a much wider area. On the Pliocene clays, muddy in winter and baked hard in summer, *coltura promiscua* is much less general; in the valleys of the Orcia and the upper Ombrone, a characteristic area, extensive wheat cultivation dominates the land-use and mediocrity of the clay-based soils helps to explain the low population density of Siena province (71 per sq km). In the Val di Chiana, whose marshy alluvial floor, drained northwards by the Canale Maestra, was only satisfactorily reclaimed in the nineteenth century, an intensive *coltura promiscua*, locally aided by irrigation, has been established.

The Apuan Alps and the longitudinal intermontane valleys so characteristic of the southern flank of the Tusco–Emilian Apennines (Lunigiana, Garfagnana, Mugello, Casentino) have already received attention; we are concerned here with the rest of the *regione* which consists of a hilly upland flanked on the north by the three small plains of the Arno basin, on the west by a discontinuous coastal lowland and on the east by the Val di Chiana depression. This upland is mostly developed on Tertiary sediments through which a basement of folded Permian and Triassic rocks is revealed in a number of the higher zones. The Permian is mainly represented by conglomerates and other siliceous rocks, for example in the southern Colline Metallifere and in M. Pisano, while the Triassic rocks are calcareous, notably in the Montagnola Senese and the summit of M. Cetona inland and in M. Argentario and the Mti dell' Uccellina along the coast. Most of these areas have experienced some degree of metamorphism with which mineral veins and, in the case of Montagnola, marble are associated. The soil covering is usually thin and unrewarding although *terra rossa* occurs on some of the limestone surfaces.

The Permo–Triassic rocks are widely overlain by folded Eocene clays, marls, schists and sandstones very similar to those already described as being so typical of the northern Apennines; they are well represented in M. Albano, the Chianti hills, the Colline Metallifere, Pratomagno and the platform on which stands the extinct volcano of M. Amiata. In general they present rolling hills and plateaus but where the clays and schists are exposed there is no shortage of more active erosional features (*frane, calanchi*, etc.). Rocks of Miocene age, mostly chalks and marls locally containing alabaster, salt and sulphur, are less extensively exposed but they are of some importance south of Volterra. The radial movements to which the whole peninsula was subjected in the post-Pliocene and which was accompanied by vulcanicity throughout the Anti-Apennines, revealed wide expanses of Pliocene clays and sands sometimes to heights of over 800m. They occur widely in that part of the Tuscan uplands drained by the Era, Elsa and Pesa, where the overlying sands have been extensively preserved, and in the valleys of the Orcia, Arbia and upper Ombrone further south where clays and marls predominate. These Pliocene sediments, which also occupy much of the Val di Chiana, have been moulded by erosion into a sea of hills whose morphology varies locally in response to minor structural peculiarities. In general the permeability of the sands gives them greater resistance than the clays so that tabular forms are not unusual and the valleys tend to be narrower and more steep-sided; occasionally, as in the *balze* of Volterra, the sandy plateaus end abruptly in precipitous cliffs. The clays favour a rolling landscape of gently rounded hills often gullied in their lower slopes; the marls of the Crete Senesi, whose surface is in a state of continuous disintegration, present many of the features associated with badland.

Since the Mesozoic 'Tuscany' has been the scene of repeated earth-movements, tangential at first and later radial, and these have been associated with successive volcanic phases. Deep-seated intrusions have been exposed in the granites of Elba (M. Capanne), Giglio and Montecristo and they have contributed to the metamorphism and mineralization of the Colline Metallifere. Topographically the most obvious product of vulcanicity is the Pliocene cone of M. Amiata; like M. Calvi and Capraia it is mainly trachytic. At present volcanic activity is confined to those phenomena associated with decadence, notably thermal springs and *soffioni*; the former support several spas (Montecatini, Chianciano, Bagni di Lucca) and the latter, besides providing borax, are used to generate thermal electricity at Lardarello in the Cecina valley.

Throughout the Tuscan uplands *mezzadria* is the commonest form of operation and there is a high degree of dispersed settlement. The *poderi* vary in size from about 5 to 15 hectares in the north where sands predominate to about 15 to 30 hectares in the less intensive clay zones further south. The landowner's home farm (*fattoria*), usually set on a hill, is easily distinguished by its size and outbuildings from the more modest farmsteads of the *mezzadri*. The Tuscan upland is dotted with little towns, almost invariably perched defensively on a hill or plateau, each of which has provided at least a footnote in the colourful pages of Italian Medieval and Renaissance history, and many can claim a place in the broader tapestry of European art. Siena (61,000) is the only sizeable town on the Tuscan plateau; it has agricultural processing and craft industries but, like its ancient rival Florence, it leans heavily on tourism. The same can be said of Arezzo (75,000), the largest of several towns flanking the Val di Chiana.

As its valley widens below Pontassieve the Arno passes successively through three lowlands separated by M. Alburno and M. Pisano. The alluvial and lacustrine deposits flooring the Florence and Fucecchio basins were not satisfactorily reclaimed until the late eighteenth century, and the drainage of the deltaic plain below Pisa was not completely achieved until the 1920s. These lowlands are now occupied by an intensive *coltura promiscua* recalling that of Veneto; the dampness of the subsoil permits the cultivation of maize and lucerne and in the area south of Pisa there are water meadows comparable with those of Lombardy. The basin margins are devoted to terraced tree crops which thin out upwards into evergreen and deciduous woodlands; the olive oil of Lucca enjoys a particularly high reputation. With one or two exceptions, notably Pisa, the older towns and villages are sited above the former marsh on the marginal hills. Florence (Firenze, 440,000), Roman Florentia, was of no great significance until the Middle Ages, possibly because of the persistence of marsh over so much of the Arno basin. Today it focuses several trans-Apennine routes (two railways from Bologna, the older one via Pistoia and the other via Prato, as well as a line from Faenza; the Futa and Porretta roads in addition to the Strada del Sole) and passes them on either through the Val di Chiana to Rome or along both margins of the Arno basins to the coast. The city retains many of its traditional crafts (glass, leatherwork, metalwork, lace, jewellery) for which the main requirements are skill and taste; these qualities have also helped to establish Florence's reputation in the world of *haute couture*. Other industries represented in the area include agricultural processing, machine tools, scientific instruments, electrical goods, oil drilling equipment and railway repair shops, but more than anything Florence depends on the tourist trade for which her unique prestige in the world of art and culture provides such a powerful attraction. Cotton textiles and electrical engineering are among Pistoia's (85,000) activities; Prato, on the edge of the same basin, is the biggest woollen centre outside the Valle Padana and it specializes in shoddy. Lucca (88,000) and Pisa (91,000), whose mutually hostile gaze in the Middle Ages was blocked by M. Pisano, are provincial centres with agricultural and cotton textile industries. Pisa's airport is a useful asset for her tourist trade. Leghorn (Livorno, 161,000) is by Tuscan standards a town with no pedigree. After the eclipse of Pisa it was developed as the Grand Duchy's main port by the Medici whose liberal trading policy contributed to the spectacular growth of the port in the seventeenth century. In recent years Leghorn has been handling some 5 million tons composed mainly of oil to feed local refineries. It is also an important fishing port and the base of the small Italian fleet operating beyond Gibraltar. The city's other interests include agricultural processing, chemicals, foundries, engineering and shipbuilding. Recent plans for the rationalization of Italian shipbuilding cast doubts on the future of the Leghorn yards.

The Maremma coast is characterized by a series of shallow bays edged with low wave-built sandbars (*tomboli*) festooned between rocky headlands, some of which (M. Argentario, M. Massoncello) were islands in recent geological times. The extensive lagoons which once lay to the rear of the *tomboli* have been silted up almost entirely by the heavy detritus load of the rivers draining the erodible hinterland. The evolution of a satisfactory drainage system on these alluvial flats has been hindered by the torrential character of the rivers and by the difficulty they experience in penetrating the fringe of *tomboli*. Under the Etruscans the Maremma seems to have been closely settled but with the relentless deforestation of the uplands, the worsening hydrological disorders in the plain below, accompanied by malaria, banished permanent settlement to the neighbouring hills and by Dante's day the Maremma had long been notorious as the haunt of snakes and pestilence. Later the Barbary pirates provided an additional hazard. The reforming legislation of the House of Lorraine slackened the hold of the powerful traditional landowners, among whom the Church and other charitable bodies were in a majority; in the nineteenth century, under the guidance of Count Fossombroni, the first serious attempts were made to reclaim the area but as late as the 1940s the Maremma presented a landscape of mournful desolation. The wild boar still lurked in the macchia and pinewoods of the dunes, and vast tracts of the alluvial flats behind, baked out in summer, reverted to marsh in winter. There were more fortunate zones (e.g. near Cecina) and there were enterprising improvers who had taken advantage of the 1933 legislation which gave assistance to groups of proprietors (*consorzi*) prepared to combine in developing the basic amenities of their estates (*bonifica integrale*), but all too many of the great landowners (*latifondisti*) were content to devote their broad acres to sheep rearing and extensive wheat production. This state of affairs was characteristic not only of the alluvial plains but of the neighbouring uplands. The transformation of the Maremma since 1950 deserves more detailed consideration.

In that year the government created a number of agencies (*enti*) each of which was charged with the application of the Land Reform within a given zone (*comprensorio*). In Sicily and Sardinia the reform was made the responsibility of the autonomous authorities and in the Sila a special law applied, but everywhere else, including the Maremma, came under the so-called 'Stralcio' law. As far as this zone was concerned the main aims were to co-ordinate all previous development schemes; to carry out the fundamental rehabilitation of the land by means of drainage, soil conservation, re-afforestation, the provision of water supplies, etc.; to appropriate land from existing *latifondisti* and settle peasants on the land thus made available in *poderi* and smallholdings (*quote*); to carry out any necessary improvements, for example deep ploughing and tree planting, and provide houses, farm buildings, wells, etc. on these holdings; to assist with the provision of facilities for processing, marketing, technical advice, the hire of machinery and the purchase of stock and fertilizers through co-operatives; to build up the infrastructure especially as regards transport; to employ labour gainfully throughout the year and to encourage greater intensification (for example by reducing the former dependence on wheat in favour of fodder crops and meat and milk production) with the object of raising the income per hectare.

The *comprensorio* of the Ente Maremma which covers 995,390 ha (96% of it 'productive') stretches from Volterra to the Tiber above Rome and extends inland anything from 20 to 75 km. In 1951 the situation was as follows: 50% of the productive area was classed as arable, 29% as woodland, 13% as pasture and 4% as under tree crops; less than 1% of the proprietors owned 73·5% of the area in holdings of over 100 ha and 50% of it belonged to owners holding over 500 ha. Of those engaged in agriculture about one-fifth were landless and of the rest the majority owned so little that they were forced to engage themselves as *mezzadri* or hired labourers. Whatever the peasant's status the average number of days worked per year did not exceed 160 and throughout the *comprensorio* the average density of population was only about 56 per sq km, about one-third of the national average.

Between 1951 and 1955 some 192,000 ha belonging to over 600 landowners were declared subject to appropriation. Model farms were exempt but other properties were vulnerable roughly on the principle that the larger the estate and the lower the degree of intensiveness achieved the greater the area subject to appropriation. Landowners were compensated with 5% twenty-five-year bonds equivalent to the value of the land concerned. In fact some 167,000 ha were appropriated outright; another 25,000 ha were made up of 'residual thirds', that is tracts of land half of which the landowners could retain provided they carried out the necessary improvements on the whole tract. Of the land thus made available about 110,000 ha have been divided into *poderi* averaging 15 ha and intended to provide whole-time work for the family, and some 33,000 ha have been carved into smallholdings averaging 3 ha. A system of priorities in general favouring local men already working on the appropriated land as share tenants (*mezzadri*), sharecroppers (*comparticipanti*) or day labourers (*braccianti*) was evolved and in cases where applicants were of equal merit the choice was made by lot. In fact the vast majority of applicants were accommodated. The colonists, in all some 17,000 in the Maremma, are buying their holdings by instalments over thirty years at 3½%; the sum involved covers the cost of the land plus a proportion of the cost of providing the house, buildings, water supplies and other improvements.

To a substantial degree the original targets which included nearly 10,000 new houses and 1600 km of roads as well as service stations, reservoirs, aqueducts, stores, plants for processing wine, fruit, sugar, milk, etc., social centres, churches and schools, have been achieved. While the traditional interplanted Mediterranean field and tree crops are still well represented on the new *poderi*, their owners are encouraged to devote about half of their acreage to grass and leguminous fodder (at the expense of wheat) in the interests of veal, pork and milk production. Sugar beet and the specialized cultivation of vegetables, fruit and tobacco, where possible with the aid of sprinkler irrigation, are now appearing significantly in the land-use.

Inevitably the Land Reform and its associated activities have been the object of severe criticism. On economic grounds it is asserted that the vast sums involved are disproportionate to the probable increase in production; that the schemes are bureaucratically top heavy; that the co-operatives are too rigidly controlled from above and do not help sufficiently in remedying the lack of working capital; that *poderi* of 15 ha (still less *quote* of 3) can no longer be considered viable units and that to create more peasant family farms is to underpin an inefficient system incapable of surviving the economic climate of the Common Market; that the schemes were aimed too much at providing work and too little at encouraging efficient production; that in the context of a rapidly expanding industrial country such peasant settlement schemes were irrelevant. No doubt there is much substance in these strictures, in particular as regards the size of holdings, but the shortcomings of the reform must be seen against the strong political and social pressures of the late 1940s. As far as the Maremma was concerned the maintenance of the *status quo* was indefensible. In fact, thanks very largely to the skill and experience of the Tuscan peasant, the Ente Maremma can claim a substantial measure of success.

Tuscany, like Sardinia, possesses a rich variety of minerals but for the most part the deposits are small and scattered. The mining of lignite, some of which is used in thermal electric plants, is significant in view of the poverty of the area in other forms of energy. The better-quality lignites are found in the Miocene sediments of Grosseto province but the vast majority of the production (roughly half of Italy's 1,000,000 tons) is now of inferior fuel extracted from the Pliocene and Pleistocene lacustrine deposits of the upper Arno and Siena districts. The iron ore of eastern Elba (haematite, magnetite and limonite), mined since Etruscan times, is smelted with imported coal at Piombino; the furnaces of Portoferraio, damaged during the war, have not been rebuilt. Salt, borax and gypsum in the Cecina valley and pyrites from Gavorrano and Rovi provide the raw materials for a number of small chemical plants. In the M. Amiata area antimony and mercury are mined; the latter have become relatively more important since the loss of the Idria mines to Yugoslavia in 1946. Other minerals represented are ferro-manganese in M. Argentario and silver-lead and copper at Massa Marittima. The architecture of Tuscany is enriched by a variety of building stones, among them the marbles of Montagnola and the Apuan Alps.

The economy of Tuscany is still heavily inclined towards agriculture, and its industries, based for the most part on the processing of agricultural products and minerals, are mainly organized in small units; the steel works of Piombino, the shipyards of Leghorn and the motor-cycle plant at Pontedera are exceptional. Yet despite this agricultural bias and the poor showing of industry, traits common to most of the Centre and South, Tuscany's demographic evolution seems to be more in step with that of the North. With some local exceptions the pressure of population on the agricultural resources has been less severe than in most of peninsular Italy, and although emigration never reached proportions experienced in many other areas (Veneto, Calabria) the population rose only 23% to its present 3,291,000 between 1911 and 1961 – much less than the national average. In fact, only Liguria, Piedmont and Friuli–Venezia Giulia have lower birth rates than Tuscany (13·4‰). The population density varies widely from over 240 per sq km in the more intensively cultivated and more heavily urbanized provinces of Pistoia, Florence and Pisa to 71 and 49 respectively in Siena and Grosseto provinces. A drift from the land, steady rather than spectacular, has been evident over the last decade, but Florence and Grosseto excepted, the cities of Tuscany have shown no special growth.

## IV[e] *Lazio*

The area here considered, consisting of the provinces of Viterbo, Roma, Frosinone and Latina, differs from the administrative *regione* in omitting Rieti province whose limestone massifs and intermontane basins have more in common with Umbria and the Abruzzi. Historically the area so defined is recognizable in the Medieval Patrimony of St Peter rather than in ancient Latium, which was much less extensive and lay almost entirely south of the Tiber. Bordered inland by the calcareous massifs of the Mti Simbruini and the Mti Sabini, it falls entirely within the Anti-Apennine zone, whose recent geological history has been dominated by the post-Pliocene uplift and by the volcanic outbursts which accompanied it and continued through the Quaternary into immediately prehistoric times. From the geological standpoint the outstanding contrast within the higher features of this sector of the Anti-Apennines lies between the folded Mesozoic limestone massifs of the Monti Lepini, Ausoni and Aurunci in the south and the volcanic hills and plateaus lying northwards from (and including) the Colli Albani; but it is more satisfactory geographically to recognize the identity of the Rome lowlands (with their encircling hills) leaving northern and southern Lazio for separate treatment.

The core of northern Lazio consists of a volcanic upland falling away sharply to the Tiber valley on one side but much more gradually to the coastal lowlands on the other; its highest point is not much over 1000m (M. Cimino). The foundation of this vast accumulation, which, to judge from the volcanic ash in the Apennine moraines, grew rapidly in the Quaternary, is provided in part by sediments laid down in the shallow waters of the Pliocene sea, and in part by more severely disturbed Eocene–Miocene clays, marls and sandstones. The former are revealed in the Tiber trench and in the Marta valley, while the latter are exposed in the Monti della Tolfa where they are penetrated by a trachytic lava mass, a relic of a much earlier eruptive phase. The character of the Lazial volcanic upland owes much to the predominance of the consolidated pyroclastic material (*tufo*) of which it is overwhelmingly composed; lavas do occur, notably on the western slopes of the Mti Volsini, but elsewhere they are limited in extent. The tufi, basaltic and trachytic in composition, vary in compactness and resistance (*peperino* is the toughest) but in general they are permeable and their agricultural value depends much on the extent to which weathering has produced a satisfactory depth of soil. Its ubiquity and the ease with which it can be cut and then 'rendered' with cement or plaster recommend tufo as a building stone. Travertine 'marble' of which Augustine Rome was rebuilt is another common building material found in irregular masses in the tufo beds. Each of the major centres of volcanic activity, the Monti Volsini, Cimini and Sabatini, is a complex of major and parasitic cones, some partially destroyed by later eruptions; for example, M. Venere, half enclosed by Lago di Vico, lies within the main crater of the Mti Cimini, and Lake Martignano occupies a parasitic crater of the main Bracciano cone. Lakes Bolsena and Bracciano, both about 150m deep, cover 114 and 57 sq km respectively. In general the Lazial upland presents an open rolling landscape whose outlines do not obviously reveal the complex volcanic accumulation underlying it; in fact one can be unaware of a massive cone until at the end of a long incline one finds oneself, as at Montefiascone, overlooking an obvious crater lake. Each of the major volcanic masses is incised by a radial pattern of drainage so that not infrequently the open sweep of the landscape is lost and one finds oneself involved in a system of deep valleys edged with steep wooded bluffs (Via Cassia near Sutri). The abrupt fall-away to the Tiber valley, fretted by a succession of wooded ravines, softens as the Pliocene sediments are reached. The bluff-like edge of the plateau provided defensible sites for a number of villages some of which are being forced to retreat from their perches because of *frane*. Many of their inhabitants are obliged to waste time and energy in reaching their work in the valley, which was unhealthy and poorly exploited when the villages were established.

The volcanic upland offers the farmer few outstanding advantages. Over large areas the soil is too thin for agriculture and about one-third of the total area is classed as forest, much of it stunted oakwood (*bosco*) regularly worked over for fuel, although in the higher areas, notably the Mti Cimini, there are some fine chestnut stands giving way to beech higher up. On the flanks of the cones there are numerous perennial springs but their discharge is small and is barely sufficient to supply the domestic needs of the villages. The only areas where irrigation is possible are on the shores of the larger crater lakes, notably Bolsena where fruit is of some importance. In the vicinity of the villages a dry Mediterranean poly-culture, based on wheat, olives and vines, is practised but over large areas the tree crops thin out into open low-yielding wheat land, grazed by sheep after the harvest. As elsewhere there is a tendency to concentrate vine and olive cultivation in specialized fields. *Mezzadria* is the commonest form of operation and although dispersed settlement in *poderi* is modestly represented, the mass of the land is worked from villages whose cramped and inconvenient sites reflect the insecurity which reigned here till the later nineteenth century. The pleasant walled city of Viterbo (52,000) is the only place of any size; it is a provincial market centre where Medieval popes more than once found refuge from the uncertainties of their capital. A narrow-gauge, privately owned railway reaches it from Rome across the plateau. Montefiascone has an ancient reputation for its wine (Est-est-est), and numerous other centres, many of them of absorbing historical interest because of their associations with the Etruscans and the patrician families of Rome, benefit from the summer exodus from the capital.

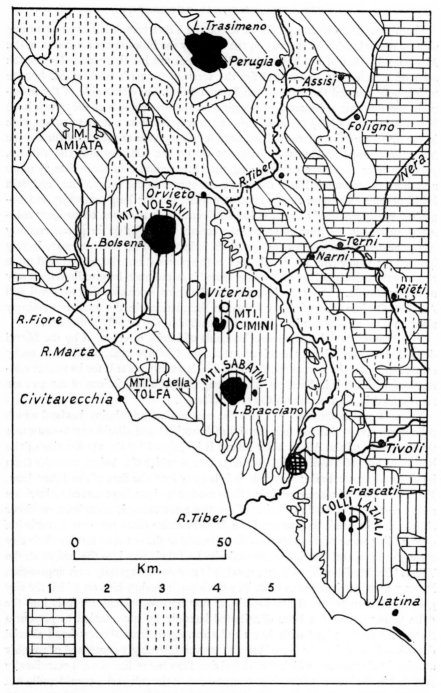

*Fig. 35.* Northern and central Lazio, geological. **1** – Mesozoic limestone hills and mountains. **2** – Eocene clays and sandstones. **3** – Pliocene sands, clays and marls. **4** – Volcanic deposits, mainly ash (*tufo*). **5** – Quaternary sediments and recent alluvium

From Orvieto to within 30 km of Rome the Tiber trench is bordered on one side by the volcanic plateau and on the other by the limestone whalebacks of the Mti Sabini. West of the Tiber these limestones are locally responsible for the spur on which Orte stands and for the serrated dragon's back of M. Soratte which once marked the limit of the Roman world. On either side of the floodplain the Pliocene sediments outcropping on the lower slopes of the trench have been eroded into a hilly marginal zone, narrow in the west but up to 10 km wide in the east where the Pliocenes have been uplifted on the shoulders of the Sabine hills. Tree crops and oakwood coppice clothe the hillsides and the villages, perched defensively, are experiencing the inconvenience of their sites as more and more the economic life of the area concentrates in the valley. The floodplain itself, never much more than a kilometre wide, was for long unhealthy and neglected but, particularly over the last half-century, it has been thoroughly colonized, mainly in the form of *poderi*; the control of the Tiber for power recently has provided opportunities for sprinkler irrigation. The ancient roads largely ignored the valley (the Via Cassia prefers the plateau) but the railway and more recently the Strada del Sole have established it as the main longitudinal routeway of the peninsula. Orte is the junction for the trans-Apennine line to Terni and Ancona. Orvieto, one of many Etruscan foundations in the area, is strikingly sited on a tufo platform; its wine and its cathedral are equally renowned.

The character of the Maremma lowlands of Lazio, interrupted by the Monti della Tolfa, have already received attention. Civitavecchia, sited on a rocky sector, and once the port of the Papal States, is mainly notable for its packet connections with Olbia in Sardinia. The strong Etruscan associations of the area are represented in Tarquinia and Cerveteri (Caere).

Rome (Roma 2,320,000) occupies the centre of an undulating lowland which rolls north-westwards towards the rim of Bracciano and climbs south-eastwards up the flanks of the Alban hills; inland it is defined by the abrupt rise of the limestone hills of Tivoli (Mti Tiburtini) through which the Aniene cascades from its elevated upper basin; seawards it falls away into the flats of the Tiber delta. Dozens of little streams, emanating from modest springs, have carved an intricate radial pattern into the flared skirts of the two great volcanic complexes on either side so that in detail the sweep of the Agro Romano often presents a confusion of low hills; some of these streams flow directly to the sea after forcing their way through the coastal dunes, but the majority find their way into the Aniene or the Tiber. The bluff-bordered Tiber floodplain narrows irregularly as it approaches Rome where the river has to force its way through the low hills on which the city grew up. Downstream, the floodplain, at first narrow, widens abruptly into the delta whose debris has been distributed laterally by wave action to present a flattened triangle edged with dunes and spits. Apart from the restricted alluvial deposits of the delta, the Agro Romano is overwhelmingly composed of roughly stratified tufo through which the underlying Pliocene sediments are occasionally revealed in the lower valleys. The composition of the tufi varies considerably but

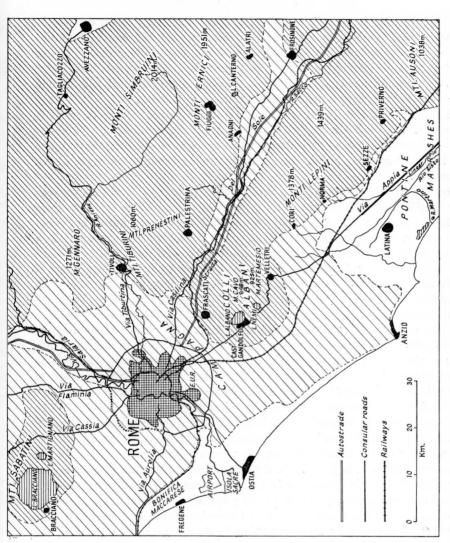

*Fig. 36.* The environs of Rome. Open diagonal shading – undulating and dissected hill country below about 200m; closer shading – higher hill and mountain country

they are generally permeable; many of the lesser valleys are virtually dry but the poor drainage of others contributed to the notorious unhealthiness of the Campagna (strictly speaking the area south of the Tiber) as, with the decline of Rome, such matters were neglected. Before the Augustine rebuilding of the city, Rome was largely constructed of brick and tufo. *Pozzolana*, a volcanic ash laid down in or resorted by water, was used to make cement as it is today.

The Alban volcano is a complicated structure in some respects recalling Vesuvius. The central cones (M. Cavo, M. Jano) are surrounded by a horseshoe depression part of which is deeply pitted by the steep-sided craters occupied by lakes Albano and Nemi. An incomplete outer rim reaches 925m in M. Artemisio.

For centuries travellers to Rome have been impressed by the contrast between the magnificence of the city and the poverty of its immediate environs. Even today the Agro Romano, increasingly encroached on for new suburbs and penetrated by new roads, still has a neglected, empty air. Wheat, its stubble grazed by sheep in winter, still dominates the land-use although there has been some expansion of olive cultivation and of sprinkler-irrigated fodder crops aimed at milk and meat production. With its peppering of very large farms (*casali*), frequently well equipped with buildings and machinery, the landscape has much in common with the *latifondi* zones of the South; indeed, the traditional patrician families of Rome are still well entrenched here. The picture changes at the Tivoli hills where olives become dominant, and on the slopes of the Alban hills where vines are almost a monoculture; from Velletri through Genzano to Frascati is one huge vineyard, source of the Castelli wines. The higher areas of the volcano, including M. Cavo and M. Artemisio, where the soils are thin, are left under chestnut woodland which is coppiced to provide vine supports. The springs of the inner depression have long contributed to Rome's water supplies.

The deltaic coastlands widening southwards from Ladispoli, formerly malarial marsh and once the shame of the capital, were reclaimed between the wars and have been organized in *poderi*. The Isola Sacra and the Bonifica Maccarese contain the only large irrigated area in Rome province. In general they support a mixed economy including milk and meat production based on irrigated fodder, but the 'fossil' dune zones are exploited for wine and dessert grapes. A state hunting reserve, heavily wooded with umbrella pines, occupies much of the southern part of the delta. Ostia, Fregene and Ladispoli are summer bathing resorts of the capital. Part of the reclaimed delta has been sacrificed for the Rome (Fiumicino) airport which replaces Ciampino.

Whatever the circumstances of its foundation, Rome grew up on the Tiber's left bank on a group of tufo bluffs known as the Seven Hills (the Quirinale, Viminale, Esquilino, Capitolino, Palatino, Celio and Aventino). They provided defensible sites near enough together to be enclosed later within the fourth-century (BC) Servian walls and they overlooked the river at a point where it could be most easily bridged. At a time when the extension of the Etruscan power southwards into Campania demanded a satisfactory crossing of the Tiber, the engineers' task was simplified by the absence of a floodplain here and by the presence of the Isola Tiberina resting on a rocky sill, which incidentally determined the head of navigation. The expansion of Rome politically revealed the favourable situation of the city in its wider aspects; it controlled the most important of the three lowlands penetrating the mountainous peninsula and was the natural focus of the inner and coastal longitudinal routes along the western side of it. Later the organizing talents of the Romans reinforced the nodal position of their capital with a radiating system of roads.

The heart of Imperial Rome still lay on the Seven Hills but its boundaries, as defined by the third-century (AD) Aurealian walls, had expanded markedly, even to include part of the right bank, significantly enough that sector opposite the Isola Tiberina. Rome was not to be so extensive again until the twentieth century. By the Middle Ages the classical city was a desolation, its forums grazed by sheep, its ruined public buildings the makeshift fortresses of feudal factions. The life of the city now lay mainly along the river and among the tortuous streets of the Pantheon quarter. Under the Renaissance popes the Eternal City began to assume a new magnificence and throughout the next two centuries Italians found some balm for their political humiliation in the ornate ostentation of the baroque; the low-lying quarter between Piazza Venezia and Piazza del Popolo (formerly the Campus Martius) bears its stamp as do many famous churches, squares, gardens and palaces celebrating the names of princely papal families. When Rome became the capital of a united Italy its population was still below 250,000 but since then the pace of expansion has quickened relentlessly (1910 – 500,000; 1930 – 1,000,000; 1950 – 1,500,000; 1960 – 2,300,000). Each period has left its characteristic mark, that of the Savoy monarchy in the station quarter, the turn of the century on the right bank, and the fascist era most typically in the Foro Italica and the 1942 Exhibition zone. Since 1950 few areas of the periphery have been spared the block-like proliferation of ferro-concrete.

More than two millennia ago Rome ceased to be dependent on its immediate environs, no doubt a contributory factor in the neglect of the Agro Romano thereafter. In classical times it drew tribute from an empire and as that declined it found a new resource in the tithes of all Christendom; with the establishment of a united Italy its prestige and its transitional position between North and South made it the obvious choice for a capital so that modern Rome continues to draw on the resources of the country as a whole. It is essentially a city of bureaucrats, lay and ecclesiastical (Vatican City), national and international (FAO) and most of its industrial activities – transport, servicing, food processing and above all construction – are engaged in supplying their needs. The devotion of the Catholic world and the city's unique tourist attractions provide the other main source of income. Many of its industries are of a type commonly associated with capitals – railway and vehicle servicing, printing, films, clothing and *haute couture*, furniture, household goods and pharmaceuticals. Electronics, rubber,

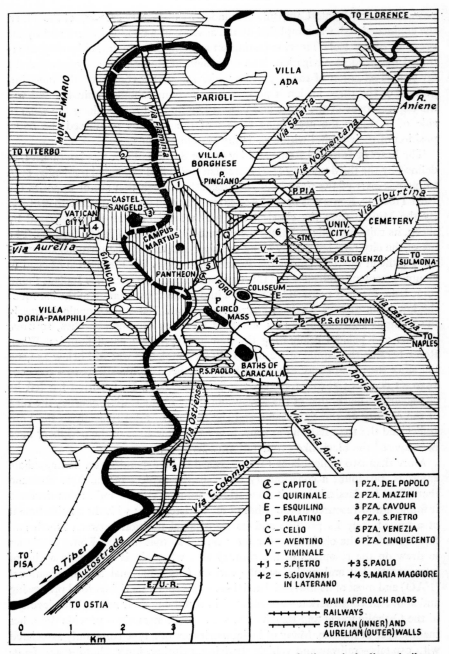

*Fig. 37.* Rome. Vertical shading – built-up area *c.* 1600; horizontal shading – built-up area 1964

oil refining and light engineering, generally more recent and organized in larger units, fall into a different category, but as a centre of commerce and manufacture Rome is still of the second rank. The older industrial quarters lie in S. Lorenzo and along the Via Ostiense, but many new ventures have been sited on the periphery, a tendency encouraged by financial concessions available within 'depressed' areas impinging on the city. Rome is obviously the main centre of roads and railways in the peninsula and its equipment has been reinforced recently by the Strada del Sole. It is the most important airport not only of Italy but of the whole Mediterranean area and is well placed to serve routes from north-west Europe to the Middle East, the Far East and East Africa.

Between the Mti Prenestini and the Alban hills the ancient Via Latina, accompanied by the railway and the Strada del Sole, passes over the low Palestrina col into the Sacco–Liri trench (Valle Latina). To the north the Cretaceous limestones of the Monti Ernici–Simbruini, their rugged slopes clothed in oak and beech scrub when not completely barren, offer a landscape suggestive of nearby Abruzzi; Lake Canterno is of karstic origin. Occasionally, in a basin or on a shelf (Fiuggi), a more generous soil, sometimes containing far travelled volcanic ash, permits the cultivation of olives and other dry tree crops. Much of the Valle Latina is hilly, particularly near Frosinone (32,000) where Miocene marls and sandstones occur, but the lower section round Pontecorvo is the bed of a Quaternary lake. Locally irrigation is practicable but in general a dry polyculture predominates. The northern hilly margin with its line of perched settlements (Anagni, Ferentino, Roccasecca) is grey with olives. The Monti Lepini, Aurunci and Ausoni, folded and faulted Cretaceous limestone blocks like the Mti Simbruini, repeat many of the features of that range. Much of their surface is good only for sheep grazing or coppiced woodland but patches of *terra rossa* support the olive groves of the hill-top villages overlooking the Pontine Marshes (Cori, Norma, Priverno, etc.).

Something has already been said of the unfortunate past of the Agro Pontino (p. 41). Fundamentally it contains two types of country, a region of Quaternary dunes and a region of marsh. Before its improvement, the first, stretching inland some 6 to 8 km, was largely macchia and oak *bosco*, part of which is preserved in a national park. The danger to health here came mainly from the lagoons (lakes Fogliano, Sabaudia) lying between the Quarternary dunes and a line of *lidi* anchored at their southern end to the isolated limestone block of M. Circeo. The traditional fishing industry using elaborate traps (really sluices) survives, but the *lidi* are being increasingly exploited for bathing resorts. The undulating Quaternary dune zone has been systematically colonized in large *poderi*. Subterranean water is tapped by tree crops, especially vines, and the field crops, notably wheat, fodder and groundnuts, are assisted with sprinkler irrigation where possible. Eucalypts have been used imaginatively to give shade and shelter along the roads and round the farms.

The second region, with its organically rich alluvial soil, would soon revert to marsh but for pumping. It presents a more intensive form of *bonifica* landscape than the dunes; the layout of fields, drains, roads and settlement is monotonously rectangular and the damper soils, irrigated over about half of the total area, produce high yields of maize, wheat, beet, vegetables and fodder crops. The traditional buffalo, whose *ricotta* was once the main product of the marsh, has disappeared but meat and milk production is important in the economy. *Coltura promiscua* is not usual and the region still retains something of its former sadness.

The Fondi plain, which repeats many of the features of the Pontine Marsh, has only been satisfactorily reclaimed since the war. About 20% of it is under citrus, a crop which becomes increasingly significant from Terracina southwards.

Except in the food processing, constructional materials and paper sectors, industry in southern Lazio is poorly represented, a matter which is receiving attention from the *Cassa del Mezzogiorno*. A recent addition is the paper mill, using rag as the raw material, at Cassino, a town which has paid dearly for its strategic position on the Valle Latina approach to Rome. Lazio has two atomically generated electric plants, one on the Garigliano and the other at Latina (50,000) the main town of the Agro Pontino.

## IV[f]  *The Abruzzi Highlands*

Many would assign the Abruzzi[1] to the South on historical and socio-economic grounds; until 1860 it formed part of the Kingdom of the Two Sicilies and its economic backwardness, as revealed for example in its overwhelmingly pastoral and agricultural character, is certainly a southern trait. In fact the area under consideration excludes half of the Abruzzi–Molise *regione*; it consists essentially of the provinces of Aquila and Rieti, the latter administratively part of Lazio and both falling within the orbit of Rome. In terms of geographical features it lies between the Gran Sasso–Morrone–Maiella massifs in the north-east and the Monti Sabini–Simbruini ranges in the south-west.

This area derives its special character from its interior position, its high and rugged relief, the dominance of limestone in its lithology and the importance of tectonic movements in its structure. The general NW–SE trend of the Apennine folding has been complicated here by severe faulting, longitudinally and transversely; much of this tectonic disturbance occurred during the post-Pliocene uplift, but to judge from the area's continued susceptibility to earthquakes, it is still incomplete. The result as far as relief is concerned has been to produce a series of blocks aligned NW–SE separated by narrow intermontane basins. The latter are drained by the longitudinal courses of the major rivers which are obliged to escape to the sea transversely by means of deep narrow valleys. The blocks are overwhelmingly composed of limestone which may vary in age from the Eocene to the Triassic, and in character from chalk to dolomite; in fact, the Cretaceous limestones are the most extensive. In the higher massifs the Quaternary

[1] Abruzzo, the singular form, is also used.

glaciers have scooped out cirques and dumped moraines below them, but in general the summits, though rugged, are rounded or whalebacked rather than pyramidal; the Gran Sasso ridge rising to 2914m in the dolomitic bastions of Corno Grande is exceptional. The lower slopes of the massifs as they rise from the basins are usually steep, smooth and deeply incised, but further up wide shoulders and extensive plateaus occur, frequently studded with karstic depressions; although too high to be typical, Campo Imperatore, pitted with dolines and strewn with glacial debris, is a well-known example. The principal intermontane basins, that of Sulmona excepted, are higher than their Umbrian counterparts. In some of them, for example the Liri and Scanno valleys and the Carseoli and Aquila depressions, Miocene and Pliocene deposits, among them erodible marls, appear in the lower part of the basins; these have been moulded into a marginal hill zone contrasting with the starker limestone slopes above. Alluvial and lacustrine sediments, Quaternary to recent in age, are responsible for the flatter floors of the Sulmona and Rieti basins.

It may help in unravelling the complicated pattern of relief to recognize three main groups of roughly aligned blocks. The highest, consisting of Gran Sasso, M. Morrone and M. Maiella (2793m) falls abruptly to the Adriatic Sub-Apennine hill zone. Immediately inland lie the Aquila and Sulmona basins; they are drained by the Aterno and Pescara which join to cut their way to the sea through the Popoli defile, incidentally providing a path for the ancient Via Valeria and the railway. The second 'range', which enfolds the Fucino basin, stretches from the Monti Reatini (Terminillo 2213m) through M. Velino and M. Sirente into the high plateaus surrounding Scanno; it is pierced below Antrodoco by the transverse course of the Velino. The third and lowest group, consisting of the Mti Sabini and Mti Simbruini, lies to the south of the trench drained northwards through the Rieti basin by the Salto, and southwards to the Sora basin by the Liri; within a few miles of Rome it presents the Via Salaria (salt road) and the Via Valeria with their first serious barrier as they force their way to the Adriatic via Rieti and Avezzano respectively.

Their height and their interior position combine to give the Abruzzi highlands the severest winters of the peninsula; snow lies for five months on the summits and the higher roads are frequently impassable. Except where they are exploited for skiing (e.g. Campo Imperatore) vast areas are practically deserted in winter and in really severe spells wolves can be a nuisance. Even so olives survive to about 800m and all the basins are thoroughly cultivated. The two most important are those of Rieti and Fucino, both of which were occupied by lakes into historical times. The Romans took the first steps in draining the Rieti (or Velino) lake by cutting through the travertine sill over which the Velino tumbles in the Cascate di Marmore, a spectacular sight now rarely witnessed because of the diversion of the river for power. Lake Piediluco is the largest of three small remnants of the former Velino lake. Lake Fucino too was drained first by the Romans, under the Emperor Claudius, but during the Dark Ages the exit conduits to the Liri became choked. The area was finally reclaimed in 1875 by Principe Torlonia who divided it into *poderi* of about 25 hectares each. Even so, until the recent intervention of the Land Reform authorities, there was little dispersed settlement and the mass of the population continues to live in the peripheral villages. The centre of the basin (actually not the lowest zone) is irrigated as are one or two detritus fans on the margins, but the emphasis in the land-use is none the less on cereals, sugar beet, potatoes and fodder; vines and tree crops are limited to the older settled areas on the basin margins which are better drained and incidentally less troubled by temperature inversion. In the Rieti basin, which has been worked and settled for a much longer period, tree crops and *cultura promiscua* are better represented but cereals, beet and fodder are also important. The Sulmona basin averaging only about 350m is somewhat lower than the other two; much of it, in particular the hilly margins, is devoted to vines, olives and almonds but cereals, beet and fodder occupy the alluvial floor where intermittent irrigation is possible. Saffron and tobacco are of some note in all the lower basins.

The second element in the Abruzzi highlands is provided by the calcareous massifs. The highest of them rise above the upper limit of trees (approximately 1850m) and their rock-strewn summits support only summer pasture. Even lower down very little forest has survived, and that mainly beech coppice, but extensive areas are now being replanted with conifers by the state. The national park is exceptional in that it has retained some fine stands of beech; chestnuts, which prefer a siliceous soil, were never extensive in the Abruzzi. On the lower cols and plateaus the humid rendzina soils are coaxed into producing cereals, potatoes and hay but in general the massifs are only economically important as the host region for migrant sheep moving up in summer from the Campagna and the Tavoliere di Puglie. The wealth of these flocks lies in their wool and their milk from which *pecorino* cheese is made. They are in the charge of professional shepherds whose personal stake in the flock is usually small. Transhumance is on the decline and road transport is replacing the drives along the traditional drover tracks (*tratturi*) but in summer the total of sheep in these highlands still approaches 800,000. In these rugged zones there is little permanent settlement and what there is is concentrated in defensively sited hamlets. In fact, even in the populous intermontane basins the degree of dispersed settlement is low, a reflection at least in part of the lawlessness which prevailed here until the late nineteenth century.

Industrially the Abruzzi highlands are of little account. Bauxite is mined, notably in the Maiella massif, and it is processed at Terni, but the area's two main assets, water and hydro-electric power, accrue mainly to the benefit of neighbouring provinces. Agricultural processing, for example sugar refining at Rieti and Avezzano, is the most important industrial activity. Sulmona's speciality, essentially a domestic industry, is sugared almonds (*confetti*), an indispensable item at all Italian weddings.

The area, which offers an escape from the heat of Rome in the summer and offers good skiing in winter, is being increasingly equipped for tourism but its sombre lakes and rugged mountains are an acquired taste which may not appeal to the masses who now flock to the beaches and to the Alps.

For over a century the dour and hardy stock of these highlands has been accustomed to the bitterness of an exile imposed by a niggardly soil. Together the provinces of Rieti and Aquila have a population density of under 60 per sq km; in the decade 1951–1961 the population declined by 57,000 to 465,000 and that of the two provincial capitals remained almost static. In recent years the precarious construction industry of Rome has been the main single attraction for the unskilled Abruzzi emigrant.

## V THE SOUTH

To the mass of Italians living north of Rome, the South, if not a foreign country, is at least an unknown one, whose character they find difficult to reconcile with the Italy with which they are familiar. Post-war novels, magazine articles and films have done much to arouse the national conscience to an awareness of its responsibilities in the area, but the ingrained scepticism which assumes that the South will never be anything but a depressed area is still a common attitude among Northerners. Post-war governments, however, have not been able to afford the luxury of this passive attitude; that Italy cannot remain two nations, and at the same time avoid social and political upheaval, is fully realized in Rome, but any governmental action has had to contend not only with Northern objections that capital sunk in the South is good money thrown after bad, but also with Southern cynicism, born of despair. Measured by any yardstick the South is poor. In 1955 the five Southern regions (Abruzzi–Molise, Campania, Apulia, Basilicata and Calabria) and the Islands, which together comprise 40·5% of the area and contained 37·4% of the population of Italy, accounted for only 21·6% of the national income; the average income *per capita* was calculated at 105,000 lire in the South and at 225,000 lire for the rest of the country. An official inquiry gave the percentages of the population living in 'a state of poverty' in various parts of the country as 1·5% in the North, 5·9% in the Centre, 28·3% in the Continental South and 24·8% in the Islands. Comparisons between North and South as regards railway mileages, electricity consumption, telephones, cars and motor scooters, persons per room, sanitation, tapped water supplies or unemployment told much the same story. Ten years devoted to rectifying this situation have raised the Southerner's *per capita* income some 50%, no mean achievement, but the gap between Northern and Southern living standards has widened rather than closed.

How far the Southern problem stems from the physical environment of the area and how far it is the legacy of deep-seated historical and social forces will always be a matter of controversy. Certainly the *Mezzogiorno* suffers from serious environmental disadvantages. Set in a relatively stagnant Mediterranean world, it is isolated from the economically dynamic zones of Italy and Europe. Quite apart from the difficulties presented by relief, the shape and fragmentation of the South hinder communications and favour a number of isolated areas of development rather than one major one comparable with the Valle Padana; this aggravates the problem of achieving large-scale, balanced and well-integrated industrial development.

The South (including the Islands) is further handicapped by its relief and lithology; 35·3% of its area is classed as mountainous, 41·6% as hilly and only 23·1% as plain. Many mountain zones are condemned to a closed economy because of their isolation and over large areas the combination of unstable and erodible rock surfaces, steep slopes and excessive deforestation have been disastrous, not only for the uplands, but for the plains below; nowhere is it more necessary to treat the catchment basin as a unit. The worst offenders are the *argille scagliose* and Eocene clays of the Apennine flanks, the Pliocene clays and sands of Basilicata and Sicily and the schists of Calabria, but many of the limestone zones, even when tabular in form, are notoriously devoid of soils. With few exceptions (notably that of Campania) the plains have offered inadequate compensation for the sterility of the uplands. Their exploitation and settlement have been retarded by hydrological disorders and malaria, as well as by maladministration, neglect and insecurity; for centuries the coastlands were harried by piratical attacks which contributed to the overcrowding of the hill country and encouraged settlement in cramped and inconvenient defensive sites.

Except in very high areas the temperature regime favours a varied and intensive agriculture provided adequate water supplies are available either from precipitation or from irrigation, but it is precisely in this respect that the South is at a disadvantage. Annual rainfall means, which fall below 600 mm in Apulia, Sardinia and Sicily but frequently exceed 1000 mm in the mountainous west of the peninsula, are misleading in that they mask the intensity of evaporation as well as the seasonability and unreliability of the rainfall. The summer drought encourages the cultivation of olives and autumn-sown wheat, but, because of the difficulty of providing fodder in the summer, it discourages a more mixed type of farming in which cattle rearing could play an important part. Sheep and goats are the typical Southern livestock; the former feed on the fallow stubble and are frequently moved considerable distances in search of pasture; the latter graze the wastelands to whose sterility they further contribute. It is frequently forgotten that winters in the mountains can be severe and snowy and even at low altitudes, where prolonged frosts are rare, there is no immunity from freak weather including bitter spells capable of destroying winter grain and ruining delicate tree crops (Feb. 1956, Feb. 1965). Drought, hail and the incidence of rainfall in short, often violent storms are other hazards with which the peasant has to contend.

In the *Mezzogiorno* there are no environmental problems more fundamental than those presented by the hydrology. A few areas, notably in Campania and eastern Sicily, where rivers tap reservoirs of permeable rock, are relatively well endowed with water supplies, but over vast upland areas where impermeable rocks predominate, water control for power, irrigation and domestic purposes is ruinously expensive when not practically impossible. Even so the resettlement of the coastal plains and the intensification of their agriculture hinges on the successful establishment of water control. Although limestone areas may provide useful reservoirs for neighbouring districts their own surfaces are often almost entirely lacking in surface water. An obvious case is the Murge tableland whose large urban population relies on supplies brought by the Apulian aqueduct from the headwaters of the Sele river. The shortcomings of the Southern environment as it affects industrialization will receive attention below but it should be noted in passing that the availability of reliable water supplies, which even in England is now taken less for granted, is a powerful locational factor tending to restrict the number of zones which can hope to develop industry on a large scale.

Any attempt to isolate and assess in detail the historical forces which have contributed to the relative economic backwardness of the South would be out of place here but it may be useful to suggest a few lines of inquiry:

1) The long periods of insecurity to which the South has been subjected; it has been fought over by a succession of destructive invaders – Goths, Vandals, Lombards, Byzantines, Arabs, Normans, French and Spaniards – and the coastlands in particular have been repeatedly the prey of sea raiders from the days of the Vandals to that of the Barbary pirates.
2) The relative unimportance of the trading city as it developed in the North, to the great benefit of agriculture; Naples is an obvious exception.
3) The Spanish occupation which is condemned by many Italian historians not only for its oppression and maladministration but for the inculcation of certain unhelpful social attitudes.
4) The support of the authorities, from the Middle Ages onwards, of powerful pastoral elements, particularly in Apulia, whose interests often ran counter to a more effective occupation of the land.
5) The excessive concentration of activity in the capital under the Bourbons and the neglect of its estates by an absentee aristocracy; the survival of feudalism until the French occupation and of feudal attitudes long after it.
6) The failure after 1860 to match political unity with economic unity; the collapse of infant Southern industries in the face of Northern competition.
7) The complacency with which overseas emigration was for long regarded as the natural solution to Southern poverty.

Whatever their origins it is generally admitted that over the centuries Southern society has accepted certain characteristic attitudes not all of which are helpful in the present situation. (Some would assert that in this respect the South is merely Italy writ large.) For example, there is a profound distrust of the authorities and an unwillingness to co-operate actively with them, an attitude which a century of political unity and the imposition of the Piedmontese system of administration have done little to remove. There is still a widespread feeling that the administration is at best a necessary evil from which the ordinary citizen can expect little in the way of sympathetic treatment unless he has access to influential intermediaries. The most powerful element in society is the family, loyalty to which is almost an article of faith; this reveals itself most favourably in the generosity of emigrants whose remittances ease the lot of thousands of families; less so in the acceptance of nepotism and a reluctance to recognize the claims of the wider social group. Southern society is male-centred and the place of women is still widely regarded as exclusively in the home; this outlook has sometimes been a hindrance when female labour had to be recruited for newly established factories. At least in the remoter areas the town or village is a closed community, stagnant economically, conservative and rigidly stratified socially. The individual's hopes for a better life are easily frustrated by poverty, illiteracy and the lack of economic opportunities, and he tends to resign himself to a fatalistic acceptance of a situation in which there seems to be no place for initiative or self-help. In the past the only escape was to emigrate and even in a new environment he might find himself obliged to join, at least for a time, another closed community composed of his own compatriots. The contribution of Southerners to the national life, particularly in the fields of politics, diplomacy, letters, the law and the church, is generally recognized but the qualities which made for success in industry or progressive agriculture have been less conspicuous; the 'tycoon' is almost exclusively a Northern figure. The generally accepted practice of investing securely in land or in bricks and mortar has discouraged more enterprising forms of investment. Furthermore, the ownership of land, preferably without having to work it, still confers prestige mainly because it allows one to enjoy leisure and dispense patronage. In Southern towns *rentiers* constitute an important element among the middle classes and their standards are widely accepted among those less fortunate. Those members of the bourgeoisie who are obliged to earn a living have always shown a preference for the liberal professions, the church and the civil service – occupations mainly desirable for their security and the status they confer. On a humbler plane the *Meridionale* with a measure of education seeks similar advantages in a pensionable post in the petty bureaucracy, the police, the railways or the para-military forces. No doubt these attitudes are crumbling but their wide acceptance till recently goes some way to explaining why the *Mezzogiorno* lacked the entrepreneurs, the technicians, the managers and even the skilled artisans indispensable to modern industry. One of the most encouraging signs has been the experience of employers that Southern workers recently recruited into industry, whether in the North or the South, are proving themselves industrious, adaptable and receptive of training.

Perhaps the most important aspect of the socio-economic pattern of the *Mezzogiorno* is the excessive pressure of population on the economic resources. In 1964 the birth rates in Campania, Calabria and Sicily were 25·6, 23·2 and 21·7 per thousand respectively compared with 15·7, 14·5 and 18·6 in Piedmont, Liguria and Lombardy, while in the same year, thanks to an older average population, the death rates were slightly higher in the Northern regions than in the Southern. In fact, for many decades the rate of population increase in the South has far exceeded that in the North; in recent years the excess of births over deaths per thousand inhabitants in the South has been about 15, roughly three times the Northern figure. No rapid fall in Southern birth rates can be expected unless there is a marked rise in living standards and an acceptance of Northern social attitudes, a development which is likely to be delayed by the certainty that population will continue to increase for a very long time. This situation, which would have been more explosive but for the contribution of emigration, underlines the urgency of promoting every form of economic progress in the South and even this is unlikely to remove the need for continued emigration to the North, overseas and into Europe.

The demographic problem of the *Mezzogiorno* is rendered more intractable by the overwhelming dependence of the area on agriculture, the most stagnant and least efficient sector of the economy. On the basis of the dominant crops grown, the mode of operation and the size of holdings the South exhibits a variety of farm types each of which makes its contribution to a characteristic landscape. Considering each of the main farm types in turn it becomes immediately apparent that the medium-sized (25 ha) commercialized unit, whether owner-worked or rented for cash, is scarcely represented. The consolidated unit, commonly between 5 and 15 hectares and worked under a share tenancy contract (*mezzadria appoderata*), is almost exclusively restricted to the coastal hill country of the Abruzzi. The land-use of this type of farm, so typical of Tuscany, Umbria and the Marche, is a dry Mediterranean polyculture in which field crops, mainly wheat, maize, beans and fodder, are usually interplanted with fruit trees (*coltura promiscua*). The presence of a farmstead on the *podere* ensures a fair degree of dispersed settlement. In most other parts of the South where a form of *mezzadria* is practised tenures are less secure, holdings are smaller and dispersed, and no farmstead is available.

In some areas, usually those blessed with some particular advantage in soil, rainfall, irrigation facilities or communications, a more intensive form of peasant cultivation is recognizable. It is well exemplified in the plains and low hills of Campania, the northern and eastern coasts of Sicily and the lower Murge tablelands. This is a highly commercialized form of agriculture catering not only for the cities of the South but for more distant markets and therefore implies a well-developed marketing and processing organization as well as good communications. Heavy yields are obtained and there is frequently a high degree of specialization, for example the vegetables and fruit of Campania, the citrus of Calabria and Sicily, and the olives, wine and almonds of Apulia, but this achievement is offset by the intense pressure of rural population. Most holdings are under 2 hectares and they are usually dispersed in several parcels. Sharecroppers (*compartecipanti*) and share tenants (*mezzadri*) are well represented but most of this zone is worked by peasant proprietors. The villages which house the majority of the rural population include a large landless element (*braccianti*) which has difficulty in finding sufficient work, despite the labour-intensive character of the cultivation. In fact many proprietors own so little land that they are often obliged to operate also as *mezzadri* or as labourers.

The rest of the cultivated area of the South supports a much less intensive form of agriculture dominated by the production of wheat, olives and sheep. One recognizable form of exploitation is the *latifondo capitalistico* in which the main element is a large commercial unit managed by a tenant or the owner's bailiff and concentrating on wheat production with the aid of machinery and hired labour. Sometimes part of the estate is let to share tenants and sharecroppers who, together with a large landless element, inhabit the agro-towns with which the area is studded. The other characteristic feature of the settlement pattern is the *masseria*, the headquarters of the estate, which consists of a large group of farm buildings including the bailiff's house and accommodation for permanent employees, machinery and animals. Such farm groupings – in Lazio they would be called *casali* – stand isolated in an empty countryside whose treeless, steppe-like landscape is often referred to as the *Mezzogiornon udo*, as opposed to the *Mezzogiorno arborato* to which tree crops make a significant contribution. The *latifondo capitalistico* is most characteristically represented in the Tavoliere di Puglie, Basilicata, eastern Calabria and the Sicilian interior. Its preoccupation with wheat is a comparatively recent development which was encouraged by the autarchic policies of the inter-war years. For centuries previously its economy was concerned with the rearing of sheep which were moved up to the summer mountain pastures along traditional drover tracks (*tratturi*); the movement between the Abruzzi and Apulia was of particular importance. Transhumance now is on a much reduced scale but the lowland fallows still help to support large numbers of sheep. In a part of the country hungry for work and land the *latifondo capitalistico* has inevitably been the target of criticism on the grounds of its size, the extensive nature of its cultivation, its inability to provide regular work throughout the year, and the indifference of its owners, frequently absentees, towards the need for economic development and the demands of social justice. These strictures are most difficult to refute in those neglected lowland areas which, given the necessary investment, are capable of supporting a more intensive form of agriculture combined with a more equitable distribution of property. In fact, the land reform has already achieved a transformation in many areas formerly dominated by the *latifondo capitalistico*.

Throughout much of the hill country of the southern Apennines and Sicily, where the surface is often unstable and erodible, the land-use varies between low-grade cereal cultivation and an open form of *cultura promiscua*; this latter frequently occurs as a circle round the villages. The vast numbers of strips and parcels into which the land is divided without any visible boundaries are worked in part by hired labourers, in part by peasant proprietors and in part by share tenants and sharecroppers. These last are concerned with the fortunes of only one season's crop; the *mezzadri*, many of whom are working for absentee owners, have few of the advantages, especially as regards housing and security of tenure, enjoyed by their Tuscan counterparts. This type of agriculture, which in terms of landscape belongs mainly to the faceless *Mezzogiorno nudo*, is sometimes referred to as the *latifondo contadino* – the peasant *latifondo*. Its essential char-acteristics are great pressure of population on the land resources; an excessive dispersal and fragmentation of holdings; rudimentary equipment – often nothing more elaborate than the mattock and the wooden plough; low yields and tradi-tional methods (e.g. the worked fallow); a minimum of diversification and an excessive preoccupation with wheat; the small number of work days available (rarely more than 150 days a year) to all classes of peasants; and the concentration of settlement in sizeable villages.

With this brief review of the characteristics of Southern agriculture in mind it may be useful to list the main lines on which future developments should pro-ceed. These would seem to be:

1 *A drastic reduction of those engaged in agriculture.* In fact, between 1953 and 1963 over two million Southerners left the land and the proportion of the Southern labour force engaged in agriculture fell from 52% to 40% (25% in the North). Many have been usefully absorbed into industry, mainly in the North, and others into construction work (a notoriously precarious occupation), but in part this movement represents a rather aimless drift to Rome and the Southern cities encouraged by the removal of administrative restrictions on internal migration and motivated by a growing distaste for the land. Unfortunately far too many former peasants are eking out a living in the slums and shanty towns of the big cities by means of odd jobs and petty trafficking.

2 *A withdrawal from cultivation of large areas*, especially in the eroded uplands, and their incorporation into conservation zones. Progress in this respect depends on 1.

3 *The creation of viable consolidated holdings* suited to the application of modern methods, including mechanization, and capable of supporting a thoroughly com-mercialized farm economy. As the drift to the towns continues and landowners become increasingly disillusioned with agriculture as an investment, peasants are being presented with the opportunity to increase their holding and low-interest loans are available for this purpose. The enormous task of assembling dispersed plots into consolidated units has scarcely begun. Criticisms of the size of *poderi* and *quote* created under the land reform have already been noted.

4 *The reclamation of the plains.* This is essentially a water control problem.

Many schemes initiated in the inter-war years and taken over by the land reform authorities are well on the way to completion, notably in the Tavoliere di Puglie, the Volturno and Sele plains, the Metaponto coastlands, the Crati lowlands and the Catania plain.

**5** *Intensification*. Three principal means are involved – the greater use of fertilizers; the extension of irrigation facilities; and the application of more intensive cropping methods. Almost everywhere there has been a notable increase in the use of chemical fertilizers, and the irrigated area in the South has increased since 1949 from under 300,000 to over 700,000 hectares. As regards cropping methods there is still much room for improvement, for example in the suppression of the worked fallow in favour of forage crops.

**6** *Diversification* with the principal aims of increasing the return per hectare and of reducing seasonal unemployment. This would imply a reduction in the area under wheat, an easy crop favoured both by the small farmer, whose family exists mainly on bread, and by the large operator, who at least until 1965 received considerable benefit from governmental price support. Among the vested interests concerned with maintaining the dominance of wheat are the *Federconsorzi*, agricultural associations whose financial strength lies in their control of the administration of grain supplies. With rising living standards and the increasing demand for meat there is a strong argument for reducing the wheat area in favour of forage crops. Much of the South is climatically handicapped in this respect but there is scope for extending the cultivation of drought-resistant grasses and leguminous forage crops such as vetch, sulla, lupinella and bersim; lucerne is better suited to the damper areas. A programme of technical instruction will also be necessary if a swing to animal rearing is to be achieved.

**7** *The improvement of the infrastructure* especially as regards transport facilities without which many areas were condemned to a closed economy. This has been substantially achieved; in fact there has been some criticism that money has been wasted on roads in areas which will soon be abandoned.

**8** *The provision of better facilities for credit, hire of machinery, technical advice and education, processing, marketing, etc.* and the encouragement of self-help through co-operatives.

Most of these objectives (especially 4, 5, 7 and 8) have been accepted and have been actively pursued under the programme for the rehabilitation of the South which, after a hesitant start in the late 40s with a number of reconstruction and public work projects financed mainly by the European Recovery Programme, assumed a massive and co-ordinated form with the passing of the land reform

DELTA
260,000 h.

FUCINO 155,000 h.

MAREMMA
TOSCO LAZIALE
956,600 h.

PUGLIA-LUCANIA
1,453,180 h.

CAMPANIA

SARDINIA

SILA
503,779 h.

SICILY

0    100    200
Km.

*Fig. 38.* The land reform zones

laws and the establishment of the Southern Development Fund (*Cassa per il Mezzogiorno*) in 1950. As originally conceived the reform was to apply to the whole country; in fact, of the two laws passed in 1950 one applied specifically to La Sila and the other (the so-called '*stralcio*' or partial law) applied to a number of zones covering the whole of Sicily and Sardinia, the Maremma, the Po delta, the Rieti and Fucino basins, the lower Volturno and Sele plains, the Tavoliere di

191

Puglie and much of Basilicata; in all some 8,141,000 hectares of productive land were involved. In each major zone (*comprensorio*) the administration of the reform was entrusted to an agency (*ente*) responsible either to the central government or, in the case of Sicily and Sardinia, to the autonomous regional authorities. One of the main functions of the *enti* is to effect basic rehabilitation of the land by means of drainage, flood control and the provision of irrigation facilities; the inclusion of large areas of upland within the jurisdiction of the *enti* recognizes the fundamental interdependence of upland and plain in the establishment of water control. The *enti* are also responsible for the co-ordination within the overall plan of earlier improvement schemes such as those effected directly by the fascist government or under the law of 1933 which subsidized associations of landowners (*consorzi*) prepared to carry out a co-ordinated improvement plan (*bonifica integrale*); this law is still in force. Not the least of the tasks assigned to the *enti* was the expropriation of land and its distribution among peasant families in *poderi* and *quote* on the lines described above (p. 168). The method of expropriation under the Sila law differed from that under the *stralcio* law; under the former landowners possessing more than 300 hectares (in any part of the country) were vulnerable, while under the *stralcio* law only model farms were entirely exempt. In fact only 106 farms totalling 45,000 ha measured up to the required standards. Of the 700,000 ha made available under the reform, either by expropriation or purchase, over 610,000 ha have been assigned to some 108,000 peasant families. Not all the assignees are new owners; many merely added to their previous holdings. About one-quarter of the total area, involving half the assignees, consists of non-viable *quote*.

Some of the criticisms levelled against the reform have been touched on above (p. 169). It pleased neither the political right, whose supporters among the landowners resented the attack on their privileges, nor the political left, which stood to gain most from rural unrest; its main support came from the Catholic centre, which regards the God-fearing peasant family, preferably a prosperous one, as one of the most worthy and stable elements in the state. A decade of trial has revealed some of the miscalculations of the reform. Some colonists have proved themselves incapable of achieving the required standards; others, often those with most drive, have been lured from the land altogether by the greater opportunities in industry. Abandoned *poderi*, particularly in hilly districts of intractable clay where irrigation is impossible and intensification is difficult, are by no means uncommon. But despite its shortcomings and local failures the land reform can claim to have transformed the economies of several formerly stagnant areas, to have improved the lot of thousands of peasant families, and to have provided millions of man-days of useful work on construction projects. Its solid achievements in the field of rural re-settlement and public works are undeniable. Above all it was a practical expression of the state's concern for the plight of the South at a particularly difficult time when the upsurge of industry and the opportunities for emigration later available were still far from assured.

The *Cassa per il Mezzogiorno* is responsible for the co-ordination, direction and financing not only of the land reform and its associated activities but of the overall development programme for the South. Originally endowed in 1950 with 1000 billion lire to be spent over ten years, the funds at its disposal, part of which was raised abroad, have been twice increased and its life span has been similarly extended (1952, 1965). Given the South's appetite for capital and the deep involvement of the state in its fortunes, the *Cassa* seems likely to become a permanent institution. Its first ten years were mainly occupied with assisting agriculture through public works, land reclamation and improvement, and the implementation of the land reform generally, but in recent years the *Cassa* has increasingly directed its efforts towards industrialization.

It has long been obvious that agriculture alone is incapable of providing a solution to the problems of the *Mezzogiorno* and that if agriculture itself is to be put on an efficient basis the numbers engaged in it must be drastically reduced. Short of a massive emigration abroad, the redundant manpower of the South, relentlessly reinforced by natural increase, must be increasingly absorbed into industry either in the North or in the South itself. According to the industrial census of 1951 only 722,000 Southerners were employed in industry (including construction and mining), approximately 17% of the national total; in 1961 the corresponding figures were 851,000 and 15%. As yet only Naples and to a lesser extent Bari can claim to be significant industrial centres with any diversity of activity. In the South generally the best-represented sectors are quarrying, mining, construction, constructional materials, agricultural processing, clothing, textiles and engineering. As in so much of Italy a high proportion of the workers is employed in very small units, many of them simply craft workshops. In recent years the steel (Taranto) and petro-chemical (Gela, Bari, Augusta, Brindisi) sectors have been powerfully reinforced but progress towards a complex of varied manufactures has made little headway outside Campania. Apart from the discouraging aspects of the social and economic *milieu* touched on above, the most serious obstacles to Southern industrialization would seem to be:

1) The isolation of the *Mezzogiorno* from Europe's richest markets and its most rapidly developing zones.
2) The poverty of the local market for consumer and capital goods.
3) Illiteracy and a lack of industrial skills (Naples excepted).
4) The super-abundance of labour which tends to discourage the adoption of labour-saving factory techniques and to perpetuate the small unit.
5) Lack of capital and the preoccupation of the moneyed classes with investment in land and buildings.
6) The niggardly endowment of the area in water supplies, hydro-electric power resources, minerals and fuels. In recent years the South has been responsible for no more than 15% of the country's electricity output; its mineral production, with the exception of that of sulphur, lead–zinc and potash, is very

modest and the producing units are small, inefficient and scattered; and hopes of discovering oil and gas in really large quantities have not been realized.

Inevitably much of the initiative for industrialization in the *Mezzogiorno* has come from the state. Directly or through the *Cassa* it has done much to improve the infrastructure especially as regards roads, railways, shipping and water supplies. Through various state-controlled bodies it has been able to provide credit and direct investment; the *Istituto per la Ricostruzione Industriale* (IRI) and the *Ente Nazionale Idrocarburi* (ENI), for example, are obliged to channel 60% of all new investment into the *Mezzogiorno* and the Taranto steel works and the Gela petro-chemical complex are fruits of this policy. The *Cassa* too has financed directly or indirectly a number of projects, for example in paper, chemicals, synthetic fibres and agricultural processing. In the long run, however, much must depend on the extent to which Northern firms can be persuaded to extend their activities into the South; to this end the authorities assist manufacturers in finding suitably equipped factory sites, make sizeable concessions on taxes and on duties payable on imported machinery, provide credit for plant and assist with training. In fact, a number of well-known foreign and Italian companies, notably those concerned with oil, chemicals, vehicle assembly, office machinery, rubber, plastics, synthetic materials and photographic goods, have invested substantially. Inevitably industry has been mainly attracted (or directed) to a limited number of zones with special advantages as regards ports, communications, water supplies and skilled labour, notably Campania, the Bari–Taranto–Brindisi triangle and eastern Sicily. It was hoped that these areas, well equipped with such basic industries as steel, chemicals and oil processing, would constitute natural 'development poles' to which a much wider range of manufacturing activity would be attracted. In fact, this spontaneous 'snowballing' process has been less successful than was hoped; it is clear that something more is needed besides the establishment of a few basic activities if an area is to develop into a diversified industrial complex. This is diagnosed as the environmental influence of a concentration of manufacturing enterprises mutually dependent for parts, by-products and services.[1] It is therefore proposed to encourage the simultaneous establishment of a group of closely inter-connected manufacturing activities of the type best suited to the geographical and economic conditions of the *Mezzogiorno*. To be competitive each activity has to be capable of supporting production on a fairly large scale, a condition which ruled out many products because of the limited demand of the South and its remoteness from possible markets elsewhere. As far as the Bari–Taranto–Brindisi 'pole' was concerned the consultants reduced the list of manufacturing groups likely to be successfully established to synthetic materials and mechanical engineering. Unfortunately for the South, the sort of industrial environment which it is hoped to create exists already in the North and the congestion there has not yet reached a point

[1] *Economist*, 7 Nov. 1964.

where further development is being discouraged. Indeed, the spread of manufacturing into those rural areas within the general industrial environment is one of the commonest distributional trends in the Valle Padana.

## V[a] *Campania*

The heart of Campania lies between the shores of the Gulf of Naples and the outer bastions of the Apennines; this was the base from which Greek civilization, established in the cities of Cumae, Neapolis and Pompei, first penetrated the central peninsula. The modern *regione* stretching from the Garigliano to the Gulf of Policastro and thrusting deep into the Apennine highlands, is much more extensive and its limits are less easily defined in terms of natural features; such unity as it has is provided by the powerful attraction of Naples which brings Campania's five provinces (Caserta, Benevento, Napoli, Avellino and Salerno) within its orbit. In many respects Campania is not typical of the South; it enjoys great natural advantages in climate, soil and water supplies favourable to intensive cultivation; in Naples it has a port of international stature which has stimulated enterprise in both agriculture and industry; above all it has always been accessible from the north along the coast and down the Valle Latina. Along these routes, bent on war and trade, came the Etruscans who, from their base in Capua, briefly dominated Hellenic Campania. Later the Campanians, glad to accept protection against the Samnite hill tribes, fell easily within the Roman sphere; Puteoli (Pozzuoli), served by the Via Appia and other Roman roads, thrived as the acknowledged port of Rome (at least until Claudius developed Ostia), and under Augustus's reorganization Latium and Campania were combined in one *regio*. Today the accessibility of Campania is adequately assured by roads, motorways and railways and the port of Naples serves Central Italy much as Puteoli once did.

Within the complexity of Campania's relief and geology a number of physical elements may be identified each of which has tended to evoke a characteristic human response. They are:

1) The coastal plains, further divisible into
   a. the plains of Campania Felix,
   b. the alluvial plains of the lower Garigliano, Volturno and Sele.
2) The volcanic zones of Roccamonfina, Vesuvius, the Phlegraean Fields and the islands of Ischia and Procida.
3) The Apennines, within which two main zones are recognizable:
   a. the limestone bastions, blocks and peninsulas with their associated basins and
   b. the Eocene clay–sandstone (*flysch*) zone of the Apennine interior.

The plain of Campania Felix, forming an arc from Aversa through Acera to Nocera, is distinguished from the other plains of Campania not only by the natural fertility of its soils but by the ease with which it has been exploited to support an intensive form of cultivation from classical times onwards. The majority of its surface is composed of basaltic volcanic ash, deposited *in situ* or resorted by water. Because of the permeability of the tufo large areas are without surface drainage but the high water table keeps the subsoil moist and irrigation

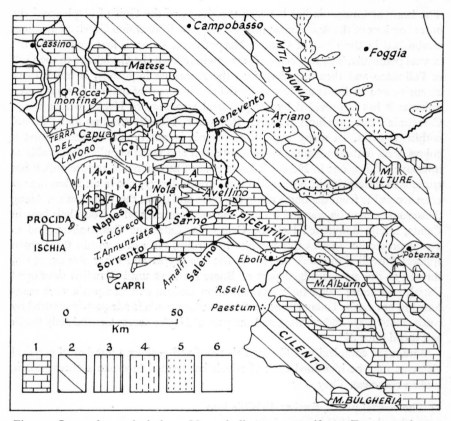

*Fig. 39.* Campania – geological. 1 – Mesozoic limestone massifs. 2 – Eocene sandstones and clays (*flysch*). 3 – The volcanic massifs. 4 – Ash-covered lowlands. 5 – Pliocene basins. 6 – Quaternary and recent alluvium

water from wells is readily available. Springs issuing from the marginal limestone bastions to the north of the plain are the other main source of water; they serve two particularly extensive irrigated zones, namely the Sarno plain and the Caserta–Nola–Casória triangle. The former is drained by surface streams and is more alluvial in character than the rest of the plain. Although there are innumerable nuances in the land-use, in general Campania Felix is an area of *coltura promiscua* intensified where possible by irrigation. Locally, as towards Capua, the tree crops are wider spaced and the emphasis lies with the field crops, but in many of the more densely populated areas the landscape closes in to become an open orchard. The soil, which is demanding increasing quantities of fertilizers, is never idle; maize, wheat, beans, sugar beet, hemp, potatoes, lucerne, clover and an almost unbroken succession of vegetables are the main field crops. The tree crops, either grown 'mixed' or in specialized orchards, include peaches, cherries, plums, pears, almonds, olives and hazel nuts. Vines, skilfully festooned to form screens between pollarded elms and poplars, are a typical feature of the landscape. More than anywhere else in the *Mezzogiorno* cattle, pigs and poultry have an important place in the economy. The agriculture of this part of Campania is highly commercialized and much of the produce, for example, the stone fruits and tomatoes and the market-garden crops of the coastal strip between Naples and Castellammare, are destined for foreign markets, either fresh or in the form of essences and preserves. Unfortunately the proverbial bounty of Campania Felix is more than offset by the fecundity of the inhabitants and the rural population density often exceeds 500 per sq km and locally reaches 1000 in the Aversa–Afragola zone. The vast majority of the land is worked by direct cultivators (*coltivatori diretti*); most of them own at least some of the land they work but they often supplement their incomes by hiring extra plots on a cash or *mezzadria* basis. Even so the peasant's 'farm' frequently amounts to no more than 2 hectares; in Naples province 64% of the cultivated area is worked in units of 3 hectares or less. Inevitably most villages have a large landless element. Here and there a *masseria* survives, shorn of most of its land, but the vast majority of the rural population lives in large concentrated settlements (Acera, Afragola, Frattamaggiore) many of which retain the rectangular Roman street plan orientated N–S and E–W. The narrow basalt-paved streets are commonly flanked by three-storied tenements built round a courtyard (*cortile*) which is approached through an archway from the road. Each *cortile* is occupied by several families who reach their quarters by means of stairways and balconies surrounding the courtyard.

In marked contrast to Campania Felix the alluvial plains of the lower Garigliano, Volturno (Terra di Lavoro) and Sele (Plain of Paestum), once marshy and malaria-ridden, repelled settlement until quite recently. Spasmodic attempts were made to cure their hydrological disorders (the Regi Lagni canal dates from 1600) but little serious progress was made until the 1930s. With the renewed impetus of the land reform reclamation and colonization are being pushed ahead and these plains once monopolized by *latifondi* are gradually assuming the orderly landscape characteristic of recent colonization. Large areas on the Garigliano and Sele plains are now irrigable and in addition to the traditional Mediterranean crops meat and milk production are becoming increasingly important, particularly on a number of highly efficient capitalist farms. Oddly enough with the passing of the marsh the cow has not entirely displaced the buffalo whose rich milk fetches high prices.

Although somewhat more extensive, the extinct cone of Roccamonfina may be regarded as a dead Vesuvius; it is about the same height (1005m) and its basalt ash and lava are of similar composition. Its summit (in contrast to the sterile crown of Vesuvius) is clothed with chestnut coppice and its thickly populated lower slopes are devoted to vines, olives and *coltura promiscua* worked from a ring of large villages. The steep ash cone of Vesuvius is separated by a circular depression (Atrio del Cavallo) from the precipitous rim of the caldera which was left after the eruption of AD 79. The caldera edge, which is highest on the northern side (M. Somma, 1132m), has been breached frequently since then; lava flows reached the sea in 1760 and 1861, and in 1944, the most recent serious eruption, Massa and S. Sebastiano were destroyed. The lower skirt of the mountain, up to about 200m, is a vast orchard in which stone fruits and hazel nuts are prominent; directly above the vine takes over until the chestnut woods are reached. The inner cone is completely sterile but in the Atrio del Cavallo broom and conifers are doing their pioneer work. The density of settlement on the outer slopes is astonishing even when one expects it; besides the large nucleated villages strung along the road ringing the mountain, the terraced countryside is dotted with box-like houses, each with its garden from which expert hands wring every possible ounce of produce. On the rugged islands of Ischia and Procida the pressure of population on the resources is no less; with a combined area of about 35 sq km, together they have about 50,000 inhabitants. Fortunately they have much to offer the tourist.

Volcanic activity in its constructive and destructive moods is responsible for the chaotic relief of the Phlegraean Fields. Low ash rings, often incomplete, jostle each other to encompass flat-floored crater basins. Some of these contained lakes which have been profitably reclaimed; the most famous, Averno, is connected to the sea by a canal. The highest hills are clothed with vines and capped with chestnuts, but the dominant impression is that of a densely populated orchard of sub-tropical exuberance.

The Campanian and Lucanian Apennines stretch from the Sangro–Volturno line in the north to the Scalone pass in the south. In this sector the Apennines have swung back to the Tyrrhenian side of the peninsula and the general NW–SE trend of the folding is obscured by severe transverse and longitudinal faulting (mainly associated with the post-Pliocene uplift) which has produced a number of roughly aligned isolated massifs; these massifs are most obvious on the western flank. Within the highlands two significant elements may be recognized, namely, a discontinuous Mesozoic calcareous zone in the west and an Eocene clay-sandstone zone which is most extensive in the east (fig. 39).

The calcareous zone, severely disturbed tectonically, reveals itself in a number of isolated blocks emerging abruptly through the Eocene sediments (*flysch*). In some cases the latter merely envelope the lower slopes of the limestone massifs but in several areas they have survived more extensively (Cilento). The main massifs, which were once islands in the Pliocene sea, are identifiable in the Matese group, M. Maggiore, M. Taburno the Mti Picentini, the Mti Lattari,

M. Alburno, M. Cervati, M. Vulturino and M. Pollino. They vary in character from chalk to dolomite and in age from the Cretaceous to the Triassic. Except for the Mti Picentini, the dolomites occur mainly outside Campania proper. The lower flanks of the limestone blocks are generally terraced for dry tree crops but otherwise they are of little agricultural value. Much of their surface is a rocky karst whose meagre pastures are grazed by transhumant sheep; the rest is oak and beech scrub occasionally improving to respectable stands on the summits. The importance of these blocks, which exhibit many interesting karstic features (Lake Matese; the dolines of M. Alburno), lies in their ability to act as reservoirs; the regimes of most Campanian rivers, notably the Lete, Sarno and Sele, benefit from the regulating effect of karstic springs, and the lowland corridors and the margins of the adjacent plains are heavily dependent upon them. The springs of the Mti Picentini, tapped to supply Naples (Serino aqueduct) and the cities of Apulia, are particularly valuable.

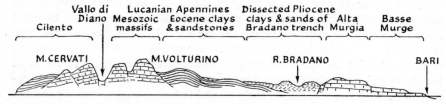

*Fig. 40.* Simplified geological section from Cilento to the Murge

Penetrating the blocks along fault zones are a number of lowland corridors and basins in which the *flysch* covering has survived. Their floors and hilly margins, which in northern Campania are extensively enriched with volcanic ash (Avellino basin, Montesarchio basin) are intensively cultivated under *coltura promiscua*. They also provide a number of routeways into the Apennine highlands, some transverse (e.g. the Cadore valley to Benevento), some longitudinal (e.g. the Vallo di Diano). The latter, overlooked by the impressive scarp of M. Alburno, is a tectonic trench whose exploitation has demanded extensive drainage works.

The Sorrento and Cilento peninsulas deserve special mention. The former is tilted northwards to produce a magnificent southern coast. The rugged interior of the peninsula is scrub-covered but the coastal margins have been painfully terraced to support a flourishing arboriculture; the walnuts of Sorrento are particularly renowned. In the Cilento highlands the underlying limestone block, folded NW–SE, is exposed in M. Bulgheria, M. Alburno and the M. Vesole–M. Cervati ridge; elsewhere it is masked by Eocene clays and sandstones. The latter are extensively devoted to figs, olives and vines, associated with a form of *coltura promiscua* in the valleys, but the limestone areas, when not just barren karst, support little but scrub woodland.

The main exposure of Eocene clays and sandstones – the second element in the Campano–Lucanian Apennines – forms a wide strip to the east of the limestone massifs from Maiella to the Gulf of Taranto (fig. 39); it covers all but the coast-lands of Chieti and Campobasso provinces, much of Benevento and a good deal of Basilicata. The general character of these sediments has already received attention; seen from a height the clays present a monotonous succession of rounded ridges interrupted locally by tougher sandstone outcrops. The difficult terrain is in the valleys whose unstable slopes and gravel-filled floors are avoided by both roads and settlement. The land-use, typical of the *latifondo contadino* to which most of this zone can be assigned, is dominated by wheat, and tree crops only occur extensively in the vicinity of the hill-top villages where most of the population is concentrated. Despite the unpromising environment the population density is surprisingly high (Campobasso 75 per sq km, Benevento 144) but there has been a marked decline in recent years. Where Pliocene sediments overlie the Eocenes (e.g. the Benevento basin) they are mostly clays and there is little fundamental change in the landscape or in the land-use.

The teeming city of Naples (Napoli, 1,196,000) dominates Campania as securely as Milan does Lombardy, and throughout the continental South it retains much of the status it enjoyed as the capital of the Two Sicilies. The population has doubled in the last half-century and in the decade 1951–1961 its total, swollen by the quickening flight from the countryside, rose by 17%. Inevitably this exacerbates the problem of providing housing and useful employment. With Bagnoli, Naples ranks second to Genoa among Italian ports and has regular sailings not only to the Mediterranean ports but to the Americas, Africa, Australia and the Far East. Averaging 12·5 million tons it has handled about half the tonnage of Genoa in the recent years and although its passenger traffic is less than in the days of massive overseas emigration before 1915 and of colonial adventures in the thirties, it is still more important than Genoa in this respect. As in almost all European ports imports greatly exceed exports; they consist mainly of fuels and raw materials especially Middle East oil, American coal, West African iron ore, cotton, jute, timber, oil seeds and phosphates. The processing of these commodities provides one of the main industrial activities of Naples and its satellite towns. Its cotton, jute, rayon and paper mills are the most important in the South, and although they add little to the beauty of the bay, its oil refineries, chemical plants and the full-cycle iron and steel works at Bagnoli illustrate the diversity of its manufacturing activities. The metal-working and engineering sectors are represented in the tube works at Torre Annunziata and the old-established shipyards at Castellammare; unfortunately the latter have suffered from the rationalization of Italian shipbuilding. Recently established factories producing artificial silk, typewriters, ball-bearings, cars (Alfa Romeo), rubber and pharmaceuticals are some of the fruits of the policy of encouraging industrial investment in the South. The more traditional industries of the area include hundreds of craft workshops and agricultural processing based on local and imported supplies (pasta, olive oil, soap, fruit and vegetable preserves). Naples continues to enjoy a high cultural reputation whose traditions stretch back through the Middle Ages (when Frederick II founded the university) to their Greco–Roman roots.

Salerno (123,000), reached from the north through a narrow gap between the Mti Lattari and the Mti Picentini, occupies a similar position in relation to the Gulf of Salerno as Naples does to its bay. Almost entirely rebuilt since the devastation of 1943, it is now a provincial and market centre and a modest port with cotton and food processing among its industrial activities. Its importance may be expected to grow as the potentialities of the Sele plain are more fully realized. Caserta (54,000), the Versailles of the Kingdom of the Two Sicilies, owes its existence to the grandiose ambitions of the Neapolitan Bourbons, but the recent establishment of a photographic material factory and of the biggest nylon plant in Italy are of greater contemporary significance.

The Campanian coasts and islands which are of absorbing interest to the historian, the archaeologist and the geologist and present a perfect setting for the civilized cultivation of idleness, have attracted wealthy expatriates and tourists in all their guises since the time of Cicero and Tiberius. Sorrento, Amalfi, Positano, Capri and Ischia have become almost entirely dependent on them.

### V[b] *Molise*

Although administratively part of the *regione* of the Abruzzi and Molise,[1] the area covered by the provinces of Chieti and Campobasso deserves separate recognition, partly because its relief, landforms, lithology, land-use and settlement are strongly influenced by the dominance of erodible Tertiary rocks, especially clays, and partly because of its isolation; it is something of a no-man's-land between the more positive regions of Campania, Apulia and the limestone massifs of Abruzzo. In the west and south the area is bounded by the limestone highlands of M. Maiella, M. Greco and Matese; in the east it falls away across the Fortore river to the Tavoliere di Puglie. A distinction may be drawn between the dissected coastal hill country developed on Pliocene clays, sands and conglomerates (Astian sands over Piacenza clays) and the higher interior zone of Eocene clays and sandstones. The physical characteristics and the human response to them of both these types of country have already received some attention above. Put very briefly the coastal strip, varying in width from 10 to 30 km, is favoured by a milder climate and by the partial survival of Pliocene sands on the interfluves, especially south of the Sangro. These advantages are reflected in a greater diversity of land-use (including tree crops) and a greater density of population; *mezzadria appoderata* is also better represented here than anywhere else in the South. The interior zone of Eocene clays whose vicious habits are particularly well illustrated in the Monte del Frantani, may be generally assigned to the *latifondo contadino*. The following figures bring out some of the salient features of the agriculture of the two provinces:

[1] Molise in the strict sense is practically coterminous with Campobasso province and Chieti province is associated administratively with the Abruzzi.

|  | | Chieti | Campobasso |
|---|---|---|---|
| Percentage | mountainous | 30 | 55 |
| ,, | hilly | 70 | 45 |
| ,, | of total area cultivated | 75 | 70 |
| ,, | of total under cereals | 33 | 41 |
| ,, | of total area under tree crops | 11 | 4 |
| ,, | of farm area in units of 5 ha or less | 49 | 31 |
| Population density per sq km agro-forest land | | 153 | 85 |

Given the meagre agricultural resources and the almost complete absence of industry it is small wonder that the population is drifting away; the decline between 1951 and 1961 was 11% in Chieti and 15% in Campobasso but the density is still excessive.

### V[c] *Apulia*

Apulia's communications with the rest of Italy compare unfavourably with those of Campania; indeed, in certain phases of its history it was drawn out of the Italian orbit into that of the eastern Mediterranean. In classical times, as part of Magna Graecia, it fell first within the Hellenic sphere and later served as a springboard and a highway (Via Appia, Via Egnatia) for Roman penetration into the Balkans. For centuries it was an outpost of the Byzantine Empire but it was none the less harried repeatedly by Saracen pirates, and when the Empire fell it was seriously menaced by the Turks. Even in modern times its extra-Italian associations have occasionally reasserted themselves; in the fascist period Bari was the base for Italian activity in the Balkans and the Middle East, and Brindisi, whose fortunes were briefly revived in the later nineteenth century with the establishment of a rail and steamer service from Calais to Egypt and India, has now renewed its Balkan connections by means of a car ferry to Igoumenitza, Patras and Athens.

In terms of physical features Apulia's limits are set by the lower Fortore river, the Sub-Apennines (Mti di Daunia) and the edge of the Bradano (Pre-Murgian) trench; this defines an area corresponding broadly with the five provinces of the *regione* (Foggia, Bari, Taranto, Brindisi and Lecce). Structurally it consists of two Cretaceous limestone platforms connected by the near-horizontal, Pliocene to recent sediments of the Tavoliere di Puglie. These sediments occupy the northern end of the Bradano trench which is itself part of the much longer Apennine foretrench stretching up through the Marche into the Valle Padana. In Pliocene times practically all of Apulia except the highest parts of the limestone blocks was submerged. Since then the whole area has been uplifted; the blocks emerged first and there has been time for most of the Pliocene–Quaternary covering to be removed by erosion, but the emergence of the Tavoliere is of recent date. The stages in the uplift, which to judge from the seismic instability of Gargano is still incomplete, are associated with marine abrasion platforms cut in the two blocks.

What variations there are in the general uniformity of climate are introduced by altitude and this reinforces the customary threefold division of the area on the basis of relief and geology into the Gargano peninsula, the Murge and the Tavo-liere. The Gargano block falls very sharply to the north either directly to the sea or to the two lakes of Lesina and Varano which have been sealed off from the sea by longshore drift from the north; their alluvial fringes, once malarial, have now been reclaimed. The southern flank descends in two massive terraces; the upper one is traversed by the E-W road through S. Giovanni and the lower one extends due westwards from Manfredonia. Much of the plateau top, which reaches 1000m, is a rocky karstic waste pitted with shallow depressions and occasional dolines (particularly in the dolomitic areas) but forest, mainly beech and pines, has survived in the north-east (Bosco d'Umbra) and on the northern flank, where it gives way to tree crops below. On the upper terrace of the southern flank, where several patches of Quaternary sediments remain, the karst is relieved by olives and other dry tree crops; on the lower terrace the Quaternary covering is extensive and the land-use differs little from that of the Tavoliere (see below). With these exceptions the peninsula is of little value agriculturally; apart from a few springs issuing near sea level its surface is almost entirely devoid of water and at best its threadbare mantle of *terra rossa* is shallow and discontinuous.

Between the Fortore and the Ofanto the Eocene clays of the Sub-Apennines roll down to the Tavoliere di Puglie, once known as Daunia or the Capitanata (the Byzantine designation). It is bordered by a narrow and incomplete fringe of Pliocene sediments, mostly clays, where the terrain is hilly or undulating rather than flat. The plain proper, falling gently to the Candelaro 'gutter' and the dunes fringing the Gulf of Manfredonia, is surfaced with shallow marine clays, conglomerates and sands of Quaternary and recent date whose intercalation pro-vides well water at shallow depths. Torrential rivers, which scarcely survive as far as the coast, lace the plain with alluvial strips; their shallow valleys and the lagoons into which they flow offered ideal conditions for the development of malarial marshes. On the interfluves, silts, conglomerates and especially soft calcareous sandstones (*tufi*) are widely represented; these last produce a porous, floury soil while the conglomerates provide a concretionary, less easily workable surface. In the lower areas the water table is very near the surface and the soils, rich in humus, may be classed as black Mediterranean soils (*tirs*). Although in classical times the coast and the upper margins of the Tavoliere were colonized (there is evidence of centuriation, and Lucera and Sipontum were sizeable Roman towns), until recently Man's efforts to settle and exploit the area system-atically have always been frustrated by hydrological disorders and malaria. In the Middle Ages it became the preserve of powerful pastoral elements whose privileges were later confirmed by the Aragonese; the network of *tratturi* was extended, defined and protected, and over large areas tillage was restricted by law. Despite the establishment of a few small colonies by the Bourbons at the end of the eighteenth century (Orta, Ordona, Carapelle, Stornara) and the liberal legislation introduced during the French interlude, no fundamental change took place in the character of the Tavoliere till the 1860s. With the arrival of the railways and the decline in wool prices in the face of overseas competition, the *masserie* began to take an increasing interest in wheat production, an activity which dovetailed well with sheep rearing. At the same time an influx of labourers transformed the villages into towns without greatly changing their function. Although at harvest time the Tavoliere attracted temporary labour from all over the continental South, the permanent *giornalieri* suffered from serious under-employment and their livelihood was increasingly menaced by mechanization. Between the wars *consorzi di bonifica* made some modest progress in improving the area which now assumed an important rôle in the 'Battle for Grain'. The conversion of Lake Salpi into salt pans was completed, Lake Salso was reclaimed by *colmate*, and a number of settlements, based on *poderi*, were founded under the aegis of ex-servicemen's organizations (e.g. Mezzanone). The environs of the towns were increasingly taken over by small cultivators, and tree crops, notably olives round Cerignola and vines near S. Severo, continued to modify the traditional land-use, but in 1946 the Tavoliere was still essentially a vast cultural steppe, studded with *masserie* and overcrowded townships. Since 1950, under the land reform, the hydrological problems have been tackled with vigour. Malaria has been practically eliminated; over 57,000 hectares in Foggia province have been appropriated and settled; and some 125,000 hectares are being provided with irrigation along the lower Fortore, on the right bank of the middle Ofanto, and most extensively between the Candelaro and the Foggia–S. Severo road. Although about 38% of Foggia province is still in properties of over 50 hectares, a very high figure for Italy, the trend towards a more intensive and varied land-use and a wider distribution of ownership is firmly established. Even so the problem of rural overpopulation is far from solved; towns like Foggia (118,000), which has managed to attract food processing, agricultural machinery and textile industries on a modest scale, must be further industrialized and it is unlikely that emigration can be avoided for a long time yet.

The Murge and the Salentine peninsula constitute a structural unit but they are best considered separately. Lying between the Ofanto and a line joining Brindisi and Taranto, and rising to 686m in Torre Disperata, the Murge table-land is composed of Cretaceous limestone gently folded on a NW–SE axis. On its southern flank, where the limestones are down-faulted, the plateau falls abruptly and irregularly to the Bradano trench and the amphitheatre of Taranto. Northwards it descends to the sea across three escarpments; the first and highest of these, which corresponds roughly with the 300m contour, marks the edge of the high plateau top – the Alte Murge. The other two much lower escarpments, running roughly parallel to the coast, convert the lower Murge into three shallow steps. The relative importance of faulting and of marine or sub-aerial peneplan-ation in the formation of these steps is variously assessed. Although the plateau is lapped by Pliocene–Quaternary sediments on its southern and western flanks, and similar deposits have survived on its upper surface (notably along the coast between Barletta and Bisceglie, near Bari, south of Monopoli and at Gioia) it is essentially a karstic block, at best incompletely veiled by residual soils – rendzinas in the very highest areas, *terra rossa* elsewhere. East of the Ofanto there are no rivers and although locally the occurrence of non-calcareous sediments over the limestone may force water in minor quantities to the surface, in general the availability of water from springs or wells depends on the position of the place concerned in relation to the body of fresh water, lens-shaped in section, which is floating on the sea water saturating the base of the block. In fact, in the interior of the Murge the water table is unattainable by wells and along the coast well water is often brackish; what few springs there are issue immediately above or below the shoreline. Almost every settlement of any size now depends on the Apulian aqueduct (p. 199) for its domestic supplies, but the dearth of local sources is an obvious handicap to both agriculture and industry. Karstic phenomena are best represented in the Alte Murge where shallow elongated depressions and dolines occur; the recent discovery of large caves just below the surface at Castellena suggest that such features may be more common than was once thought. The edges of the plateau are occasionally scored by dry valleys; the *gravine* of the southern flank (e.g. at Massafra and Castellaneta) are deeper and more tortuous than the *lame* of the Adriatic side. Where *terra rossa* has accumulated on their floors they provide valuable agricultural land.

On the rugged, undulating tableland of the Alte Murge (aptly called *Puglia petrosa*), where the *terra rossa* covering is thin when not absent altogether, large expanses are occupied by low macchia, garrigue and steppe. In general the area is still one of large properties and *masserie* dependent on extensive wheat production and sheep rearing, but in some areas peasant colonization has achieved an extraordinary transformation over the last ninety years. This is best illustrated in the Murgia dei Trulli lying between Ostuni, Conversano and Noci where a thrifty, tenacious and hardworking peasantry has gained possession of the land and converted it into a multitude of very small compact farms[1] producing wine, olives, almonds, stone fruits and vegetables. This transformation was favoured by the social and economic circumstances immediately following the unification of Italy. With the fall of wool prices in the face of overseas production many landowners were willing to sell while others sought a profitable alternative to wool and wheat. The former group found willing buyers among those peasants who could raise a loan or who had amassed a little capital, usually with the aid of emigrant relatives. Other landowners installed peasants on their estates under *enfiteusi* and contracts of improvement. Under *enfiteusi* the peasant was assured of the use of the land provided he paid a small rent; under contracts of improvement part of the land was retained by the peasant provided he improved the whole. Thus by various means the land gradually came into the possession of a host of small proprietors. Furthermore, it happened that the crop most suited to these ungrateful soils, the vine, could be profitably expanded because, as a result

[1] In Locorotondo 51% and in Alberobello 43% of the commune was worked in units of under 2 hectares in 1957 (V. Ricchioni).

of the phylloxera epidemic in France, high alcoholic wines suitable for blending were in great demand. Olives and later almonds were other crops with an assured market, but the peasant growing them had to be prepared to wait much longer for his return. This specialized and essentially commercialized form of agriculture was encouraged by the extension of the railways into Apulia. The improvement of these unpromising lands is a monument to the tenacity of a land-hungry peasantry. First the ground was cleared of rocks which were used to build terraces and protective walls round the little fields. This task was made easier by the flaggy nature of the limestone which also lent itself to the construction of the characteristic *trulli* – beehive-shaped dwellings from which the area takes its name. The preparation of the fields involved the removal of the *terra rossa* layer and of the loose stones below; then the irregular rock surface exposed was levelled and broken up as much as possible while the loose stones were broken and graded to form a subsoil into which tree roots could penetrate and find moisture; finally the *terra rossa* topsoil was replaced. All this with pick, shovel and basket. The area now presents a neat pattern of small walled fields closely dotted with *trulli* (p. xxb); nowhere else in the South is there such a high degree of dispersed settlement.

The Murgia dei Trulli trespasses into the lower Murge, an area which is climatically more suited than the Alte Murge to delicate tree crops and is locally favoured by residual patches of Pliocene–Quaternary sediments. The coastal strip has enjoyed a reputation for olives and wine since classical times but after 1860 practically all the Murge Basse underwent a transformation similar to that described in the *trulli* zone. The main difference is that here the peasantry preferred to remain concentrated in large villages whose original function was to serve an extensive economy based on wheat and sheep. Thus at certain periods this huge orchard of olives, almonds and vines seems quite deserted, despite a high density of population (Bari province 246 per sq km). At harvest times, however, the peasants move temporarily on to their holdings where they are 'housed' in box-like stone cabins. Provided their root systems are not in competition (e.g. vines and olives) dry tree crops can be grown *in promiscua*, but the cultivation of each crop in separate plots is preferable; in Apulia, which in 1964 produced 15% of Italy's wine and 40% of her olive oil, two-thirds of the olives and the vast majority of the vines come into this second category. Much of the wine of Apulia is used to make vermouth. In recent decades early vegetables have become increasingly important in the economy and where soils are deep and retentive of water the vinegrower has turned his attention to dessert grapes.

The low platform of the Salentine peninsula, like the Murge Basse, is underlain with Cretaceous limestone which is exposed in the low ridges of the Murge Tarentine and Murge Salentine, but it has preserved more of its covering of post-Cretaceous sediments. Of these the most extensive are the calcareous sands, conglomerates and clays of Quaternary age which cover the Tavoliere di Lecce.

At Lecce itself impure Miocene limestones include the famous honey-coloured *pietra leccese* which was used in the extraordinary baroque architecture of the town. Unfortunately almost all these sediments are permeable and there are no streams and very few springs. As elsewhere in 'rocky' Apulia the colonizing energy of the peasantry has converted a niggardly steppe into expanses of vines, olives and figs, but some of the limestone ridges are beyond redemption. Since 1900 tobacco, which is suited to the deeper, moister soils, has become important; it demands much labour and is grown mainly by sharecroppers.

The Quaternary sediments which only partially hide the limestones of the Taranto amphitheatre cover a wide area in the west of Taranto province. Traditionally this is *latifondo* zone and large tracts are still used mainly for extensive cereals, but much of the immediate hinterland of Taranto is now devoted to dry tree crops. Further west the formerly marshy strip behind the coastal dunes has been closely settled in *poderi* created under the land reform. The provision of irrigation facilities makes possible a wide range of crops including citrus, tobacco and early vegetables (artichokes, fennel, cauliflowers, etc.).

The transformation of Apulian agriculture over the last hundred years in terms of the enthusiastic expansion of a small range of crops has been marked by a succession of booms and slumps which recall the vicissitudes of the Brazilian economy. The expansion of viticulture stimulated by the French phylloxera epidemic and the French commercial treaty of 1863 received a rude check when that treaty was abrogated in 1886. An agreement with Austria–Hungary did something to retrieve the situation but not enough to prevent widespread bankruptcy and a mass emigration overseas. A worse disaster befell Apulia with the arrival of phylloxera in 1899 which obliged still more Apulians to emigrate and incidentally stimulated the expansion of tobacco and almonds as alternatives to vines. Since the restoration of the vineyards with the aid of American stocks the vinegrowers' main problem has been overproduction; hence the growing interest in dessert grapes. The olive, which is notoriously erratic in yield from year to year and from area to area,[1] and demands some fifteen years before giving a worthwhile return, has made the steadiest progress but it has not been without its misfortunes; in particular the olive fly epidemic before and after the First World War caused havoc and encouraged a switch to almonds and tobacco. These crises in Apulian agriculture have been all the more serious because the peculiar geography of the area restricts the range of alternative crops to which the farmer can turn.

The rise in living standards which might have been expected to follow from the conversion of agriculture from a cereal-pastoral economy to one based on specialized arboriculture has been frustrated by a relentless rise in population. Between 1861 and 1961 the birth rate fell from 43·8‰ to 23·9‰ but the death rate dropped from 30·5‰ to 8·4‰ so that, despite massive emigration, the population rose from 1,352,000 to 3,309,000 over the century. The other main

[1] In the Taranto area the yield is six times the Apulian average.

features of the demographic situation, some of which have already been touched on, are:

1) The much higher density of population in 'rocky' Apulia compared with that of Foggia province, potentially the richest region but one whose development demanded something more than individual peasant enterprise.
2) The high proportion of the population concentrated in large villages and towns, whose function is mainly agricultural, both in 'rocky' Apulia and in the Tavoliere. The *trulli* zone is exceptional.
3) The close succession of towns along the coast north of Bari, which despite their size (Barletta 70,000, Trani 34,000, Bisceglie 40,000, Molfetta 59,000) are mainly dependent on agriculture directly or indirectly. For many centuries these towns suffered from the insecurity of the Apulian coastlands and their expansion dates from the 1860s.
4) The line of sizeable agricultural towns some 10 to 15 km from the coast (Andria 70,000, Bitonto 40,000), the most important of which were originally Roman townships along the Via Egnatia. Following the collapse of the Roman and Byzantine power these interior towns tended to become more important than the coastal settlements whose safety from sea raiders was not assured till the nineteenth century. This is a common theme throughout the South.
5) The absence of coastal towns between Monopoli and Brindisi where the coastline is backed by superficial Quaternary sediments whose surface here encouraged the development of malarial flats. Roman Egnatia never recovered its earlier importance.

The old city of Bari (317,000) with its tortuous medieval layout stands on a low rocky peninsula; the old harbour lies to the south of it and the modern artificial port to the north. Like most coastal Apulian towns it languished till the unification; thereafter with the arrival of the railways and the agricultural transformation of its hinterland it began to expand on the geometrical pattern which today is one of its main features. Between the wars it benefited from its selection as the main springboard of Italian ambitions in the Near East. Its Fiera di Levante, established at that time, claims to be the southern equivalent of the Milan Fair. In the post-war period it has been chosen as one of the main nuclei of industrialization in the South. Its traditional industries are concerned with agricultural processing; the addition of cement, rubber, steel pipes, engineering, chemicals and oil refining have helped to make Bari the second most important industrial town in the South. Oil imports account for most of the traffic in the port.

Taranto (201,000), Spartan Taras, was founded in the eighth century BC on an island which, with the adjoining peninsula, separates the inner Mare Piccolo from the outer Mare Grande enclosed by the Isole Cheradi. The modern town which has a rectangular layout and was rebuilt after its destruction in the war, occupies much of the peninsula. For nearly a century its main function was that of a naval base but with the decline of this activity it hopes to restore its fortunes in terms of industry. The Italsider full-cycle steel works using American coal and west African ore is the most important development so far.

Brindisi (76,000) where a vast petro-chemical plant (Shell–Montecatini) has recently been established is the third corner of Apulia's triangular 'pole of development'. The town itself lies in the fork between two submerged 'fossil' valleys.

## V[d] *Basilicata*

Basilicata is the Byzantine name for the region which in Roman (and fascist times) was known as Lucania. The modern *regione* stretches westwards from the edge of the Murge across the Lucanian Apennines to the Gulf of Policastro, and southwards from the Ofanto to the Gulf of Taranto. Certainly one of the most isolated and neglected regions of Italy, it consists of three main physical elements – the Lucanian Apennines, the Bradano trench and the small volcanic area of M. Vulture.

The Lucanian Apennines are less of a range than a series of isolated massifs; the dislocation of these highlands is associated with a series of faults the most important of which are orientated NW–SE (Vallo di Diano), while others trend less obviously NE–SW (Platano and upper Basento valleys). The cores of the massifs consist of Triassic limestones (M. Maruggio, M. Volturino, M. Sirino, Sra. Dolcedorme) often dolomitic in character, which emerge boldly through an extensive cover of Oligocene–Eocene clays and sandstones (*flysch*). These in turn are masked locally by Miocene sediments, mainly marls, or by Pliocene sands and clays (*molasse*). The latter are represented in several transverse valleys which were submerged to form straits by the Pliocene sea from which only the higher parts of the Lucanian Apennines emerged as a chain of islands, but they are most extensive in south-eastern Potenza province between the Agri and the Sinni. Their altitude, sometimes over 800m, testifies to the extent of the post-Pliocene uplift. The limestone massifs, most of which exceed 1500m, are of little agricultural value; over most of their surface the destruction of the forest cover of beech and oak has produced a sterile karstic waste suitable for little but sheep grazing, but neighbouring areas reap some benefit from springs issuing from the sides of the massifs (Vallo di Diano). The vast expanses of Tertiary sediments, lying mainly to the east of the massifs, present a dreary landscape of rounded ridges separated by open valleys. Huge tracts are left under scrub and threadbare pasture, and although there are patches of *coltura promiscua* (upper Sinni valley) most of the cultivated area is devoted to wheat. Hill-top villages and the preference of the roads, most of them fantastically tortuous, for the ridges under-line the instability of the clays. In fact the concentration of settlement in sizeable villages, the fragmentation and dispersal of property, and the extensive character of the land-use assign most of this zone to the *latifondo contadino*.

From the point of view of human settlement the second main sub-region of

Basilicata, the Bradano trench, is scarcely more rewarding. A succession of rivers (Bradano, Basento, Cavone, Agri, etc.) have carved the predominantly clayey infilling into a succession of rounded ridges whose unstable flanks are extensively fretted by *calanchi*. Locally, where Pliocene and Quaternary sands and conglomerates have survived, the interfluves assume a tabular form. The debris-filled valley floors, laced with braided channels, are extensively denied the cultivator because of their liability to disastrous flooding. Along the Gulf of Taranto, behind a chaotic barrier of low dunes, the rivers have built up a continuous strip of alluvial flats from which human settlement was banished by malaria for some fifteen hundred years. This strip is now being colonized under the land reform; the Bradano has been dammed to form a large reservoir and the other rivers are being similarly controlled. Many of the new *poderi* are irrigated so that citrus fruit, sugar beet, early vegetables and tobacco can be grown as well as the usual dry Mediterranean crops. The interior uplands of the Bradano trench offer little scope for improvement. Traditionally a *latifondo* stronghold, much of the area is still held in large properties worked from *masserie*.[1] Towards the Murge, however, the dominance of wheat and sheep in the land-use is relieved by arboriculture, particularly where Quaternary sands cover the down-faulted terraces of the western Murge.

The small isolated volcanic zone of M. Vulture (1327m) has much in common with Roccamonfina; it is similarly composed of basaltic lavas and tuffs, is capped by chestnuts and is flanked by vines and tree crops supporting a relatively dense population. An outer rim encloses two small crater lakes.

With the exception of those few more fortunate areas noted above, Basilicata presents the Southern environment at its worst – a hilly or mountainous terrain developed on unstable impermeable rocks whose surface is rapidly wasting away, worn-out soils, a rainfall unreliable and often destructively violent, rivers dry half the year but often raging torrents in winter. With a population density of only 65 per sq km most of Basilicata is overpopulated. The peasantry, concentrated in squalid isolated villages, lacks land, capital and useful work. Emigration overseas is an old tradition here but the internal drift from the land is less marked than in many other Southern regions (between 1951 and 1961 the population fell by only 2·4%). If it were possible to introduce a more rational system of land-use, the majority of Basilicata would be restored to forest leaving only those areas under cultivation which are capable of sustained improvement. To an inadequate degree this is taking place with the drift of population from the uplands and the concentration of activity on the reclaimed coastlands. The problem of rural overpopulation is aggravated by the lack of industrial advantages; agricultural processing and constructional materials were the only sectors represented until recently. The only notable raw material is the gas of the newly developed Ferrandina field; part of its output goes to Bari but part (thanks less to

[1] In 1961 properties of over 50 hectares occupied respectively 50% and 42% of the agricultural and forest land in Matera and Potenza provinces.

economic planning than to the vehemence of local opinion) is used to support a petro-chemical plant at Pisticci. The two largest towns, Potenza (44,000) and Matera (38,000), are administrative and agricultural in function. Until it was rehoused by the *Cassa* a large part of Matera's population lived in cave dwellings cut in the edge of a Cretaceous limestone platform – a fact which was often quoted as a measure of the backwardness of the *Mezzogiorno*.

## V[e] *Calabria*

The landscapes of Calabria are as numerous and varied as those of Apulia and Basilicata are few and monotonously repetitive. This diversity is most attractively displayed along the coastlands where the intimacy of mountain and sea recalls the homeland of the Greek settlers who first colonized the area in the eighth and seventh centuries BC. Thanks to the nature of the relief, the variety of climate is equally striking; on the sparsely populated Sila plateau, where Mediterranean Man was never really at home, the snow may lie for two or three months, while on the coast, particularly the Tyrrhenian coast, the mildness of the winters and the almost complete absence of severe frosts permit the growth of the most sensitive Mediterranean crops.

The northern barrier of Calabria is provided by the last of the Apennine limestone massifs which overlook the Crati lowlands from the Scalone Pass to the Pollino group. With their wooded summits and their sterile karstic flanks they differ little from their more northerly counterparts, but the flourishing oasis along the Cascile valley above Castrovillari is indebted to their springs (pl. xixb).

South of a line joining the Scalone Pass and the mouth of the Crati the relief of Calabria is dominated by two crystalline Hercynian horsts linked by the low isthmus of Catanzaro. Like the limestone massifs further north their summits emerged as islands from the Pliocene sea the sediments of whose bed, subsequently uplifted with the rest of the area, are exposed on the flanks of the horsts. The whole area, continuing into north-east Sicily, is seismically unstable, especially in the fault zone occupied by the Straits of Messina; the earthquakes of 1783 and 1908 were particularly destructive. The most northern of the blocks is unequally divided by the tectonic trench of the upper Crati. To the west lies the Catena Costiera composed very largely of mica-schists, impermeable below but frequently masked by a deep unstable layer of weathered debris. The steep sides of the range have been scored by a succession of torrents (*fiumare*) whose violence is fed by a seasonal and disastrously erratic rainfall averaging over 1800 mm. Along the Tyrrhenian coast these torrents have built a chain of small alluvial plains and detritus cones whose exuberant arboriculture, irrigated where possible, contrasts with the intervening expanses of rock and macchia. The forests of oak and chestnut, often in fine stands, which clothe the main ridge have a vital conservational rôle. On the seaward slope they give way to terraced olives at about 700m but on the opposite side they extend down as far as the dissected Tertiary hills which flank the Crati trench.

The Sila plateau, rising to 1929m in Botte Donato, is composed of granite in the east and of mica-schists in the west and south-west. Its peneplaned surface presents an almost monotonous alternation of rounded summits and wide open

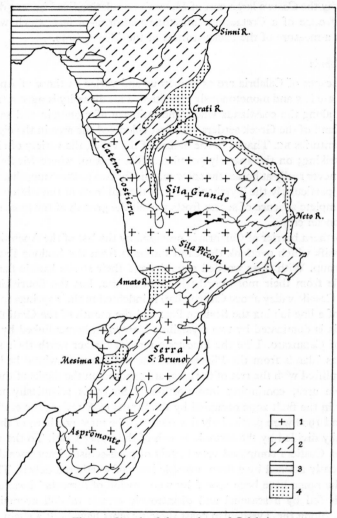

*Fig. 41.* Sketch of the geology of Calabria

1 – Granites, gneisses and schists. 2 – Mainly Neogene clays and sands. 3 – Mesozoic limestones. 4 – Alluvium

valleys whose floors, deeply lined with granitic sands, are often poorly drained. The highest part of the plateau drains to the Neto, three of whose tributaries (the Lese, Arvo and Ampollino) have been dammed to provide power; they have also added to the tourist attractions of the area. Although there are extensive deforested areas whose moorland pastures are grazed by transhumant flocks and herds in summer, the majority of the plateau is still forested with black pines, oak, chestnut and beech. Until recently the permanent population, few in number and concentrated in a handful of villages, was largely dependent on forestry work, but since 1950 the Ente Sila has established a number of agricultural settlements. Rye, potatoes, clover and grass are the crops best suited to the area and milk is the main cash product. The Ente is also developing the tourist trade by providing roads and encouraging investment in accommodation. The western edge of the plateau falls away abruptly to the dissected Pliocene hill country which flanks the eastern side of the Crati valley. The change is clearly reflected in the land-use; woodlands and pastures give place to terraced tree crops worked from a generous sprinkling of hill-top villages. The existence of these hard-won terraces is always at the mercy of freak storms breaking over the Sila and he is a fortunate peasant who has not seen part of his holding washed away at least once in a lifetime. Eastwards the Sila descends more gently into hill country where the crystalline rocks are lost beneath a covering of Tertiary sediments. In Marchesato these are represented by Pliocene clays and marls whose unstable nature have been repeatedly referred to. Marchesato was once the unchallenged domain of *latifondisti* who relied mainly on sheep and extensive wheat production, but since 1950 sizeable areas have been redistributed under the Sila law. This project has shown a higher than average failure rate; inexperience among the settlers is one cause but the environment itself is unfavourable to the small farmer. From Strongoli round to Rossano the rugged coastal hill country is developed on Miocene marls and limestones which are no more promising agriculturally than the Pliocenes; large areas are unstable and remain uncultivated.

The Silan coastlands are much less spectacular than those of the Catena Costiera; for long stretches the hills crowding down to the sea tolerate a narrow lowland strip which widens occasionally into a sizeable alluvial plain. Such areas (the Neto mouth), once malarial, and still repeatedly menaced by floods, are now being won for permanent settlement. Even so the irrigated area along the coast is very restricted.

Reference has already been made to the highly dissected Pliocene hill country flanking both sides of the upper Crati. Its terraced tree crops and *coltura promiscua* support two rows of villages which face each other across the valley at a height of between 300 and 600m. The alluvial floor of the valley, much of it occupied by the braided bed of the Crati and punctuated on either side by detritus fans, is mainly used for cereals rather than tree crops. Locally the fans lend themselves to irrigation. As the valley widens northwards the Pliocene hills fall more gently to form a rolling steppe-like landscape; the higher margins are rich in olives but lower down extensive wheat, fallow and pasture still monopolize the land-use. The alluvial flats of the lower Crati, below which Sybaris and Thurii lie buried, have proved difficult to tame and much remains to be done before the area can be securely resettled.

South of the Catanzaro isthmus the other main Calabrian horst presents a bold high ridge (Le Serre, 1423m) which merges without a break into the dome of Aspromonte (1956m). The ridge is mainly of granite while the dome is predominantly of gneiss; the first retains much of its forest cover but on the middle slopes of Aspromonte deforestation has reduced large areas to heath. The western slopes of the Serre, and, even more obviously, the flanks of Aspromonte, are interrupted by broad erosion terraces. Lower down the crystalline rocks are hidden below Tertiary sediments; in the Gioia lowlands and the Mesima valley these are mostly of clay but above the eastern shore Eocene arenaceous rocks are extensively represented. Although considerable areas, notably in the Mesima valley, remain under cereals, the descent into the peripheral Tertiary hill country usually coincides with a transition from forest to tree crops – olives, figs, vines and stone fruits. In their lower courses many torrents reach the sea in alluvial fans; the river is hopefully confined by massive walls while the rest of the fan, tapped for irrigation water, is utilized in an extremely intensive mixture of arboriculture and horticulture. This is well exemplified on the coast between Scilla and Melito where oranges and lemons are joined by an interesting speciality, the bergamotte, another citrus fruit whose oil is used for fixing perfumes and essences. Climatically it is even more demanding than the lemon; it will tolerate neither frost nor mist.

To an outstanding degree Calabria illustrates the fundamental problem of the *Mezzogiorno*, overpopulation. In the essentially agricultural provinces of Reggio and Catanzaro the population densities in 1961 were 191 and 141 per sq km respectively, and in the coastal huertas the oppressive figure of 800 is sometimes reached. Repeated pulsations of emigration, notably to America before the war of '15 and more recently to northern Italy, Germany and Switzerland, have eased the intolerable burden but while the death rate has declined below the national average the birth rate remains one of the highest in Italy. Between 1951 and 1961 the total population declined by only 2·4% and there seems no alternative to continued emigration. Agriculture offers no solution and it would be difficult to imagine an area with fewer natural advantages for industry than this remote mountainous peninsula. Apart from constructional materials and agricultural processing the only notable industries represented are textiles at Reggio and the chemical works at Crotone which utilizes Silan power.

In common with most of the *Mezzogiorno* a large proportion of the rural population is housed in sizeable villages and small townships which are most numerous between 300 and 600m. In part this distribution reflects the attractiveness of the peripheral Tertiary hills but it also underlines the disadvantages of both the crystalline highlands and of the coastlands, at least until recently. Malaria and insecurity from seaborne attack were certainly major causes of the retreat of population into the hills. In the last century with the establishment of satisfactory communications along the coast this movement has been reversed so that settlements are now found frequently in pairs, one on the coast and one in the hills; the former often bears the latter's name with 'marina' attached (Gioiosa, Marina di Gioiosa). The ancient Greek colony of Locri illustrates this process; it managed to survive until the ninth century but the increasing danger from Saracen raids induced the inhabitants to establish Gerace inland. With the return of more settled times the older settlement has recovered some of its former importance. Another interesting feature of Calabrian settlement is the survival of alien communities which have retained something of their cultural, religious and linguistic identity. In southern Aspromonte the Amendoleo valley is inhabited by people of Greek descent and there are several villages composed of descendants of Albanian refugees who were given asylum when the Turks overran their country (Spezzano Albanese, Vaccarizzo Albanese, Falcanara Albanese).[1]

The three largest towns, all of them provincial capitals, Catanzaro (74,000), Cosenza (79,000) and Reggio (152,000), serve also as market centres for the most productive zones. The train, car and passenger ferries to Messina operate from Reggio and Villa S. Giovanni.

## VI SICILY (SICILIA)

Throughout the 3000 years of its history every power in the Mediterranean has sought to possess this island either for its own sake or for its strategic position at the crossroads of the Inland Sea. In turn Greeks, Carthaginians, Romans, Byzantines, Arabs, Normans, 'French' and Spaniards have occupied it wholly or part; even the British controlled it for a short period during the Napoleonic wars. These successive occupations, several of which can be measured in centuries, have not only contributed to the racial composition and the cultural fabric, but they may be held responsible, at least in part, for certain social traits which are more deeply rooted here than in any other part of Italy. Thus among this fundamentally conservative and insular people, who find it bitterly difficult to reconcile their present miseries with the riches of their cultural heritage, the family has retained its traditional force both as an economic association and as a source of moral strength; indeed, in the eyes of Sicilians the family has proved itself again and again to be the one trustworthy and sympathetic element in a society often indifferent when not actively hostile. It is almost a corollary of this narrow outlook that the Sicilian should have grown to expect little to his benefit from official authority which he tends to regard as something to be circumvented. This trait may be explained in part by the fact that so often in the past authority has been not only oppressive but alien, and even the governments of united Italy have had little success in dispelling this suspicious attitude. Thus life in Sicily tends to be lived on two associated but separate levels and the peasant, from a position of weakness imposed by poverty, hopes to achieve what seems impossible on the official plane by recourse to 'arrangements' contrived by intermediaries,

[1] Similar Albanian communities were established in Apulia immediately to the east of Taranto but the Albanian tongue survives in only one village, S. Marzano.

if possible members of the family, but otherwise powerful patrons or clandestine associations. And yet despite the numerous occupations of the island and the cultural and social influences they exerted, the links which Rome first forged have held, and Sicily has emerged from the centuries Italian, but Italian with a difference, a difference which since 1946 has been recognized in a large measure of regional autonomy.

From the human viewpoint the two outstanding features of the relief and geology of Sicily are firstly the high proportion of the island's area occupied by mountain (25%) and hill country (61%) compared with the low proportion under plains (14%); and secondly the great extent of impermeable rock surfaces, particularly clays, marls and shales.[1] Together these two features combine to encourage rapid runoff and erosion and this is particularly unfortunate in an area with a marked summer drought,[2] intense evaporation for most of the year, and less than 6% of its surface under woodland. Some 40% of the island is classified as 'liable to frequent landslips' and all the rivers are torrential in regime, very few of them managing to survive the summer even as a trickle. The Simeto and Alcantara, which benefit from the high rainfall and snow-melt of the Caronie (Nebrodi) mountains and from springs issuing from the permeable base of Etna, are exceptionally fortunate; the average discharge of the Simeto varies between 1 cubic metre per second in August and 40 c.m.s in January but in periods of flood it has been known to discharge 2300 c.m.s.

The sweep of the Apennines continues along the north of Sicily in the Monti Peloritani, Nebrodi and Madonie which provide a simple watershed between the short steep torrents flowing to the Tyrrhenian and the much longer rivers flowing to the Ionian and 'African' coasts. These mountain groups, which everywhere fall short of 2000m, formed islands in the Pliocene sea below which the rest of Sicily was submerged. The Mti Peloritani are composed of granite, gneiss and mica-schist, like Aspromente across the straits, but they lack the broad erosion terraces of the Calabrian massif. These crystalline rocks are deeply fissured and their surface has disintegrated to a considerable depth so that to a large extent they are permeable in character; unfortunately this advantage has to be offset against the instability of the slopes. The mountains themselves are clothed more in heath than in forest and are of little agricultural value. That part of the range known as the Caronie and Madonie, which is largely composed of impermeable clays, sandstones and shales (*argille scagliose*) of Eocene–Oligocene age, resembles the Tusco–Emilian Apennines in its structure, lithology and landforms. The flanks of the range are deeply incised and are often ruinously unstable, but the summits, despite their height, are rounded and unspectacular. By contrast the Triassic limestones, which form the highest part of the Madonie (M. S. Salva-

---

[1] About 27% of the island's surface is classed as permeable and between 43 and 53% as impermeable, according to the criteria adopted.
[2] Palermo, Syracuse and Catania enjoy respectively 2200, 2409 and 2558 hours of sunshine annually.

tore, 1910m) and emerge abruptly from the less resistant Tertiaries, introduce a harsher note into the morphology. Deforestation has spared only the highest areas, mainly on the limestones and sandstones, and what 'woodland' there is has been largely reduced to coppice. Cultivation descends extensively as far as 1200m, and particularly on the southern flank, which rolls down interminably towards the centre of the island, the landscape has all the features of the *Mezzogiorno nudo* – low-grade wheat alternating with fallows and rough pasture, isolated *masserie*, and large hill-top villages spaced at infrequent intervals. West of the Torto river, whose valley carries the main transverse railway route, the range degenerates into a series of isolated massifs composed of Triassic dolomite and limestone (M. Grifone, M. Signora, M. Sparagio); their sterile surfaces rarely carry more than scrub. They have, however, a useful function as reservoirs of spring water, but even in this respect they are disappointing because their flanks are extensively enveloped by impermeable Tertiary rocks.

The densely populated coastlands of northern Sicily from Taormina to Trapani present an alternation of narrow alluvial plains and rocky spurs which often leave little space for communications. The plains at the foot of the Mti Peloritani (like those of southern Calabria) are frequently no more than extensive detritus fans whose subterranean waters are tapped by wells and tunnels for irrigation; west of Bagheria the limestone massifs crowd down to the sea to form bold headlands and the coastal lowlands are provided by low marine terraces covered with calcareous sands and conglomerates of Quaternary age. In their land-use and the intensity of their cultivation the north Sicilian coastlands resemble those of south-western Calabria. The lower hills are terraced for olives, vines and figs, and the plains, wherever water is available, are exploited for oranges, lemons, medlar fruits, and market-garden crops. The citrus groves, such as those of Bagheria and the Conca d'Oro, are regarded as particularly valuable not only for their high cash return but because they engage the peasant's time profitably for most of the year. On the plain of Castellammare and some of the other marine terraces there is so far little irrigation and the land-use is dominated by vines and olives. Everywhere the density of population is oppressive and although property is more widely distributed here than in most of Sicily, the degree of fragmentation is inevitably excessive.

The majestic pile of Etna (3263m) had its origin in a shallow gulf towards the end of the Pliocene and has been active ever since. In summer, when the snows have disappeared, the mountain above 2000m presents a black infernal landscape of loose ash and tortured lava pock-marked by over 200 large parasitic ash cones. To the east an awe-inspiring chasm, the Val di Bove, reveals a huge, steep-sided caldera, and scores of lava flows, many of them originating in the flanks of the mountain, radiate in all directions; one of these destroyed Catania in 1669. As one descends, tufty grasses and cushion-like plants colonize the ash; at about 1500m pines, beech and chestnut share the land with broom and pistaccio, and here and there Man has begun his colonizing work, building terraces and planting

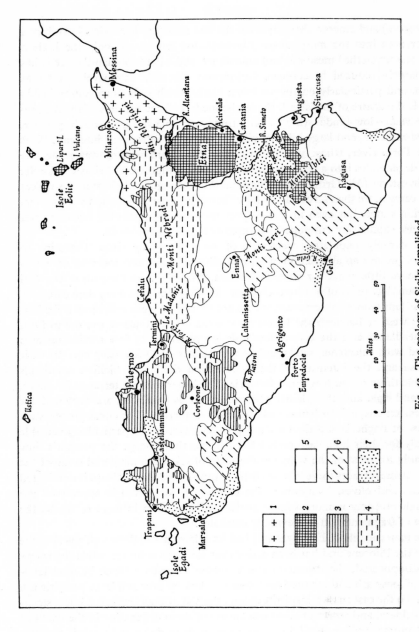

*Fig. 42.* The geology of Sicily simplified

1 – Ancient crystalline rocks. 2 – Volcanic rocks. 3 – Mesozoic limestones. 4 – Eocene conglomerates, sandstones, etc. 5 – Miocene marls, clays and limestones. 6 – Pliocene clays and sands. 7 – Quaternary deposits and recent alluvium

fruit trees where soil has accumulated in pockets of the chaotic terrain (pl. xxiiia). Below 1000m, except where lava flows have left a broad sterile swathe, cultivation is continuous. Vines, occupying much of the higher areas, are succeeded below by almonds, figs, stone fruits, olives and market-garden crops. Lower still the proverbially fertile basaltic soils are irrigated from springs issuing from the tortuous interbedding of ash and lava. The citrus groves along the coast between Giarre and Catania, some of them no more than gardens hemmed in by tongues of lava, are particularly valuable. Another belt of citrus stretches along the middle Simeto valley which benefits from the spring line along the junction of the volcanic rocks and the uplifted Quaternary sea bed. Unfortunately the crescent of intensive peasant cultivation occupying the lower southern skirt of the mountain from Adrano to Giarre is obliged to support a density of rural population which sometimes exceeds 800 per sq km, and although the land is mainly in the hands of those who work it, the average holding is desperately small, rarely more than 2 hectares.

The hilly interior of Sicily, wedged between the Apennines and the 'African' shore, presents a brutal contrast with the perennially exuberant 'huertas' described above; this is attributable in part to the climate with its long summer droughts, intense evaporation and low, fickle rainfall, and in part to the peculiarities of the lithology. Much of the area is surfaced by saline Miocene clays, occasionally varied by conglomerates and sandstones, and the erosion of these essentially impermeable rocks has produced a rolling sea of rounded hills and ridges separated by wide, open valleys. In spring this vast cultural steppe is green with young wheat relieved here and there by magenta strips of sulla, the commonest fodder crop; in summer it is a desert of stubble and fallow grazed by sheep. The aridity of the climate and the tendency of the clays to bake out and fissure discourage tree crops, but there is usually a sprinkling of them round the widely spaced hill-top towns in which most of the population is concentrated. In this traditional stronghold of *latifondi* the majority of the land is still held in large properties worked by hired labour and sharecroppers, but for some decades there has been a steady increase in smallholdings in the immediate vicinity of the towns and villages. Unfortunately these peasant holdings are only marginally more productive than the *latifondi*, so small are the cultivators' resources and so daunting are the physical conditions. In fact, in this desolate interior zone there seems to be no practical alternative to some form of extensive cereal–pastoral economy; any attempt to create a mass of *poderi* to replace the present large units would be desperately expensive and would almost certainly prove a failure.

In much of Agrigento and Caltanissetta provinces the Miocene clays are overlain by sulphur-bearing marls and chalks, also of Miocene age, but the land-use and the landscape are different only in degree; the mining of lens-shaped sulphur deposits employs some 3000 men who are housed in settlements no less squalid than the agricultural villages. In the west the dominance of the clays is interrupted by rugged platforms of Triassic limestone (Rocca Busambra, M. Rose,

M. Cammarata); they are even more unrewarding than the clays through which they emerge and the towns on their edges (e.g. Corleone) are often quoted to illustrate the Sicilian socio-economic environment at its worst. The south-east of the island, rising to nearly 1000m in the Mti Iblei, is composed of almost horizontal Miocene limestones which present a succession of tablelands descending by steps to the sea. These platforms are deeply incised by rivers some of which (e.g. the Anapo) are slightly less irregular in regime than most Sicilian rivers. Their waters are used for irrigation, notably in the citrus groves of Syracuse. The upper calcareous tablelands are extensively lacking in soil, but the lower peripheral platforms, especially where Quaternary marine sediments have survived, are used for wheat and dry tree crops. The coastal lowlands south of Syracuse carry a surprisingly high rural population density, often over 200 per sq km. In the north of the Mti Iblei the Miocene limestones are intercalated with and are overlain by basaltic ash and lava of contemporary age. Detritus derived from these volcanic rocks contributes to the fertility of the Lentini area whose citrus groves rely mainly on well water.

The Pliocene sediments of Sicily, which occupy large areas to the north-west and south of Caltagirone, are mainly conglomerates and sands; they produce a more active relief than the clays. They are also more amenable to cultivation and although the higher areas of the Mti Erei differ little from the rest of central Sicily in land-use, the lowlands, for example near Vittoria, produce a variety of crops including vines, olives, almonds and tomatoes.

Along the southern shore of Sicily, low cliffs alternate with dune-fringed alluvial plains the largest of which extends on either side of Gela, but between Sciacca and Trapani a series of broad marine platforms may be identified. They are covered with calcareous sands and conglomerates (Quaternary) and they support the biggest concentration of viticulture in the island. This is the home of Marsala, a fortified wine, somewhat similar to port, which was first introduced to a wider market at the time of the British occupation during the Napoleonic wars. Although the process has not gone so far as in the Murge, the peasantry here is also gaining possession of the land and using it more intensively; this has been accompanied by a dispersal of settlement. Near Trapani, one of several ports interested in tunny fishing, the coastal flats have been converted into salt pans.

The only large alluvial plain in Sicily is that of Catania, once notoriously unhealthy and still proving difficult to exploit. Its erratic rivers are being controlled by the *Cassa* and limited areas have been diversified for tree crops, tomatoes, artichokes and sugar beet, but most of it retains its extensive character.

Within the Italian agricultural economy as a whole Sicily is mainly significant for its oranges (60%) and lemons (90%); it is also a notable producer of wine (15%), olive oil (10%), almonds, wheat and vegetables (artichokes, fennel, early potatoes). The wheat is almost all of the hard variety used for making pasta and although one expects a lower return with this type, yields are very low indeed. The physical conditions discourage animal rearing but sheep fit well enough into the economy of the extensively cultivated areas. It is indicative of the primitive conditions in much of the island that it possesses one-quarter of the country's mules and donkeys. Directly or indirectly the vast majority of Sicily's 4,631,000 people are dependent on agriculture. It will have become clear from the regional treatment above that both the intensive and extensive agricultural zones are desperately overpopulated; within the former the opportunities for further intensification or an extension of the profitably cultivable area are limited; in the extensive zones the expense involved in achieving greater production is often prohibitive and in many areas improvements are practically vetoed by the physical conditions. The most promising areas for development, as in the rest of Mediterranean Italy, are the alluvial plains where until recently the twin problems of malaria and water control have prevented their proper exploitation. In 1946 the irrigated area, mainly in the coastal 'huertas', amounted to 90,000 hectares; the regional land reform authority (ERAS) is engaged in doubling this figure, notably in the Catania plain (Simeto and Dittaino rivers, 30,000 ha), in the Gela plain (Dissueri river, 1500 ha intensively and 4700 ha intermittently) and in the Menfi plain (Carbo and Belice rivers, 7000 ha). Not without considerable political interference, ERAS has appropriated some 75,000 hectares and assigned them to 17,000 peasant families. This development, for which neither the physical conditions nor the prevailing social milieu were particularly auspicious, has been criticized for the small size of the units and the great expense involved in creating them.

The demographic situation in Sicily is a familiar one – a high birth rate (22·1‰); a low death rate (8·8‰); a relentless natural increase (13·3‰); and a long tradition of emigration at one time orientated towards America and now principally towards northern Italy, France, Germany and Switzerland; and yet the total population between 1951 and 1961 increased by 200,000. For a long time massive emigration seems unavoidable; agriculture has little to offer towards a solution and the contribution of industry is likely to be marginal. Apart from agricultural produce, Sicily's main raw materials are chemicals and oil. Sulphur, salt and gypsum have been mined for well over a century in the Miocene rocks of the Caltanissetta zone; the potash mining at S. Cataldo and Lercara is a post-war development. Fertilizers and other chemicals based on these materials are manufactured at Licata and Porto Empedocle. Oil was discovered in 1954 at Ragusa (Gulf Italia), still the main field, and later at Gela (AGIP). It is poor in quality (sulphurous and asphaltic) and hopes of an expanding production, still only 2,000,000 tons (1964), have proved illusory, but the discovery encouraged international oil concerns to establish a very large refining and petro-chemical complex in the Augusta–Priolo zone and ENI has since built a similar plant at Gela. Both developments are overwhelmingly dependent on imported Middle East crude.

Outside the chemical and petro-chemical fields, industrial progress has been hindered by the limited local market, by a lack of specialized skills and by the difficulty of attracting investment into this rather remote region, despite incentives offered by the regional authority which has also established industrial estates with the basic facilities at Palermo, Catania, Messina, Syracuse, Trapani and Porto Empedocle. Agricultural processing, constructional materials, building, textiles and metal working are the largest users of labour but a high proportion of 'industrial' workers are still employed in traditional craft units. There are three surprisingly large cities whose size cannot be easily explained in terms of their manufacturing and commercial activities. Palermo (592,000), overshadowed by M. Pellegrino and surrounded by the fertile Conca d'Oro, was originally a Carthaginian settlement which much later became the main centre of Arab[1] and Norman power. Since it became the regional capital in 1946 its baroque heritage has been challenged by an impressive rash of modern buildings. It has regular sailings to Naples and Genoa and one of its main functions is to market, process and ship agricultural produce, but its only outstanding large-scale industry is ship repairing. Catania (362,000) is the main port and business and manufacturing centre (food, chemicals, metal goods, sanitary ware) for the east coast – the island's most rapidly developing zone. Messina (257,000), rebuilt since 1908, provides the ferry link with Reggio and Villa S. Giovanni; a bridge across the straits, which it is hoped will break down Sicily's isolation, is planned for the near future. Syracuse (89,000), once one of the most powerful cities of the Hellenic world, is benefiting from the petro-chemical developments immediately to the north of it.

Sicily has been a tourist area since its 'discovery' by classical enthusiasts in the nineteenth century and the development of air communications (to Palermo and Catania) is bringing the island more and more within the range of the millions who make the annual migration to the Mediterranean in search of the sun.

## VII SARDINIA (SARDEGNA)

Until recently Sardinia was regarded almost as a colonial area; in Roman times it was a place of exile and even today the official posted to the island feels justified in accepting the commiserations of his colleagues. Sardinia (24,089 sq kms) and Sicily (25,708 sq km), although roughly equal in size, are otherwise markedly different. Despite a very much greater loss by emigration over the last century, Sicily's population is three and a half times that of Sardinia. No doubt this reflects in part the cumulative effect of malaria in damping down the Sardinian natural increase over the centuries since the relative death rates, birth rates and natural increase are now very similar in the two islands. It also suggests that the physical conditions in Sicily, if not more favourable in all respects, have so far lent themselves more easily to exploitation; Sardinia, for example, has few

[1] The Arabs and Berbers settled mainly in the west of the island (Val di Magora); they founded few new settlements but have left numerous traces of their occupation in place-names, e.g. Misilmiri, Marsala, Caltabellotta.

'huertas' comparable with those of Sicily's north and east coasts, and vastly more of its surface is classed as woodland, pasture and waste. Both islands have had their share of invaders but Sardinia seems to have been less deeply affected both ethnically and culturally. Certainly there have been immigrant groups some of which have left a permanent mark; the influence of Catalans and Ligurians, for example, is traceable in the dialects respectively of Alghero and the extreme south-west, and the reclaimed zone of Arborea was settled by Venetians as late as the thirties, but in general the influence of newcomers did not easily penetrate the isolated pastoral groups for whom the mountainous and wooded interior provided a refuge.[1] In fact it seems likely that the racial make-up has changed little since Roman times. Sardinia has also played a less important strategic rôle than Sicily and the unattractiveness of its interior discouraged those invaders who, unlike the Romans, were content with a limited objective short of complete conquest, such as the establishment of a victualling point or a trading post or the exploitation of easily accessible minerals. As long as piracy remained unchecked and malaria unconquered even the coastlands were repellent and until recently Sardinia has tended to be introspective as well as insular.

The physical geography of Sardinia too has little in common with that of Sicily or with most of peninsular Italy for that matter. The majority of its surface is composed of crystalline rocks, and although generally considered to be the product of Hercynian earth-movements, Sardinia bears evidence of Caledonian folding in the Cambrian sediments of Iglesiente and the whole island suffered from severe fracturing, accompanied by vulcanicity, during the Alpine orogenesis. Three ancient massifs may be identified; the first, La Nurra, forming the north-west corner of the island from Cape Caccia to Asinara Island, has a foundation of granite and gneiss partially overlain by Silurian schists and Mesozoic limestones. Rocky, arid and wind-swept, much of La Nurra is covered with dwarf palm macchia, but in the east, roughly on an axis from Porto Torres to Alghero, the block is concealed by alluvium which is capable of being pressed into cultivation. A pre-war settlement scheme centred on Fertilia had little success, but a more ambitious project, involving irrigation based on the meagre resources of local streams, has been undertaken by ETFAS.[2] Even so La Nurra is chiefly significant for its minerals (iron, lead, zinc) which are shipped to the mainland from Porto Torres; unfortunately the lead–zinc deposits are nearing exhaustion.

The second ancient massif, Iglesiente, lying to the south-west of the Campidano rift valley, is much higher than La Nurra but is structurally very similar. A wide tectonic trench drained by the Cixerri river bisects the massif and provides access to Sardinia's most important mineralized zone. Ores containing lead, zinc and silver are mined and processed near Iglesias, and Tertiary lignite

---

[1] The dialect of the Nuoro area is said to be much closer to its Latin roots than is modern Italian.
[2] *Ente di Trasformazione Fondiaria e Agraria della Sardegna.*

(approx. 1 million tons), now used mostly for thermal electricity, is mined in the Sulcis area. The foundation of Carbonia (30,000) and the sizeable investment in the mines which support it were prompted by the autarchic policies of the thirties when the Italian fuel position was very different; economically the development is now something of an embarrassment. The alluvial plain of Palmas (south of Carbonia) is farmed and part of it is irrigated but the vast majority of Iglesiente, with its rocky, macchia-covered slopes, frequently scarred by spoil heaps, is good for little more than sheep grazing.

The third and largest of the crystalline massifs, rising to 1834m in Gennargentu, occupies the eastern half of the island. Except for the alluvial flats of the Olbia ria, Gallura is overwhelmingly composed of granite. Only the rugged Limbara range is really mountainous; elsewhere the relief is a chaos of hills whose flanks are strewn with rounded boulders half buried in aprons of coarse detritus. The naked rock shows through extensively to present smooth, exfoliated, convex brows and kopje-like summits. The suggestion of having strayed into an African landscape is heightened by the parkland of cork oaks, interrupted here and there by dense macchia thickets, which occupies the detritus spreads of the lowlands. The influence of persistent winds (especially the *maestrale*) is apparent in the tortured shapes of the trees, and on the coastlands the wind combines with the meagre rainfall and repeated overgrazing to degrade the vegetation into low macchia or even to steppe.[1] The ria coastline and the barren Maddalena Islands, which once sheltered Nelson's ships and provided Garibaldi with a home, are perhaps the main attractions of Gallura.

Southwards from Gallura the fragmented character of the relief is replaced by continuous rolling plateaus and rounded ridges in whose outlines the remnants of several erosion surfaces have been identified. Over large areas, notably in the mountains of Gennargentu, the granites are overlain with coarse mica-schists without introducing any obvious variation into the morphology. A much more fundamental change occurs in M. Albo and in the Mti di Oliena (in the hinterland of the Gulf of Orosei) where residual platforms of Cretaceous limestone produce a landscape of tabular *causses* locally edged by steep scarps. Similar calcareous platforms occur south of Gennargentu where the schists themselves have been peneplaned into a vast tableland into which the rivers, including the Flumendosa system, have etched themselves deeply on their way to an inhospitable and faulted coastline.

Although there is no lack of minor variations in the land-use of the eastern Sardinian massif, the dominant theme is almost everywhere provided by vast expanses of open cork forest and macchia, varied by chestnut and beech in the very high areas and replaced by scrub and garrigue on the coastlands. There are one or two small irrigated zones on the coast, notably at the mouth of the Flumendosa and on the Tortoli plain (which also depends on the Flumendosa for its water), but in general the economy is essentially a pastoral one in which

---

[1] The wind is also invoked to explain the curious undercut rocks known as *tafoni*.

224

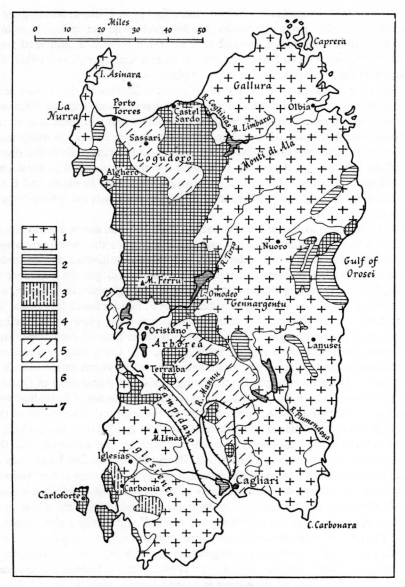

*Fig. 43.* The geology of Sardinia simplified

1 – Ancient Hercynian horsts. 2 – Mesozoic limestones. 3 – Eocene rocks. 4 – Volcanic rocks. 5 – Miocene marls, clays, etc. 6 – Quaternary deposits and recent alluvium.
7 – Conduits and aqueducts

transhumance to the lowlands still has a part. Except in Gallura, where there is some dispersal, the sparse population (Nuoro province 40 per sq km) is mainly concentrated in small villages round each of which there is a cultivated zone (hard wheat, oats, vines). Nuoro (23,000), the provincial capital, and Olbia, the packet port for Civitavecchia, are the only places of any size.

Except for an extensive exposure of Miocene sediments in the Sassari area, most of north-western Sardinia is developed on basaltic and trachytic lavas and tuffs of Tertiary age. The higher relief is generally tabular in form (e.g. to the north of Bosa) but in the M. Ferru area it becomes more chaotic. Sizeable areas are devoted to extensive wheat, with long fallows, and to vines, olives and plums round the infrequent villages, but in general the area is mainly a pastoral one. The Miocene limestone zone of Sassari, which specializes in olives and has a number of small irrigated patches, is by Sardinian standards exceptionally productive.

The Campidano lowlands are approached from the east across a wide belt of Tertiary sediments, Miocene chalks and sandy marls for the most part, whose undulating hills, completely deforested, are mainly cultivated for extensive cereals with patches of vines and tree crops near the villages. In a number of places, the gently rolling outlines, parched and glaring white in summer, are abruptly interrupted by the steep columnar sides of tabular basalt lava flows. To judge from the *nuraghi*[1] posted round their edges, these *giare* offered refuge regions for a pastoral people. Scrub and pasture cover most of their upper surfaces with here and there a shallow marshy lake. The Campidano is a tectonic trench, alluvial and once marshy at its northern and southern extremities, but elsewhere surfaced by very gently undulating sands and coarse wash of Quaternary age; on its eastern margin these latter deposits are arranged in shallow terraces but on the Iglesiente side detritus fans are more typical. The aridity of the Campidano is almost African; the effectiveness of the rainfall (600 mm), which is scanty, seasonal and unreliable, is much reduced by the *maestrale* and the *scirocco* as well as by prolonged insolation. Except in the two low-lying areas at either end, it presents a steppe-like landscape whose lack of trees is emphasized, rather than relieved by occasional screens of eucalypts. This is a *latifondo* zone only in the sense that its land-use is dominated by extensive hard wheat production; the majority of the area is worked in small and medium-sized peasant units. The need to accommodate sheep, both local and migrant, has favoured the retention of traditional collective arrangements whereby large tracts of the village lands are cultivated in blocks while the rest is under fallow. Gradually, however, a more diversified form of cultivation is being adopted, with beans and forage crops replacing the fallow; the vine acreage is also being extended and where water is available small patches of citrus have been established (Villacidro). This trend towards a more intensive form of agriculture has made some progress in the

---

[1] *Nuraghi*, of which there are some 3000 in the island, are neolithic peel towers of the shape of an English windmill.

immediate hinterland of Cagliari where well water is available, but the conditions were most propitious in the formerly alluvial marshland (Stagno di Oristano) lying between Oristano and Terralba. Here, in the thirties, some 20,000 hectares were reclaimed and irrigated with water made available by the control of the Tirso. The settlers, working 12-hectare holdings on a *mezzadria* basis, were mainly Venetians who could be relied upon to maintain the necessary precautions against malaria. With its rectangular fields of wheat, maize, lucerne, rice, sugar beet and fruit this Bonifica di Arborea might be mistaken for part of Romagna. Since 1954 the area has come under the wing of ETFAS and the *mezzadri* are now buying their farms like other beneficiaries of the land reform.

The importance of water control in Italy has been repeatedly emphasized; it is a particularly vital matter in Sardinia, not only because with its low and fickle rainfall, water for domestic, power and irrigation purposes is everywhere at a premium, but because the absence of control perpetuated malaria, a scourge which for centuries struck down and debilitated the population and denied it much potentially valuable land. For climatic reasons the rivers are unavoidably torrential in regime but their vicious habits are encouraged by the high proportion of impermeable rock surfaces and by the extent of deforestation. Between the wars various control schemes, originally inspired by the engineer whose name is remembered in Lake Omodeo, were put into operation. On the Tirso two power dams were built, the upper one forming Lake Omodeo, the lower one a lake immediately downstream; a third barrage still lower down provides irrigation water for the Arborea reclaimed zone which also receives supplies from reservoirs on the Mogoro. There is some conflict of interest between power and irrigation in the use of the Tirso's water; the demand for power in winter cannot be fully met unless the supplies for irrigation are limited. This situation has necessitated a power link with the Coghinas hydro-electric scheme. On the Flumendosa a dam was built pre-war on the upper reaches, partly to provide power and partly to supply irrigation water for the Tortoli area, but the full potentialities of the Flumendosa system are only now being realized under a scheme financed by the *Cassa*. Reservoirs have been constructed on the middle Flumendosa and its two tributaries, the Flumeniddu and the Mulargia; these reservoirs are connected by conduits and the water is directed through a ten-mile tunnel, with power stations at either end, to the Campidano where it is used in part to supply Cagliari and other towns, and in part for irrigation. The scheme is capable of producing some 145,000 kWh and eventually some 50,000 hectares of the Campidano will be irrigated. The chances of success for these encouraging developments in water control have been improved by what is probably the most significant event in Sardinia's history – the virtual elimination of malaria (at least for the present) as a result of an insecticide spraying campaign begun in 1947 with American financial aid.

The regional land reform authority (ETFAS), whose jurisdiction embraces the whole of the island, was fortunate in being able to take over a number of prewar settlement schemes totalling some 53,000 hectares and adapt them to its purposes; in addition 48,000 hectares were appropriated under the *stralcio* law. In all 3000 *poderi* and 700 *quote* have been created. The variable quality of the land available is reflected in the sizes of the *poderi*; some are only 5 hectares while in mountain land 50 may be needed to provide a viable holding. Inevitably the main effort is in the Campidano but evidence of ETFAS's activity can be seen in most parts of the island.

Although the vast majority of Sardinians are dependent on the land, the island makes only a very small contribution to Italy's total agricultural production and exports. It is a significant producer of cork, wool and sheep cheese, but it normally accounts for only about 4% of Italy's wine and 2% of her oil; in good years there is a modest export of wheat to the mainland for pasta making. The main features of the land-use are summarized in the table below; in interpreting

TABLE I

THE RELIEF ZONES AND LAND-USE IN SARDINIA AND SICILY

|  |  | Sicily | Sardinia |
|---|---|---|---|
| Total area (hectares) | | 2,570,785 | 2,408,934 |
| Percentage mountain | | 24·6 | 13·7 |
| ,, | hill | 61·3 | 67·9 |
| ,, | plain | 14·1 | 18·1 |
| Percentage cereals | | 26·4 | 9·6 |
| ,, | forage crops | 9·1 | 2·2 |
| ,, | other rotated crops | 21·3 | 20·0 |
| ,, | tree crops | 22·7 | 4·0 |
| ,, | permanent pasture | 9·7 | 39·8 |
| ,, | woodland | 5·1 | 13·3 |
| ,, | fallow | 1·7 | 6·7 |
| ,, | other uses | 5·7 | 4·4 |

it it should be borne in mind that permanent pasture in Sardinia usually means garrigue or steppe where there is insufficient soil for even the most meagre crop; that the yields are low in the cultivated area and methods are still primitive; and that much of the land classed as woodland is little better than scrub.

The low overall density of population (59 per sq km) tends to obscure the state of rural overpopulation which exists in much of the island; emigration to the 'mainland' and overseas (recently to Australia) has long been a tradition. No doubt the many projects undertaken since the war will make a real contribution but there is obviously a limit to what can be achieved along these lines. Unfortunately Sardinia's industrial prospects are not outstanding; its hydro-electric resources are really quite small (1% of Italy's capacity) and the lignite of Sulcis is an expensive source of energy. Water is everywhere a problem, and although Sardinia is Italy's most important mineral region, it is indicative of the island's colonial status that the majority of the output is processed and used on the mainland. Apart from lignite the most notable items are lead, zinc and silver (Iglesiente and La Nurra), and iron from La Nurra and S. Leone (north of Cagliari). Other useful minerals produced in small quantities are antimony, arsenic, barytes, kaolin, copper, manganese, fluorite, bauxite and salt from pans. In all about 20,000 miners are employed. Cement and chemicals near Cagliari are the most important additions to the traditional industries – agricultural processing, mineral concentration and handicrafts (e.g. baskets and blankets).

Cagliari (190,000), sited on a limestone promontory and flanked by lagoons, now largely converted to salt pans, is the regional capital and the main port, with regular sailings to Naples and Palermo. Its economy has benefited from investment in the island's development projects. Cagliari shares an interest with Porto Torres and Olbia in tunny fishing which takes place mainly off the west coast. The shoals, which arrive in early May, tend to follow regular tracks and they are funnelled by miles of curtain netting into a box-like net chamber. Once trapped in this cul-de-sac they are forced to the surface as the net is raised within a rectangle of barge-like boats. There, amid the churning of blood-stained foam, the slaughter takes place.

Sassari (80,000) is a provincial centre and a university town. So far it has few industries apart from olive oil processing, but it is hoped to build up an industrial nucleus in the Sassari–Porto Torres area taking advantage of the latter's connections with Liguria. In fact many of the island's enterprises, including the tunny-fishing industry, are already controlled from Liguria. In recent years Sardinia has become popular with the international tourist and large sums have been expended on roads (coaches are easily the best means of public transport) and on hotel accommodation. There are efficient packet services to the mainland and the airports of Cagliari and Alghero are used by international as well as internal airlines.

# PART IV

## Economic Geography

TABLE 2

| De facto population. Present frontiers | | Population per sq km | Live birth rate per 1000 | Death rate per 1000 | Per cent aged 15–50 | Excess births over deaths |
|---|---|---|---|---|---|---|
| 1901 | 33,370,000 | 112 | 32·5 | 22·0 | 47 | 343,000 |
| 1911 | 35,695,000 | 123 | 31·5 | 21·4 | 47 | 351,000 |
| 1921 | 37,404,000 | 126 | 30·7 | 17·7 | 50 | 493,000 |
| 1931 | 40,582,000 | 136 | 24·9 | 14·8 | 50 | 417,000 |
| 1941 | 44,357,000 | 148 | 20·9 | 13·9 | NA | 316,000 |
| 1951 | 47,032,000 | 158 | 18·5 | 10·3 | 52 | 379,000 |
| 1961 | 50,624,000 | 168 | 18·4 | 9·3 | 50 | 461,000 |

The economic geography of Italy is overshadowed by the demographic situation some of whose salient features are summarized in figs. 44, 45 and 46. Since the turn of the century, with the exception of a year or two during the First and Second World Wars, there has been a substantial annual increase, rarely falling below 350,000. The downward trend in the birth rate seems to be levelling off and any substantial drop will depend on the speed, no doubt a very slow one, with which the rest of the country accepts the social attitudes of the industrial North. At the same time the birth rate will receive support from the age structure of the population, one of whose features is the large proportion of women of child-bearing age. Furthermore, the effect on the natural increase of any eventual fall in the birth rate is likely to be substantially offset by a decline in the death rate, particularly among infants.[1] Unless some radical change occurs in the social outlook of the mass of Italians, a large annual increase seems certain for a long time to come. Unfortunately the most rapid increase will continue to occur in those areas which are least able to support it, namely the South and Islands. Until the boom years began to erode it the figure of two million officially unemployed was considered normal; and this took no account of widespread redundancy in industry and massive under-employment in agriculture. It will have been obvious from the regional accounts that agriculture has little to offer towards a solution; only continued emigration and further industrialization, especially for export, can make a significant contribution. Among young people seeking their first job those with technical skills and qualifications, provided they are prepared to move if necessary, can usually find worthwhile employment, but competition for 'white-collar' jobs among the non-technically educated is still fierce. For such people, many of them graduates in law and letters, an inflated but underpaid and generally inefficient bureaucracy has provided the traditional outlet. Particularly unfortunate is the lot of those who, because of family circumstances, are unable to continue with their schooling and are thrust on to the

[1] 151 infants per 1000 live births died in their first year in 1911, in 1963 only 40.

labour market without skills and barely the rudiments of education. This waste of potentially productive manpower is now at last receiving serious attention.

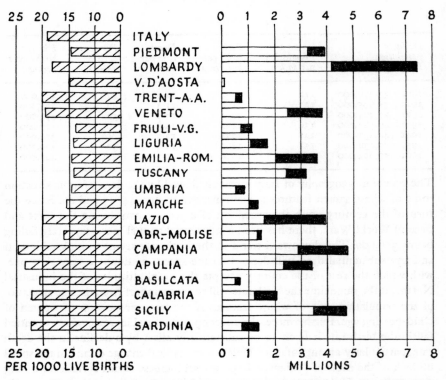

*Fig. 44.* Birth rates per 1000 live births by provinces 1961 (left); and increase (black) in population totals by provinces between 1901 and 1961 (right)

## EMIGRATION AND INTERNAL MIGRATION

Emigration in Italy is a long-established tradition. Since the Middle Ages, Italians had sold their skill throughout Europe as merchants, bankers, mercenaries, craftsmen and artists, but until the nineteenth century, always as individuals. The new movement, which first began to reach substantial proportions about 1880, was a mass one and, apart from the compelling economic circumstances, there was in it an element of gregarious imitation. Between 1901 and 1913, about 600,000 people emigrated each year; in 1913, the peak year, the figure rose to 872,000, of which 313,000 went to European countries, mainly France, Switzerland and Austria–Hungary, and the rest overseas, USA and Argentina taking the vast majority. Of the migrants to European countries the majority went on a temporary basis and eventually returned home; even so, the net emigration for

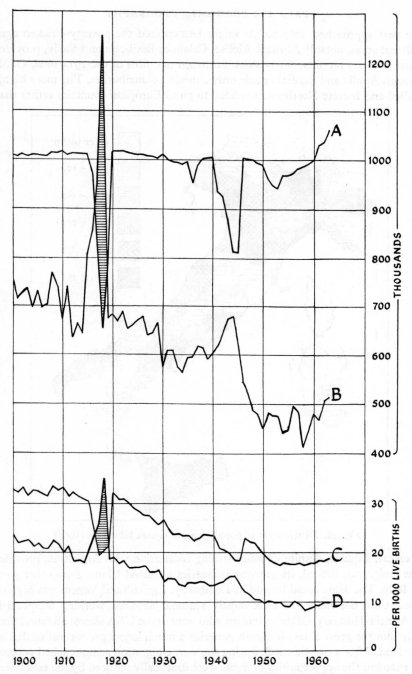

*Fig. 45.* Total births (A) and deaths (B), and birth rates (C) and death rates (D) 1900–1963

the year approached 500,000. As might be expected the poverty-stricken agricultural areas, notably Abruzzi–Molise, Calabria, Basilicata and Sicily, provided most overseas recruits. Sicily alone furnished one-fifth of the 1913 total. Oddly enough Apulia and Sardinia made only a modest contribution. The more highly skilled and literate Northerners tended to go to European countries rather than

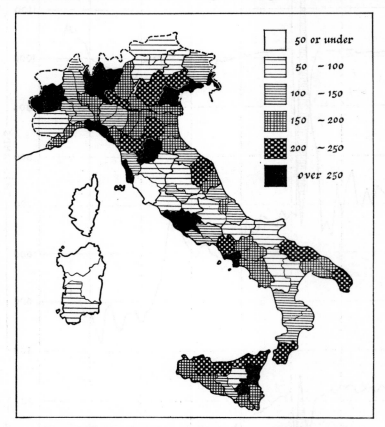

*Fig. 46.* Distribution of population per square kilometre (1961)

overseas. Liguria, despite its longstanding connection with Argentina, provided few emigrants, indeed, its growing industries attracted labour from other parts of Italy. The same could be said of Lombardy. Agricultural Veneto was high on the list but her emigrants were mostly seasonal labourers working temporarily in Austria–Hungary. Of those Italians who went to the USA almost all found their way into the great cities; in South America a much larger proportion settled on the land. After a drastic check during the war, emigration again reached 600,000 in 1920 but the opportunities overseas were drastically reduced by the enactment of new immigration legislation, particularly in the USA, where a quota system was introduced based on the proportion of immigrants in 1890, when the Italian contribution was fairly small. By 1931, over 70% of the 165,000 Italians who emigrated in that year went to European countries, but even this outlet was greatly restricted in subsequent years owing to depression conditions in the receiving states. During the inter-war years the fascist government made a virtue of necessity and planned to direct surplus population to the colonies. The colonial armies, police forces, finance guards, etc. reduced unemployment, but the number of bona fide settlers probably never reached 250,000. The post-war influx of this colonial population and of refugees from Venezia–Giulia further aggravated the employment situation.

Emigration to European countries began again in 1946 both on a temporary and long-term basis. Since then large numbers of Italian workers have been recruited into the industries of France, Belgium, Switzerland and Holland, usually in the heavy and 'dirty' sectors – mining, steel, chemicals, building and construction. An attempt to employ Italians in the British coal mines was frustrated by the trade unions at the local level but the brick industry has since come to rely heavily on their labour. With the building of the Berlin Wall and the consequent drying-up of the stream of East German refugees, West German industry has become increasingly dependent on Italian immigrants; indeed, in both Federal Germany and Switzerland it is unlikely that the pace of economic expansion could have been sustained without them. It is difficult to establish accurately the figure at any one time but the total of Italian emigrants in western European countries probably approaches two million (1965). Migration on such a scale inevitably raises serious social problems both in the receiving countries and in the communities from which the emigrants originate; there are many villages in central and southern Italy where a large part, often a majority, of the able-bodied menfolk are absent for all but a few days in the year, while in the host countries, particularly in Germany and Switzerland, the immigrant does not easily gain acceptance into the community.

In recent years emigration overseas has become numerically much less important than that to Europe, and the order of the receiving countries has undergone a change. For a time after the war the link with Brazil and Argentina was revived and Venezuela later enjoyed considerable popularity, but in the last decade Canada and Australia have received many more immigrants than Latin America. The United States continue to attract as many Italian immigrants as the quota restrictions permit. In the years 1960, 1961, 1962 the net emigration overseas from Italy was respectively 60,000, 42,000 and 41,000; in each year the United States, Canada and Australia were overwhelmingly the most important receiving countries. In the same years the comparable figures for Europe were 97,000, 147,000 and 149,000 with Federal Germany, Switzerland and France heading the list. The South and to a less extent Veneto supplied by far the largest number of migrants both to Europe and overseas.

Emigration is something to which Italians have become accustomed but an internal redistribution of population on the scale they are now experiencing is something quite unprecedented. Among the tortuous currents of migration certain main trends may be identified. Firstly, there is throughout the whole

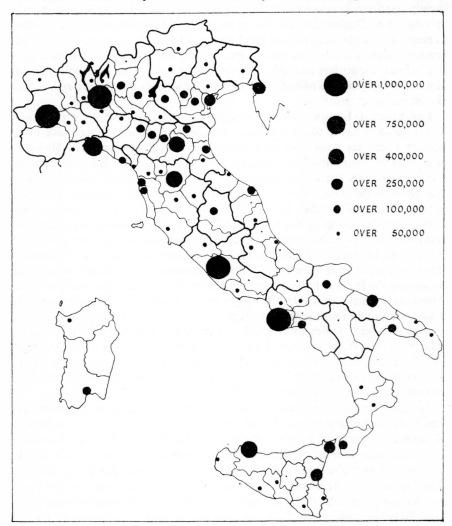

*Fig. 47.* Provincial and regional boundaries; populations of provincial capitals (1961 census)

country a powerful drift from the rural areas, particularly among young people; it is motivated in part by the attraction of the city with its promise of higher wages, regular hours and a 'fuller' life, and in part by a profound disillusionment with the land and all its associations; it is not only the poor and landless who are abandoning the countryside. 'La terra non rende piu' is a complaint heard all over Italy and few young people are content to be just peasants any more. In fact, evidence of the drift, as revealed in the landscape in the form of abandoned holdings and deserted farmsteads and of arable turned over to woodland and grazing, is more apparent in Alpine and central Italy than in the South where the economic pressures are greater but the alternative opportunities are less. Secondly, the incidence of urbanization is uneven; in the last decade the small towns, particularly in the remoter mountain and hill country, have barely held their own. They have been by-passed for the larger cities, especially Rome and the industrial centres of Lombardy and Piedmont. The capital, whose population rose 31% in the decade 1951–1961, draws its increase largely from the Centre and South; the two northern regions also attract most of their recruits from Calabria, Basilicata, Apulia and Sicily, but they are substantially reinforced from the Three Venetias. Compared with the exodus from Sicily, that from Sardinia is unimportant. Between 1951 and 1961 the populations of Milan and Turin rose by 26% and 46% respectively. The cities of Emilia, particularly Bologna, Modena and Ravenna, also registered substantial increases (20–25%), mainly from the immediate countryside, but the essentially heavy industrial city of Genoa increased by only 16%. Where special factors were at work some of the smaller urban areas recorded an above-average increase, for example Cagliari, Grosseto, Latina and Catania, which are benefiting from local development projects. Ravenna, which has found a new lease of life in terms of petro-chemicals, and Salerno, which was rebuilt during the relevant decade, fall into a similar category. Trieste, whose economic difficulties have received attention above, scarcely increased at all and Venice's performance was much below average:

### TABLE 3
### POPULATION INCREASES 1951–1961 FOR SELECTED CITY COMMUNES

In 1961 the population of the main urban communes totalled 16,526,000, an increase of 21% on the 1951 figure

| | % | | % |
|---|---|---|---|
| Turin (1,050,000) | 46 | Verona (230,000) | 23 |
| Latina (50,000) | 43 | Brescia (180,000) | 22 |
| Rome (2,246,000) | 31 | Catania (363,000) | 20 |
| Grosseto (52,000) | 31 | Palermo (593,000) | 18 |
| Cagliari (187,000) | 23 | Florence (459,000) | 17 |
| Bologna (456,000) | 27 | Naples (1,196,000) | 17 |
| Modena (143,000) | 26 | Bari (317,000) | 16 |
| Ravenna (116,000) | 26 | Genoa (796,000) | 16 |
| Milan (1,599,000) | 26 | Venice (359,000) | 11 |
| Salerno (123,000) | 26 | Trieste (273,000) | 0 |

It is quite certain that the scale of urbanization is greater than the statistics suggest; in most urban areas there is a sizeable group of new arrivals, who escape, not always unintentionally, the statistical net. In fact it is only in recent years that the administrative restrictions on internal migration have been relaxed. The internal movements now in progress are revolutionary and irrevocable; they have already raised many pressing problems in housing and education and in re-adjustment to new social environments. One wonders what the long-term conse-quences will be on the national character, on regional sentiment and on family ties and other accepted social loyalties.

## AGRICULTURE

At the risk of some repetition it may be useful to summarize here the essential characteristics of Italian agriculture. Until 1918 Italy was overwhelmingly an agricultural country and as late as 1940 the majority of Italians depended, directly or indirectly, on the land for their livelihood, so restricted in scale and so geo-graphically localized was Italian industry. The rôle of agriculture was to provide a steadily increasing population with the basic foodstuffs (bread, pasta, oil, wine, vegetables, fruit and, on a modest scale, animal products) and at the same time provide some sort of useful work for the greatest number of people. To this end agriculture was both protected and subsidized in various ways, and during the fascist period an attempt was made, with a fair measure of success, to achieve self-sufficiency in the basic foodstuffs. It may be argued that, given the political and economic climate of the 1930s, there was no alternative to this policy, but there is no doubt that it encouraged an excessive emphasis on wheat production, maintained land under the plough which should have been used otherwise, and sacrificed productivity to the demands of total production. In the last decade the pressures which previously shaped the character of Italian agriculture have slackened somewhat and it should now be possible to put more emphasis on efficiency with the object of catering for the changing needs of an increasingly affluent urban population and at the same time export more of those products for whose production Italy has climatic advantages (fruit, early vegetables, etc.). In this respect Italy's membership of the Common Market, while presenting an opportunity, also underlines the urgency of achieving the necessary reorientation.

In 1901 9·5 million Italians, some 60% of the active labour force, were engaged in agriculture; in 1963 the comparable figures were 5·3 million and 27% (table 6). In most of the South the percentage employed on the land is still about 40, while in much of the North the figure has fallen to 20. Although it may result locally in some loss of production (e.g. in the specialized wine districts of Pied-mont) this is a welcome trend which will eventually make possible more com-petitive forms of production based on viable holdings and modern methods.

At the moment there is a very great variety in the size and type of farm and in the tenure under which they are worked.[1] Half of Italy's productive area and

[1] Tables 8 and 9 attempt to summarize the land-use, form of operation and the degree of fragmentation in certain selected provinces chosen to illustrate the situation in the Alps (Bolzano); various sectors of the Northern Plain (Cremona, Padua, Ferrara); Liguria (Savona); the Sub-Apennines and Anti-Apennines (Arezzo and Siena); the central

over four-fifths of her farm units are worked by direct cultivators (*coltivatori diretti*). In effect these are family farms the majority of which are owned wholly or in part by the peasant, although less than half of the area involved is held in consolidated units (table 9). They are found in a wide variety of physical conditions, and although they may sometimes be as large as 15 hectares, holdings of between 3 and 8 hectares are more typical. The farm income they provide is equally diverse; they are most favourably represented in Piedmont, Lombardy and Veneto (table 8, Padua), usually on the upper plain where there is a large number of modest-sized family farms engaged in the production of field crops, fruit, vegetables and animal products on a commercial basis. Units of this sort are also to be found in the Arno valley and the more favoured districts of the Centre as well as in Campania, although in this last region farm incomes reflect the smaller scale of the holdings. In all these areas various types of *coltura promiscua*, a form of land use much favoured by the small producer, have long been practised. The variety of crops grown spreads the marketing and weather risks and, if the worst comes to the worst, at least the basic needs of the family are provided for. *Coltura promiscua* can also be a very intensive form of cultivation, especially where irrigation is possible, and in the Mediterranean zone its two-tier cropping (field and tree crops) fits well into the climatic rhythm; the field crops, mainly autumn sown, depend on the moisture in the topsoil provided by the cool season rains, while the tree crops can survive the summer drought on water stored in the subsoil. Yields and quality certainly suffer but the small farmer, cautious and conservative by nature, hesitates to take the plunge into specialized commercial production. This is less true of the dry arboricultural areas of Apulia and of the huertas of Calabria and Sicily, where the direct cultivator is well represented, but in these instances the peasant is very largely forced into specialization by the special physical conditions; mixed farming of the type practised in Veneto would be impossible on the Murge. As far as small family farms are concerned, incomes are lowest in the remoter hill and mountain areas, especially in the Apennines; they are often on marginal land which in a country less oppressed by rural overpopulation would be devoted to pasture or woodland. Indeed, not a few of these farms are now being abandoned. Given the size of their holdings most farmers in these less favoured areas have little alternative but to rely heavily on wheat, a crop which may be unsuited to the physical conditions but is easy to grow, demands little capital outlay and has received a degree of government support. Such is the case in much of the *latifondo contadino* (p. 189).

For at least forty years successive Italian governments have been very well disposed towards the small farmer, none more actively than the post-war

---

Apennines (Terni); the Adriatic Sub-Apennines (Teramo); an area formerly dominated by *latifondi* (Foggia); a dry arboriculture zone (Bari); a *latifondo contadino* area (Potenza); an intensive Mediterranean polyculture zone (Caserta); a varied Calabrian area (Reggio); a Sicilian interior province (Enna); and the most typical of the Sardinian provinces (Nuoro).

administrations whose land reform and reclamation projects are intended to re-inforce the small proprietor class. Unfortunately most small family farms (in-cluding some of those created under the land reform) are incapable of providing an income comparable with those obtainable in modern industry and they will have difficulty in achieving the efficiency which will be demanded in the near future. Funds are available at low interest for those who wish to enlarge their holdings by purchase, and over half a million hectares have been bought in recent years, but the problem of fragmentation, which is a serious handicap on some 20% of Italy's farmed area, is practically insoluble for three-quarters of the area concerned. Co-operation can help in overcoming some of the small farmer's difficulties but except in parts of the Northern Plain, notably in Emilia, its development has been slow. Under the fascists co-operatives were banned and unless sponsored by the government they are still regarded with suspicion in some quarters.

Not all Italy's small farmers come under the heading of *coltivatori diretti*; about 12% of the country's productive area is worked under the system known as *mezzadria appoderata* whereby an estate is divided into several compact holdings (*poderi*), usually of between 5 and 15 hectares, each with its modest farmstead. The landowner or his agent exercises a general supervision of the estate from the home farm (*fattoria*) and receives 'rent' from the *mezzadri* in kind. At one time the crops and the expenses were shared between landlord and tenant on a 50/50 basis but recently the tenant's share has been raised by legis-lation to 58%. In fact contracts vary according to the contribution of each party but in general the landowner pays the taxes while other expenses (seed, fertilizers, hire of machinery, etc.) are shared equally. The success of the system depends much on the goodwill and enterprise of the parties concerned. From the point of view of the *mezzadro* it has its advantages; he is assured of at least part of his capital needs, and since it is usual for the peasant family to remain on the *podere* year after year, permanent improvements and sound husbandry are encouraged to the benefit of both parties. *Mezzadria appoderata* is most widespread in Tuscany, the Marche, Umbria and southern Emilia; it is also represented in Veneto and the margins of the Northern Plain, but it is rare in the South. Of late the system has been attacked as an anachronism in a modern democratic state and from 1965 onwards no new *mezzadria* contracts can be legally entered into. When a *podere* falls vacant the landowner must either work the land himself with hired labour if necessary, or he must sell or rent the land to someone who is prepared to work it 'directly'. The object of this legislation seems to be either to convert the landowner into a direct cultivator or induce him to sell out. The state is prepared to advance funds at low interest to peasants who wish to purchase land but with the prevailing uncertainty in agriculture it remains to be seen whether many buyers will be forthcoming. The effect of the new legislation may well be that much land will go out of cultivation.

*Mezzadria appoderata* should not be confused with the form of *mezzadria* (*non-appoderata*) commonly practised in the South. In this case the tenant works an odd plot of land rather than a viable *podere*; no house is provided and the contract is for one year only. The landowner is often a townsman with little interest in the land or the tenant apart from the profits they provide. In much of the *Mezzogiorno* the peasant frequently has a triple rôle; he may be a proprietor but of so little land that he is obliged to rent parcels on a *mezzadria* basis and perhaps work elsewhere as a labourer.

Over one-third of Italy's agricultural and forest land is held in properties (*aziende*) of over 50 hectares, but to be concerned with mere size can be misleading; obviously 50 hectares in Milan province will yield a very different income from the same area in the mountain provinces of Aquila, Potenza or Nuoro. Even among those units with a high proportion of arable land there is a wide variety of farm types. One group engaged in producing cereals, fodder crops, fruit and animal products on an intensive capitalistic basis is most typically represented in the lower Northern Plain, especially in the provinces of Vercelli, Milan, Pavia, Piacenza, Cremona, Brescia and Mantua. A small permanent staff is supplemented by labourers whose earnings now approach those of their counterparts in industry; they are usually accommodated on the farm and their contracts are on a yearly basis. The standards achieved are high and the capital invested in building and equipment is comparable with farms in the United Kingdom. Mechanization has been encouraged by the relaxation of restrictions whereby the operator is obliged to employ labour according to the acreage and land-use. Processing and marketing, often on a co-operative basis, are also better organized here than elsewhere in Italy. It is significant that despite the vulnerable size of many of the units concerned, there has been no intervention by the land reform authorities. Although they are somewhat exceptional, efficient capitalist farms are also to be found on the Tyrrhenian lowlands of Tuscany, Lazio and Campania.

In the low-lying zones of Emilia and Veneto which have been reclaimed over the last century a rather different type of large unit may be identified. Usually in excess of 200 hectares and often run as a company, it is really an estate concentrating on the production of cereals, sugar beet, hemp, vines and fruit. It may be worked entirely with hired labour and machinery but it is common practice for part of the property to be entrusted to sharecroppers (*compartecipanti*) who are responsible, under the supervision of the operator, for a few hectares each for a season or a year; no homestead is available on the holding. With experience the sharecropper may be promoted to the status and responsibilities of a share tenant. It is one of the misfortunes of these *bonifica* zones that the demand for labour during the reclamation phase could not later be sustained, especially with the progress of mechanization. In consequence these areas have a long tradition of social unrest which has inevitably invited the attention of the land reform authorities (p. 143). The Ente Delta has also provided useful work by continuing reclamation and the lot of the hired labourer has been improved by legislation, but in the long term there is no alternative but to drain off surplus labour into industry either locally or further afield.

The third main type of large unit, generally referred to as the *latifondo capitalistico* (despite its undercapitalized nature), was identified until quite recently with the Maremma, the Tavoliere di Puglie, Marchesato, the coastlands of Basilicata and parts of the Sicilian interior. With its absentee owners it was much criticized for its low yields, for its unenterprising methods, for its pre-occupation with a small range of products (notably wheat, wool, wine and olives) and above all for its inability to provide tolerable living standards for the sharecroppers and labourers, whether local or migrant, on which the *latifondo* depended. Even before the land reform of 1950 (p. 191) the *latifondo* zones were undergoing a change; where the land was capable of improvement some progress towards higher standards and greater diversity had been made, either by direct state intervention or through the efforts of *consorzi di bonifica*, and a steadily increasing proportion of the land was passing into the hands of the peasantry. The land reform has drastically accelerated this process and has brought home to the large operators the need for a more responsible attitude towards the land. In fairness it has to be admitted that in many of the areas concerned, especially where the main problem is water control, the necessary improvements were beyond the resources of the landowners, and there are certainly vast tracts where, because of the adverse physical conditions, some form of extensive operation is unavoidable.

The output of agricultural products is very vulnerable to the vagaries of the weather but over the period 1953–1963 the index showed a rise of 22%; over the same period agriculture was responsible for a steadily declining proportion of the national income and exports. A summary of the land-use and crop areas for 1963 is given in table 10. Compared with 1953 there have been few major changes in crop areas or in yields which cannot be attributed to the weather. Soft wheat, used for bread and grown mainly in the more humid North, has tended to decline in acreage but that of hard wheat, used for pasta and confined largely to the South, has remained roughly the same. Production is sufficient for the vast majority of the country's needs. The ubiquity of wheat production and its cultivation on marginal land have already received attention. Italy is Europe's foremost producer of maize which is mainly fed to stock but is also used for human consumption, usually in the form of pollenta, a Venetian speciality. It is best suited to those areas with adequate summer rainfall or with irrigation facilities, notably in the Northern Lowlands and to a lesser degree in Campania (fig. 48). American hybrid seed, which produces double the yield of Italian varieties, accounts for half the production and is grown mainly in the North. Rice, which is used as a pioneer crop in the first stages of marsh reclamation, is declining in acreage partly because of the difficulty of obtaining seasonal labour. It is now almost entirely confined to Lomellina. Quality and yields are very high and production is sufficient to provide a modest export. The main leguminous fodder crops are

1a Pregelato in the Val del Chisone; small terraced fields on the south-facing slope, forest on the north-facing slope. Note the 'slate' roofs (*Ente Turismo, Torino*).

1b The rounded ridges and steep deforested slopes of the Triassic limestones near Limone (Maritime Alps). Only modestly glaciated but moraine in the foreground.

11a  The dolomitic mass of Sassolungo (3181m), with the northern edge of the Sella group visible behind, seen from the Alpe di Siusi. Note hay-cutting and seasonal dwellings on the plateau in the foreground (see fig. 24).

11b  View across the Campiglio valley from M. Nambino in the granitic Presanella group across to the dolomitic Brenta group. Note the contrasting morphologies of the two groups; the glaciers on the Brenta group; and the evidence of severe glaciation (cirque, arête, moraine) in the fore-ground (see fig. 23).

IIIa  Intensive viticulture in the debris-filled, overdeepened Adige valley; looking eastwards from Mezzo-Lombardo towards the Dolomites (*Ente Turismo, Trento*).

IIIb  The head of Lake Garda from the north-east. Note the massif Mesozoic limestone of the west shore, the tilted block of M. Brione and the intensively cultivated Sarca delta (*Ente Turismo, Trento*).

IVa  The Asiago plateau looking northwards from M. Kaberlaba. The valley of the Assa is visible in the middle distance. The tree line corresponds with the junction of the Jurassic limestones and the overlying marls (see fig. 25).

IVb *Coltura promiscua* on the edge of the Venetian plain seen from the foot of M. Grappa.

va The poplar-screened rice fields of the Vercellese (*Fotocielo*).

vb The rectangular pattern of fields and drains in the newly reclaimed zone of Emilia near Longastrino (south of the Valli di Comacchio (*Fotocielo*)).

VIa The rectangular layout of Turin; Pza Castello foreground right; the main station middle-ground right; the Po on the left. The pagoda (Mole Antonelliana) is a 19th-century folly (*Ente Turismo, Torino*).

VIb The Milan skyline towards the main station (*Fototeca Serv. Inform.*).

VII Venice from the west; Lido and the Porto di Lido in the distance; the islands of Murano and S. Michele on the left, and San Giorgio and La Giudecca on the right. The Grand Canal, docks, railway station and St Mark's are also distinguishable (*Ente Turismo, Venezia*).

A

B

C

VIII Farm types of the Northern Plain: A. a medium-sized modern farm near Cuneo; B. a large farm with accommodation for animals near Novara; C. a *corte* near Lodi.

ixa The rocky terraced coast at Vernazza, one of the Cinque Terre (*Fotocielo*).

ixb Grado on the lido coast of the northern Adriatic (*Fotocielo*).

xa The unspectacular summit of M. Cimone (2165m) in the northern (sandstone) Apennines. Note the height to which cultivation extends.

xb The *Strada del Sole* between Bologna and Florence (*Fototeca Serv. Inform.*).

XIa The *Balze di Volterra* (Pliocene sands over clays). The undulating Anti-Apennine plateau of Tuscany extends into the distance (*Ente Turismo, Pisa*).

XIb *Coltura promiscua* in the Tuscan hills near San Gimignano.

xiia  Mixed cultivation in the Assisi plain. Maize, tomatoes and fallow; vines supported by elms on the left, mulberries on the right.

xiib  Eroded Pliocene hills overlooking the Metauro floodplain.

XIIIa Gorge cut in the *tufo* of the volcanic plateau near Viterbo. Oak *bosco* on the sides.

XIIIb The hilltop town of Orte above the Tiber plain. Share tenant's farm in the foreground.

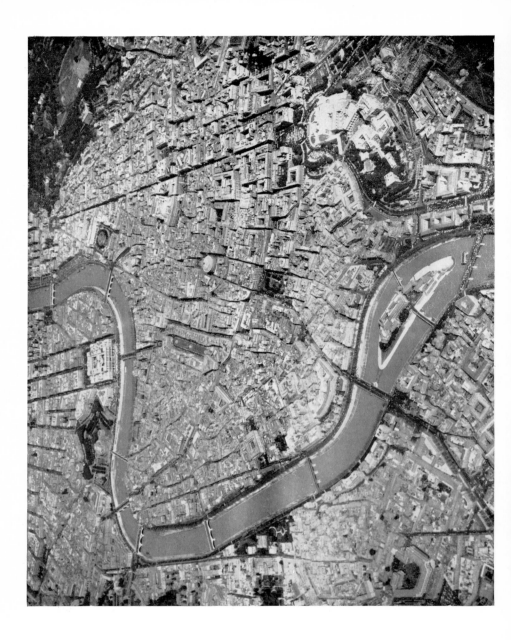

xiv  The heart of Rome – from the south. Imperial Rome covered most of the area shown on the left bank; medieval Rome lay mainly within the bend of the Tiber. The contribution of the baroque to the city's pattern is traceable between Pza S. Venezia and Pza del Popolo (top right). The Vittorio Emmanuel monument, the Campidoglio, the Corso, Pza Navona, the Pantheon, Castel S. Angelo, Pza Cavour and Pza S. Pietro are also recognizable (see fig. 37.) (*Fotocielo*).

xv  The medieval plan of Siena (A) and Bologna (B) and the baroque orderliness of Pza S. Pietro
(C) and Pza del Popolo (D). (*Fototeca Serv. Inform.*).

xvɪa Mesozoic limestone massifs overlooking the northern edge of the Fucino basin. Note the treeless reclaimed lake bed contrasting with the tree crops of the older settled higher lake shores behind.

xvɪb The limestone whaleback of M. Vettore (2478m) overlooking the karstic upland of the Pian Piccolo in the Mti Sibellini (ENIT).

XVIIa Gully erosion in the Miocene marls flanking the Scanno valley, Abruzzi. The Mesozoic limestone emerges above.

XVIIb The hilltop village of Opi in the limestone zone of the Abruzzi. The river Sangro cuts through the nearest ridge behind the village.

XVIIIa  Bundling and carting hemp in the plain of Campania (ENIT).

XVIIIb  Intensive *coltura promiscua* in the hill country of Campania; vine screen festooned between elms.

xixa  The rounded summits and pinewoods of the crystalline Sila plateau (*Ente Sila, Cosenza*).

xixb  The irrigated valley of the Cascile. The large village of Morano Calabro (near Castrovillari) on the flanks of the karst of M. Pollino is visible in the distance.

xxa The Alta Murgia near Castel del Monte, Apulia.

xxb The small walled fields and dispersed settlement of the Murgia dei Trulli (*Fototeca Serv. Inform.*).

xxia View from above Messina across the straits. Note the sickle-shaped spit protecting the harbour (ENIT).

xxib  The open cereal country of the Sicilian interior looking eastwards towards the large village of Regalbuto and Etna (ENIT).

xxiia The harbour, citrus groves and flat-roofed town of Bagheria, east of Palermo. The steep-sided limestone block is a common feature in the landscape of north-west Sicily (*Fotocielo*).

xxiib Sulphur working at Lercera among the forbidding hills of west-central Sicily (ENIT).

xxiiia  Basalt block terraces retaining volcanic ash on the southern slopes of Etna at about 1350 metres. In the background a chestnut-covered parasitic cone and a black lava flow.

xxiiib  M. San Paolino in Caltanissetta province – a Miocene chalk residual on erodible marls. The village of Sutera on the skyline to the right (*Touring Club Italiano*).

xxiva The stony walled fields of Gallura.

xxivb The macchia-covered chaotic relief of the M. Ferru volcanic zone, Sardinia.

beans (especially broad beans), peas, lentils, vetches, pulses and lupins; they are an essential element in the rotations of cereal-producing areas. Although mainly valuable as animal feedstuffs they are also used, lupins excepted, for human consumption. In the better-watered northern regions, particularly in Lombardy, lucerne and clover are the main leguminous fodders; sulla, lupinella and broad beans are more suited to the droughtier conditions of the South.

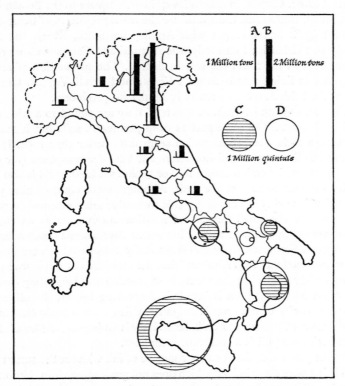

*Fig. 48.* Maize (A), sugar beet (B), lemon (C) and orange (D) production, 1961

Among the vegetables, potatoes occupy the largest acreage; they are grown throughout the country for home use, and Campania has an interest in the export of early varieties. The spring in the South is ideal for the production of a wide variety of green vegetables and salads. Processing is best developed in Campania which also exports fresh produce, particularly cauliflowers. Tomatoes, a seemingly indispensable item in Italian cooking, are particularly important in Emilia and Campania.

Sugar beet is the most important industrial crop; suited to mechanization and preferring deep alluvial soils it is concentrated mainly in the newer reclaimed lands of Veneto and Emilia. The climate is not entirely suited to the crop (the hot summers cause a loss in the sugar content) but producers receive some protection in the home market and the country is largely self-supporting in this commodity. Among other industrial crops tobacco, a labour-intensive peasant crop grown mainly in Campania, Apulia, Veneto and Umbria, is holding its own and has the marketing advantage of a state monopoly. On the other hand vegetable fibres, all of which make heavy demands on the soil and are produced more cheaply abroad, are on the decline. Cotton, in quantities quite inadequate to the demand, is produced in Sicily. Emilia and Campania are the main producers of hemp and they share the biggest flax acreages with Apulia, Basilicata, Sicily, the Abruzzi, Lombardy and Calabria; Lombardy, the Abruzzi and Campania are predominantly interested in the fibre, the rest in linseed. The production of raw silk is declining fast as living standards rise; Veneto and Friuli–Venezia Giulia, with Lombardy far behind, are now the only significant producers.

The climate, soils and terrain of much of Italy are suited to a wide range of tree and bush crops. The olive prefers deep permeable soils but it manages to thrive on most soils, even those which seem little better than rock. It is more demanding in climate and will not tolerate a humid atmosphere (for example where temperature inversion causes fog) or prolonged frosts, and it also requires a long dry summer to mature the fruit. Although some eight or nine years are needed before it begins to bear and yields thereafter are notoriously erratic, it is widely grown by the small farmers of Mediterranean Italy as an element in *coltura promiscua*. Specialized cultivation which covers some 900,000 ha (half of them in Apulia, Sicily and Calabria) is generally considered a more satisfactory method of production.[1] It is admitted that the standards of oliviculture in Italy are not what they might be; the methods of pruning and harvesting (in December) are often inexpert, there is insufficient spraying against the olive fly, and only a tiny minority of the crop is irrigated. Olive oil is a basic element in the diet of all classes of Italians but on balance Italy is an importer. The adulteration of olive oil with seed oil is a recurrent complaint.

The Italian peasant could as easily conceive of life without the sun as without wine and it is a poor *paese* indeed which does not grow some vines. Unfortunately the ubiquity of its production by thousands of peasants, who think mainly in terms of the needs of their own family or of the local market, increases the difficulty of organizing for export in the face of French, Spanish and German competition. A much higher degree of co-operation among growers is required to standardize the product and market it effectively. In 1963 Apulia, Sicily and Piedmont accounted for about half of the 1,139,000 ha under specialized cultivation, a figure which compares with 2,600,000 ha in *coltura promiscua*. Since the war the specialized acreage has increased while that under mixed cultivation has declined steadily. Apulian wine is of high alcoholic content and is used mainly in blending or in vermouth manufacture. The most important specialized viti-

---

[1] In Apulia 40 kg of olives yielding 5 kg of oil may be expected on average from a mature tree of the Cellina di Nardo variety.

culture zone in Sicily lies in the west of the island where Marsala gives its name to a fortified wine not unlike port. Elsewhere the best-known quality wines are Asti Spumante, Barbera, Grignolino, Barbaresco and Barolo from Piedmont; Chiaretto del Garda, Bardolino, Valpolicella and Soave from Veneto; Chianti from Tuscany; and Frascati, Orvieto and Montifiascone from central Italy. The production of dessert grapes demands the retention of moisture in the soil till the

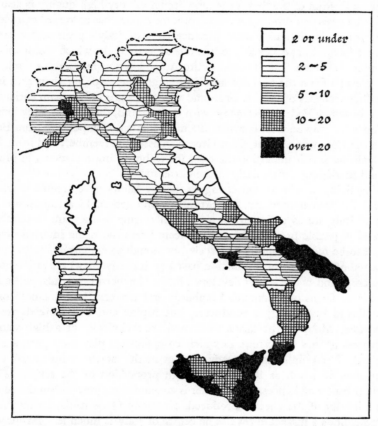

*Fig. 49.* The distribution of tree crops and vines; percentages of the provincial productive areas (1961)

autumn otherwise the grapes drop off. Production is increasing particularly in Lazio and Apulia but so far most growers seem content with the home market.

Citrus cultivation is much esteemed in the Mediterranean area because a small acreage is capable of producing a high cash return and demands the continuous attention the skilled peasant is capable of providing. Unfortunately the distribution of citrus fruit cultivation is limited by the stringent climatic requirements of the crop (long hot summers and almost frost-free winters) and by the need to irrigate in those areas climatically suitable; hence the intensive and specialized nature of the cultivation in those areas able to fulfil these requirements. Lemons, which crop very heavily and have the advantage of yielding some fruit during most of the year, are concentrated mainly in Sicily and Calabria. Oranges are less vulnerable to frost and although Sicily and Calabria lead in their production, they are also grown in Campania, Apulia and Sardinia.

The cultivation of peaches, pears and apples of very high quality is also on a specialized basis and production, much of it for export, has increased markedly in recent years. Emilia and Veneto produce 90% of Italy's pears and are easily foremost in apple and peach production, an activity in which Campania and Piedmont also share. The Trentino–Alto Adige has a reputation for apples and some growers from the area are now finding greater scope for their skill in the expanding orchards of Emilia. Fruit and vegetables are Italy's main agricultural export for which Federal Germany (with Switzerland, the United Kingdom and Sweden some way behind) provides the main market. Competition from France within the Common Market, from Greece an associate member, and from Israel and Spain outside it underline the need for technical improvements in production and marketing, particularly in the citrus sector.

Rising living standards and changing dietary habits have created a growing demand for animal products. Unfortunately the geographical conditions over much of Italy are as unfavourable to animal rearing as they are favourable to fruit and vegetable production, and in recent years the rising internal demand has had to be met by imports on a scale big enough to embarrass the balance of payments. Milk and meat production based on intensive hay cultivation and on forage crops and maize is best developed in the Northern Lowlands, particularly on the large farms of Piedmont, Lombardy and western Emilia. Dutch breeds are preferred by the larger producers, but Alpine and Swiss breeds are also represented. Many of the farms concerned are technically of a high standard and processing and marketing, in which co-operatives play their part, are well organized. Fluid milk has a ready market in the northern industrial towns and even as far south as Rome but a high proportion of the output is processed for butter and cheese. The butter is consumed entirely within the country but a minority of the cheeses produced, especially Gorgonzola, Parmesan and Bel Paese, finds a market abroad. The centre of Italy is much less favoured for cattle rearing and although in the vicinity of Rome and other large cities there is a sprinkling of large milk producers, in general the small farmer is more interested in veal. In fact, in the Centre and South, where Tuscan and Marche breeds are popular, cattle are regarded primarily as work animals and perhaps a third of Italy's 9 million cattle fall into this category. On one or two marshy coastal areas in Tuscany and Campania the buffalo survives; its rich milk is used to make *mozzarella*. Pigs are reared throughout the country for home use and for the local market but in Emilia and Lombardy, whose sausages and preserved meats enjoy a high reputation, production is on a larger and more specialized scale.

Most of Italy's eight million sheep are to be found in the drier South and Islands, particularly in Sardinia which accounts for nearly one-third of the total. Their rôle in the more extensive farming areas and in the traditional practice of transhumance, now fast disappearing, has already been mentioned. *Pecorino* cheese is made from their milk but sheep are mainly kept for their wool although most of it is used for mattresses and felts; the large-scale wool textile industries of the North rely on higher-grade imported fibres. In general lamb is obtainable only at Easter when the surplus young animals from the lambing season are slaughtered; mutton, like beef, rarely appears in the shops. The poverty of the land and the primitive conditions in the countryside are reflected in the concentration of most of Italy's 300,000 mules and 400,000 donkeys in the South and Islands; Sicily alone has half the mules.

# INDUSTRY

Within four years of the end of the war Italy had made good most of the havoc wrought on her ports, communications and factories during the migration of the front from Sicily to the Alps. This achievement owed much to the Italian genius for improvization but it would scarcely have been possible without generous American aid. For the workers it was a period of hardship and insecurity with short-time working and unemployment, while management was handicapped by shortages and by the social necessity of employing an inflated labour force. Slowly, as the general economic conditions throughout Europe improved, Italian industry passed through a period of first-aid to one of convalescence; pre-war production levels were equalled or surpassed but little impression was made on the hard core of two million unemployed. By 1953, however, Italy had entered an era of industrial expansion quite unparalleled in her history which continued unchecked until the recession of 1963.[1] For the first time the obstinate block of structural unemployment began to dissolve and a large section of the population, including an increasing number of newcomers from the countryside, experienced an unprecedented well-being.

The forces which made possible what came to be known as the Italian economic miracle are, and probably will remain, a matter of controversy. Certainly in the early fifties there was a good deal of under-employed plant and labour which could be quickly called upon to expand production, and there was a large reserve of comparatively cheap labour available for further expansion. Italy too was relatively much less handicapped as regards fuel and energy resources than before the war. The discovery of gas in the Po Valley was a lucky windfall and the increasing dominance of oil in the energy requirements of Europe put Italy on

---

[1] Between 1950 and 1962 the average annual rise in the industrial production index was 16%; *per capita* income rose from 211,000 to 570,000 lire; the share of industry in the gross national product increased from 33% to 40% while that from agriculture fell from 26% to 15%; the workers employed in industry rose from 6 to 8 millions while those engaged in agriculture dropped from 8 to 6 millions; and Italy's share in world trade went up from 2·5% to 4·0%.

a more equal footing with other European countries. Some credit must also be given to post-war governments for successfully maintaining a measure of continuity and stability without which most planning is rendered fruitless. In fact the state has not been content with a merely passive rôle; within the framework of official planning the state and private enterprise are conceived as partners in a common task. The state's contribution to this dual economy has been considerable; apart from the functions normally exercised by western governments – taxation, government spending, commercial and financial policy – the state has been able to initiate and direct investment on a vast scale, not only in the nationalized industries (notably the railways and more recently electricity), but through such agencies as the *Cassa* and IRI (*Instituto per la Ricostruzione Industriale*).[1] But perhaps the most important element contributing to the post-war expansion has been the more healthy economic climate prevailing in western Europe compared with pre-war. If instead of embracing, however cautiously, more expansionist and liberal policies, the trading nations had reverted to the narrow economic nationalism of the thirties, Italy would have been frustrated in her attempts to find markets for her industrial exports, would have been denied access to international sources of capital, would have been burdened with thousands of workers now usefully employed elsewhere, and would have been deprived of much of the foreign exchange now earned through tourism. In short, she would have been forced back on some form of economic nationalism herself. In fact, despite the slackened pace since 1963, the changes wrought in the Italian economic and social structure since 1953 are so fundamental that there can now be no going back; Italy is committed to a policy of increasing industrialization on the western European pattern.

Before reviewing briefly the various sectors, some further mention should be made of the size structure of Italian industry and of the rôle of the state. The outstanding features of the former are the small group of very large concerns at the apex of the industrial pyramid and the vast number of very small concerns at its base. The first group which is most typically represented in vehicles (Fiat), chemicals (Montecatini), rubber (Pirelli), synthetic fibres (Snia–Viscosa), electricals (CGE, Edison), steel (Finsider) and calculating machinery (Olivetti), accounts for a very large proportion of total production and exports and has contributed overwhelmingly to the expansion of recent years. The firms concerned employ a very large labour force in relatively few plants, and wages, which are negotiated through the unions, approach the levels obtaining for similar employment in other parts of western Europe. Management is efficient and often adopts a paternalistic attitude towards its workpeople, who enjoy generous fringe benefits in the form of housing, health services and holiday facilities. These firms, the majority of which are based in the North, are also outstanding in providing apprentice training facilities. In complete contrast are the thousands of small enterprises, many of them no more than backyard workshops, employing up to

[1] See page 251.

ten workers. These are common enough in the North, where some exist on work sub-contracted from larger firms, but, unlike the 'giants', they are to be found in every sizeable town in the country. Their activities include quarrying, building, vehicle repairing, metal work, furniture, tailoring, shoe-making, textiles and a host of crafts generally referred to as *artigianato* (lace, pottery, jewellery, basketwork, confectionery). They contribute little to total production and exports and the workers employed receive no fringe benefits and are paid lower wages than in the unionized factories. That such a large proportion of the labour force should be employed in small, inefficient units is regarded by some observers as a major obstacle in the way of economic expansion,[1] but such enterprises tend to be perpetuated because expansion automatically increases overheads in the form of higher wages, insurance and other welfare costs imposed by law, which may price the operator out of business. Between the many very small and the few very large concerns there is an increasing number of medium-sized firms employing a few hundred workers. They are well represented in food processing, textiles, engineering, pharmaceuticals and paper. In many cases some form of integration into larger units seems inevitable.

As regards the rôle of the state in industry there are two state-controlled agencies which deserve particular attention; one is ENI (*Ente Nazionale Idrocarburi*) which will be dealt with below (page 254); the other is IRI. The latter, founded in 1933 as a financial rescue operation, survived to perform the same function in the years after the war. With some truth it has been referred to as a hospital for sick enterprises; fortunately many of its patients have regained their health and together make an impressive list. Among the utilities IRI controls telephone networks (STET), the state airline (Alitalia), motorways (the Strada del Sole) and a large part of the mercantile marine (Finmare). Its stake in manufacturing includes Finsider, Italy's main steel-producing group, Fincantieri (shipbuilding), Finmeccanica (mechanical engineering), Siemens (electricals), textiles (Manifatture Cotoniere Meridionali) and chemicals (M. Amiata). Not least it controls three major banks, the Banca Commerciale Italiana, Credito Italiano and the Banca di Roma. Once a firm is on its feet again it has been the practice for IRI to re-sell parts of the firm's equity to the public, but except in the case of Finelettrica (nationalized in 1965), it has never relinquished its controlling interest. It is claimed that the system offers the best of both worlds; by allowing each unit to trade competitively without direct interference it avoids the bureaucratic topheaviness often associated with nationalized concerns; at the same time IRI retains sufficient overall control to 'persuade' firms to fall in line with the government's economic planning. Thus IRI has always been mindful of the plight of the South (hence the Alfa Romeo plant at Naples and the Finsider steel works at Taranto) and it is now obliged to channel about half of all new investment into that area.

[1] For a discussion of the structure of Italian industry and its effects on the economy see Vera Lutz, *Italy; a Study in Economic Development* (Oxford, 1962).

*Fuels and power*

In 1963 roughly half of Italy's energy requirements was provided by oil, over 90% of it imported; a quarter by hydro-electric power; a sixth by solid fuels and a tenth by natural gas. Nuclear power so far accounts for less than 1%. The rising demand over the next few years is likely to be met mainly from imported oil while the contribution of other sources is unlikely to change substantially.

SOLID FUELS. Italy is notoriously lacking in solid fuels. Small deposits of anthracite are worked in the Alps, notably at La Thuile in the Valle d'Aosta, but production is on the decline. The other 'coals' of note are the Tertiary lignites of Sulcis (Sardinia), where output is also on the wane, and those of Tuscany and Umbria where production steadily increased until 1963 (table 11). These deposits are mainly valuable for the production of thermal electricity and chemicals. Italy's lack of solid fuels is much less of a handicap than before the war; relatively cheap American coal can be imported for metallurgical purposes without fear of embarrassing high-cost home producers – an advantage denied the United Kingdom. Similarly her energy requirements, for example for thermal electricity generation, can be based on imported oil, the most efficient fuel, with fewer inhibitions than in the coal-producing countries. In recent years coal and coke imports, mainly from the USA, which has largely replaced the traditional European suppliers (Germany, Poland and the UK[1]), have been of the order of 10 million tons; this total is not expected to rise substantially.

OIL AND NATURAL GAS. The discovery of natural gas in the Apennine foretrench of the Po Valley in 1945 has certainly been one of the most significant events in Italy's recent economic history. Apart from its intrinsic value, the discovery acted as a psychological boost at a time when the country's economic fortunes were at a low ebb. After many lean years the efforts of AGIP (*Azienda Generale Italiana Petroli*), a state prospecting organization dating from 1926, were rewarded with gas strikes in southern Lombardy and Emilia, first at Caviaga and later at Ripalta, Cortemaggiore, Cornegliano, Bardolana, Corregio and Ravenna; more recently smaller fields have been found and tapped in the Abruzzi (San Salvo, Lentella), Basilicata (Ferrandina) and Sicily (the Catania plain). Production, still overwhelmingly from the Po Valley, stands at about 7500 million cubic metres (sufficient for 10% of Italy's energy demands in 1964) and reserves are regarded as adequate to maintain this output for some 15 years. A pipeline network totalling 5000 km serves all the major cities from Trieste to Genoa while in the south Bari and Naples are connected with the Basilicata and Abruzzi fields respectively. The gas is used principally for heat-raising in industry, thermal electricity generation (e.g. at Tavazzano), central heating and increasingly as a raw material in the chemical industry for the production of motor fuel, synthetic

[1] The NCB, however, has recently won a contract for the supply of coal to Italy (1965).

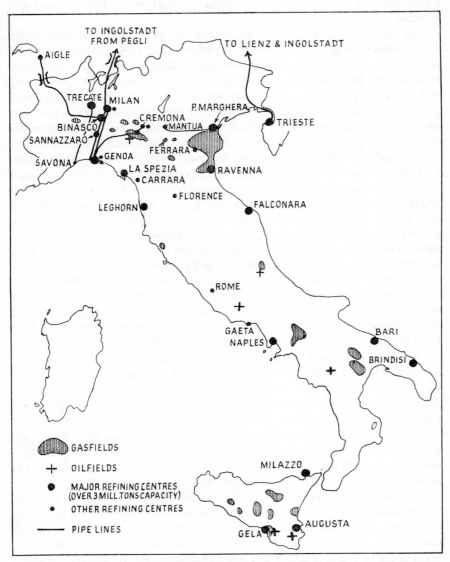

*Fig. 50.* The distribution of oil, natural gas and oil refining; principal pipelines

rubber, plastics and nitrates. The bottling of gas for domestic use has revolutionized the kitchens of thousands of homes formerly dependent on wood and charcoal.

The spectacular developments in natural gas production not unnaturally raised hopes of striking oil in sizeable quantities. Until 1949 only small amounts of oil had been located, mainly in the Fornovo–Cortemaggiore area. Inevitably a controversy arose as to what should be the relative rôles of the state company and of the private, largely foreign-owned, oil companies in prospecting and production. The state found a champion in the late Enrico Mattei; he had been appointed originally to wind up AGIP but on the strength of the Po Valley gas discoveries he gained a reprieve for the organization and lived to build it into an industrial empire.[1] In the face of some internal opposition and of pressure from the international oil companies the privileged position of the state was confirmed in 1953 and again in 1957. ENI (*Ente Nazionale Idrocarburi*), set up in 1953 with AGIP as one of its main subsidiaries, was granted a monopoly of gas and oil prospecting, production and distribution in the Po Valley. In the rest of the country ENI was obliged to compete with the Italian subsidiaries of the international oil companies which were already active in Sicily and the Abruzzi. In fact the conditions governing prospecting and production on the mainland were considered so unfavourable by the international companies that they have lost interest and have since concentrated their efforts in Sicily where the autonomous government is more favourably disposed towards them. In fact, the oil eldorado did not materialize; the richest fields are in Sicily at Ragusa, discovered by Gulf Italia in 1954, and at Gela, struck by ENI in 1956. All told the output of Sicilian oil, which is poor in quality because of its bituminous and sulphurous character, amounts to little more than 2·5 million tons (1964). The only other notable fields are at Cortemaggiore (ENI) and in the Abruzzi at Vallecupo (ENI) and Alanno (Petrosud). As hopes faded that Italy would join the ranks of the major producers, ENI, whose director resented the stranglehold of the international companies on the supplies of imported crude, sought and obtained concessions in Egypt, the Gulf coast of Persia, Libya, Morocco, Tunisia and elsewhere. When supplies were still not sufficiently forthcoming ENI made the controversial decision to import crude from the USSR and Rumania.

With its headquarters at Metanopoli, near Milan, ENI now ranks as one of Europe's industrial giants. Apart from its gas and oil interests in the Po Valley, the group controls refineries in Italy with a capacity of over 8 million tons (notably at Gela, Mestre, Leghorn, Bari, Sannazzano dei Burgondi) as well as petro-chemical plants at Ravenna, Pisticci (Basilicata) and elsewhere; it operates a tanker fleet of 500,000 tons and a large distribution network not only in Italy but in a number of African and European countries; it is competing with Marseilles and the north European ports for the central European market by means

[1] In 1964 ENI ranked 31st among Europe's major concerns as far as turnover was concerned. IRI, Fiat and Finsider were placed 5th, 10th and 23rd respectively.

of its South European Pipeline (Pegli–Ingolstadt) and the Trans-Alpine Pipeline (Trieste–Ingolstadt with a branch to Vienna) now under construction; it is active in prospecting and production abroad particularly in North Africa and the Middle East; and its engineering subsidiaries, with support from a specialized oil equipment works at Pignone (Florence), have built gasducts and pipelines abroad (e.g. the Buenos Aires–Santa Cruz gasduct) as well as a number of refineries (Ingolstadt, Mohammedia, Bizerta, Tema) in which ENI retains an interest. ENI even controls a newspaper (*Il Giorno*).

The spectacular rise of the state oil company should not be allowed to obscure the fact that the majority of Italy's refining and petro-chemical industry is controlled by the international oil companies with whose operations several Italian concerns are in association (e.g. Montecatini and Shell). Furthermore, despite ENI's connection with the USSR whence some 15% of the country's oil imports originate (1963), the vast bulk of Italy's crude oil still comes from the Middle East, especially from Kuwait, Iraq and Saudi Arabia. It has been a most fortunate circumstance that Italy's rapidly increasing demand for oil coincided with a vast expansion of world oil production so that she has been able to enjoy something of a buyer's market. In 1965 Italy's refining capacity was the largest in Europe (111 million tons[1]). The distribution of refining, shown in fig. 51, underlines the importance of the ports and of the major consuming area, namely the North.

ELECTRICITY. Between the wars the steadily rising demand for electricity was mainly met by an expansion of hydro-electric capacity. This gave an obvious industrial advantage to the North which in 1942 had 78% of the country's hydro-electric capacity and incidentally 53% of its thermal capacity. The development of industry based on electricity had the effect of favouring certain activities (e.g. textiles and light engineering) and, because of the ease with which it can be distributed, it promoted manufacturing in existing centres of population instead of encouraging new conurbations at the source of energy, as had happened on the coalfields of north-west Europe. The reliance on electrical power also affected the choice of process to be employed in some activities; for example, steel was more easily produced from scrap using electrical furnaces than by full-cycle methods. After the war Italy continued to install new hydro-capacity in the Centre and South as well as the North so that now, with a capacity of 13·9 million kW and a production of 43,500 million kWh (1964), some 80% of her hydro-electric potential has been harnessed. The development of the remaining 20% will be difficult and costly. In the same year over 70% of the country's hydro-electric output was generated in the Alps where 17 of the 21 major plants (over 100,000 kW) are located. Other major producers were the Abruzzi, Umbria, Lazio and Calabria which together accounted for 15%. In all there are over 2300 hydro-electric plants in the country. With so little unrealized hydro-electric

[1] 1950, 6 million tons.

potential available Italy has had to rely increasingly on thermal plants based oil and gas. In 1953 of a total output of 32,600 million kWh only 16% was thermally generated; in 1964 the comparable figures were 76,600 million and 43%. The distribution of natural gas once more favours the North but a growing dependence on oil puts the South on a more equal footing; in fact, 5 of the 13 major thermal plants are in the South and Centre. Some 45% of thermal production is generated from oil, 26% from natural gas, 3% from blast-furnace by-product gas, and the rest from solid fuels, only about a third of which is imported. A small contribution comes from geo-thermal installations at Larderello. Three major nuclear power generators are now in operation, one in the Pontine Marshes at Latina (an ENI project), one on the Po at Trino and one on the lower Garigliano. All three are located near good water supplies.

Until 1963 the generation and distribution of electricity were shared between a public sector, including Finelettrica (part of the IRI group), the railways and the municipalities, which together accounted for 38% of total output, and a private sector including several large firms generating for their own needs (auto-producers). In the same year, with the exception of a few small concerns and a number of auto-producers, the production and distribution of electricity were vested in a state authority (*Ente Nazionale per l'Energia Elettrica*).

## Mineral resources

The country's mineral output is summarized in table 11. Antimony, arsenic, potash, salt, lead, zinc, bauxite and manganese are produced in quantities roughly sufficient for home needs, while sulphur and mercury[1] provide a modest export. The output of tin, copper and above all iron ore is inadequate and a number of important minerals including wolfram, chrome and phosphates are unrepresented. Building raw materials are widely and plentifully available and there is no shortage of pottery clays. Marble is also well distributed (Alps, Tuscany, Lazio, Sicily) and that from Massa–Carrara provides a useful export. An increasing quantity of useful minerals, including sulphur and nitrates, is being made available by the expanding metallurgical and petro-chemical industries. All told the extractive industries employ about 100,000 workers and play a notable rôle in the economies of Sardinia, Tuscany and Sicily, but in general the deposits involved are dispersed and modest in size, and production is mainly in small, rather inefficient, units.

## Labour

It has always been one of the main handicaps of the Italian economy that it has had to carry a crushing burden of unemployed and under-employed labour; inevitably this burden has had to be shouldered by the more efficient sectors. Furthermore, the proportion of the active population actually in paid employment has always been low. This is partially explained by the wide acceptance of

[1] One of the main uses of mercury is for dental fillings.

the view, at least until very recently, that the woman's place is in the home and that those jobs available should go to the menfolk. It should be borne in mind, however, that in agriculture the family farm could not function without the contribution – usually unpaid – of the womenfolk. Since about 1953 a radical change has been taking place in the labour situation; the drift from the land generally and the exodus from the South have been accompanied, fortunately, by a rising demand for labour in the manufacturing and service industries (even in the South) and by widening opportunities for emigration beyond the Alps. There can be little doubt that the availability of labour and a reduction in the dead-weight of unemployment and under-employment helped to stimulate the remarkable expansion of industry in the fifties. The block of two million unemployed, which had come to be regarded as normal, began to melt and by 1963, despite a greater mobility of labour than the country had ever known, there were serious shortages in some categories, especially among skilled artisans. The vulnerability of this new-found prosperity was quickly revealed however in the 1963 recession when a tightening of credit soon affected many enterprises, particularly in the construction industry where many fugitives from the land had found employment. If would be remarkable if an expansion of the scale achieved in the decade 1953–1963 were to be repeated, and in view of the steady natural increase and the likelihood of more women entering paid employment in the future, it seems improbable that industry will be short of labour numerically. As in all industrialized countries the problem is more likely to be one of quality. In this respect the opportunities and prevailing attitudes in education at all levels are receiving critical attention. Many of the larger firms (Fiat, Innocenti) run excellent apprenticeship schemes but the smaller concerns contribute little. The problem is not unknown in Britain.

It will be appreciated that any comparison between labour costs in Italy and those in other countries poses problems of great complexity but one or two broad generalizations may perhaps be attempted. Italy is much more of a welfare state than is generally appreciated and whereas in Britain the employer and the employee share the cost of welfare contributions more or less equally, in Italy 90% of the burden falls on the employer. The existence of several disparate groups in the labour force has already been noted; in that group employed mainly in large efficient concerns where wages are fixed in co-operation with the unions, the hourly rates, job for job, are somewhat lower than in most of western Europe, but when holidays, welfare contributions borne by the employer, and fringe benefits are added, the discrepancy in labour costs is greatly narrowed.[1] The stronger bargaining position of organized labour[2] during the boom decade

[1] Figures published by the European Community Statistical Office showed that in 1962 Italian manufacturers in most sectors enjoyed little or no advantage in labour costs over their Belgian and Dutch competitors.
[2] In 1963, 3·6 million workers belonged to the communist-dominated CGIL; 2·4 to the Catholic CISL; and 2·5 were shared between two organizations with less rigid political or confessional ties.

resulted, naturally enough, in a marked rise in wages, probably of the order of 25%; and since the cost of living was rising more slowly the increased wages represented a very real improvement in living standards for thousands of workers. In the large-scale efficient sectors increased labour costs could be partially offset by increased productivity; this was very much more difficult in those sectors composed of small concerns or in those employing unskilled labour. Although the basic causes of slumps and booms are notoriously difficult to identify, it seems likely that the rise in labour costs in those activities where productivity could not be raised proportionately, notably the building trade, contributed substantially to the recession of 1963. Even so the boom lasted long enough to effect a revolution in the pattern of incomes, and despite the recession, Italian labour has come to expect rewards comparable with those obtainable elsewhere in western Europe. This tendency has been reinforced by the experiences of emigrant workers.

## Capital

As might be expected in a country where the living standards of a large section of the population (particularly in agriculture) are still low, the savings available provide only a modest total for industrial investment. Furthermore those with funds available tend to put them into bank deposits, government securities, small businesses, land and property rather than into industry, which is regarded as a risky investment. Thus the stock market plays a much less important rôle than in Britain and industry has to rely on the banks for much of its finance.[1] The state too is active in promoting industrial investment either directly or indirectly through IRI, which incidentally controls three important banks. In the early years of Italy's post-war recovery she received massive financial support from America; in happier days she has been able to avail herself of international sources of credit and, apart from working arrangements between foreign and Italian firms (Renault and Alfa Romeo, BMC and Innocenti), her industries have attracted sizeable foreign investments of a more permanent character, notably in oil, chemicals, calculating machinery, photographic products, and textile fibres, both natural and man-made.[2] The United States, Federal Germany, Britain and Switzerland have the largest stake. Conversely Italy has invested considerable sums abroad notably in car plants in South America and in oil ventures in Africa and the Middle East. The peculiar structure of Italian industry results in the concentration of a very large proportion of total investment in a very few firms.

## The iron and steel industry

The expansion of her iron and steel industry is often quoted as an indication of Italy's successful industrialization in recent years; between 1953 and 1963 her

[1] The restriction of credit and the calling in of loans by the banks in 1963 caused serious embarrassment, particularly in the building industry.
[2] Recent examples are Shell's investment in Montecatini, and the acquisition of a controlling interest by GEC in Olivetti, by Gevaert in Ferrania and by SKF in RIV.

output of pig iron and steel trebled to reach 3·5 and 10·1 million tons respectively. Before the war in an era of economic self-sufficiency, she was handicapped by a lack of coking coal and the meagreness and dispersal of her iron ore resources.

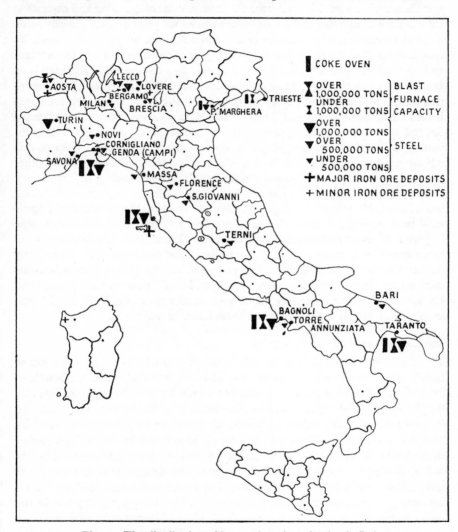

*Fig. 51.* The distribution of iron and steel production in Italy

Thus pig iron production was very limited and, except for the Aosta furnaces, was located on the coast notably in the ILVA works at Piombino, Portoferraio, Bagnoli and Trieste. The majority of Italian steel output came from electric furnaces using scrap, much of it imported. The location of the most important of these plants at Turin (Fiat), Sesto S. Giovanni (Breda, Falck), Bergamo (Dalmine) and Brescia reflected the dominance of the North as a source of power and as a consumer of steel; the Terni works was exceptional in this respect. After the war the state, through Finsider, took the initiative in reorganizing and expanding the industry (Sinigaglia Plan). Investment was aimed principally at the expansion of blast furnace capacity and the creation of full-cycle plants on the coast. To this end the Piombino and Bagnoli works have been expanded and modernized and entirely new plants with a capacity of over two million tons each have been built at Cornigliano and more recently at Taranto. The latter enterprise is equipped with LD converters; elsewhere the coastal full-cycle works employ open-hearth furnaces although Bagnoli also uses Thomas converters. The increased dependence of the Italian steel industry on imported ore and fuels, which obviously favoured coastal sites for the new developments, has so far been no disadvantage. American coal has been available at prices below that paid by other European producers for home-produced fuel, and in having to import ore Italian steelmakers are no worse off than many of their competitors. In recent years Brazil, Venezuela, India (Goa), Liberia, Sweden, Mauretania and Algeria have been among the main sources of ore imports. Italy is also a considerable importer of scrap from Europe and America. Unless there is a resumption of boom conditions, capacity seems to be adequate for most types of steel and any further increase in output will oblige producers to pay greater attention to the competitive export market. Even so there are plans for new works at Savona and La Spezia. Italy was a founder member of the European Coal and Steel Community from which she has received some financial assistance.

*Mechanical and electrical engineering*

This sector in its bewildering diversity has contributed more than any other to Italy's recent industrial expansion; it is also one in which the large Northern firms, some of them members of IRI, are dominant. The damage sustained by Italy's shipbuilding capacity was quickly made good in the post-war years and for a decade her yards enjoyed a period of activity and expansion sustained by the need to replace merchant tonnage lost in the war and by the boom in tanker construction. More recently with stiffening competition, particularly from Japan, and a slackening in world demand, the industry, despite state subsidies and several large orders for prestige passenger ships from state-controlled companies, has been going through a period of uncertainty which has prompted plans for the rationalization of production and the elimination of surplus capacity. The two main concentrations, both largely in the hands of IRI subsidiaries (Fincantieri and Finmeccanica), are at Genoa (Ansaldo) and Trieste–Monfalcone (Cantieri Riuniti dell' Adriatico). The yards at Venice, Ancona, Savona, La Spezia, Leghorn, Naples, Castellammare and Palermo are much less important and several are threatened with closure.

Other branches of the heavy engineering industry producing foundry and steel-making equipment, heavy presses, lathes, marine engines, etc. are located overwhelmingly at Genoa, Milan (Innocenti) and Turin (Fiat). The last two cities are also outstanding in the manufacture of heavy electrical equipment (Edison, CGE, Fiat) and railway equipment (Fiat, Breda) although this latter activity is also shared by Bolzano, Pinerolo, Brescia, Savigliano, Modena, Reggio Emilia, Pistoia and Naples.

No country has embraced the automobile revolution with greater enthusiasm than Italy which ranks a good fourth in Europe in production of motor vehicles after Western Germany, Britain and France; in 1964 1,090,000 vehicles were produced (a drop of 7% from the 1963 peak) and of these 331,000 were exported. As in many other fields of engineering, production is dominated by the vast integrated concern of Fiat at Turin, where Lancia's main factory is also located. Other centres interested in the industry are Milan (Alfa Romeo, Innocenti), Varese (Macchi), Brescia (OM), Modena (Ferrari), Bolzano (Lancia) and Naples (Alfa Romeo). Fear of competition from German and American-controlled producers within the Common Market and the need to exploit mass-production to the full have prompted several of the smaller producers to establish working associations with foreign firms similarly threatened (Alfa Romeo and Renault). Fiat has several factories overseas, notably in South America, as well as technical connections elsewhere (Spain).[1] The reputation of Italian designers and craftsmen is responsible for several factories specializing in luxury coachwork, for example at Milan and Modena. The Italian aircraft industry has never recovered the rank and prestige it enjoyed before the war. Production is now largely confined to engines, small planes and helicopters, many of them built under licence. The chief towns interested in the industry are Turin, Milan, Sesto Calende, Gallarate and Varese.

Cycling has lost none of its popularity as a sport but as a means of transport it has been largely superseded by that typically Italian invention, the motor scooter. The manufacture of these vehicles at Milan (Innocenti's Lambretta), Genoa and Pontedera (Piaggio's Vespa) contributes substantially to exports. Motor cycles, a branch of engineering in which Italy has earned a high reputation, are made at Milan (Bianchi), Mandello (Moto Guzzi) and Gallarate (Gilera). Naturally enough pedal cycles are also produced in most of these towns as well as at Padua, Bassano and Vittorio Veneto.

Other light engineering industries which deserve to be selected from a long and growing list are textile machinery, calculating machinery and machine tools. The first is produced on a scale sufficient to raise Italy to world rank among exporters; sewing machines are made at Milan (Singer) and Pavia (Necchi) while Italy's reputation for knitwear machines depends largely on the textile towns of Veneto. Since the war the expansion in the production of typewriters and calculating machinery has been spectacular. Output is almost entirely in the

[1] In 1966 Fiat signed contracts for the construction of a car plant in the USSR and another in Poland.

hands of one firm, Olivetti, with its main factory at Ivrea and others at Turin and Pozzuoli. It has recently come under the control of an American concern. The machine tool industry, although much expanded in recent years, is still unable to supply all the country's diverse requirements and there is a large import of German, Swiss and American products. As in so many other sectors the machine tool industry is overwhelmingly concentrated in Turin and in Milan and its environs.

## Civil engineering

In no other branch of activity was the boom decade more exuberantly and obviously manifested than in building and construction. Stimulated by an ambitious programme of public works and by a demand for more and better housing, which was a natural consequence of the rise in living standards, it was sustained by the readiness with which banks, insurance companies and individuals were willing to invest in property.[1] The recession of 1963 and the inevitable restriction of credit accompanying it caused an immediate decline in activity with serious consequences for the employment situation not only in building itself, which is the largest user of unskilled labour, but in the industries dependent on it (sanitary ware, fittings, etc.). Since the war Italian civil engineering concerns have found an outlet for their skill and experience overseas. Dams on the Zambezi, Atbara, Volta, Ladhon, Douro and Volta are among their best-known achievements.

## The chemical industry

Although most of the deposits concerned are modest in size and often inconveniently located, the subsoil of Italy provides a wide variety of chemical raw materials. Sulphur is abundantly available from the mines of Sicily, from the pyrites of Tuscany and as a by-product of oil refining; nitrates are produced from lignite, from natural gas and by atmospheric fixation; and salt is produced from pans and from the Miocene rocks of Tuscany and Sicily, which also yield gypsum. Other useful minerals present are borax (Cecina valley), fluorspar (Trentino), bauxite (Abruzzi), lead–zinc ore (Sardinia) and potash, recently discovered in large quantities in central Sicily (San Cataldo). As in other European countries the outstanding development in recent years has been the spectacular expansion of the petro-chemical industry with its multiplicity of by-products, not least rubber, plastics and synthetic fibres. In this respect the discovery of natural gas in the Po Valley and in Sicily has been most fortunate. Despite the production of so many of Italy's chemical raw materials in the peninsula and islands, the majority of the processing and manufacture is carried out in the North – the main consuming area – but the expansion of oil refining and petro-chemicals elsewhere in recent years (Naples, Bari, Brindisi, Augusta, Gela, Pisticci) has done something to redress the balance. New coking capacity is also making its contribution but

[1] Building has always been a favoured activity since no taxes are demanded on private houses or apartments until 25 years have elapsed.

otherwise the chemical industry in the South and Centre is mainly represented by a few isolated plants exploiting some local advantage, for example at Crotone (Silan power), Porto Empedocle (sulphur), Portiglione (pyrites) and Campofranco (potash). In the North the towns with a particularly strong interest in chemicals are Turin, Milan (Bovisa), Novara, Ferrara, Ravenna, Merano, Bolzano, Porto Marghera, S. Giuseppe di Cairo and Cogoleto. In common with that of all industrialized countries Italy's chemical industry has enjoyed a rapid expansion accompanied by an almost ceaseless proliferation of new products. The lion's share of production is similarly controlled by a handful of firms among which ENI, the international oil companies and above all Montecatini[1] are outstanding. In the pharmaceutical branch Italian producers have an advantage in that Italian law gives less protection than that of most countries to manufacturing processes, many of them evolved abroad after considerable expenditure on research.

### The textile and footwear industries

Textiles are a branch of manufacturing in which Italians have enjoyed a high reputation for centuries but mass-production, based on hydro-electric power and the relatively cheap labour then available, dates only from the turn of the century. In most European countries since the war the industry, except in the synthetic branches, has enjoyed none of the spectacular advances achieved in such 'growth' sectors as cars and chemicals. In this respect Italy is no exception but the industry still employs over half a million workers and is second only to engineering as an exporter. Except for silk and hemp, almost all the raw materials have to be imported, and although the consumption of textiles has risen with improved living standards, most manufacturers, especially in cottons, are in the position of having to export a large part of their output if capacity is to be fully employed. This is obviously a difficult task in view of the fierce competition in foreign markets. The structure of the industry exhibits great variety; in rayon and synthetics large units are the rule, and in cotton they are well represented, but in woollens they are much less general; indeed, there are still many woollen producers operating on a workshop or handicraft basis, for example in Tuscany and the Alpine valleys. The vulnerability of some sections of the industry has prompted a number of self-imposed and privately financed rationalization schemes aimed at the introduction of more modern machinery and labour-saving processes and the concentration of production in fewer but larger units; in cottons in particular this has resulted in a drastic reduction in the number of workers.

Over 90% of Italy's cotton spinning and weaving capacity is located in the North particularly in the upper plain of Piedmont and Lombardy (Varese, Gallarate, Busto Arsizio, Legnano). Most of the rest is to be found in Campania and Calabria where several mills damaged in the war came under the control of

---

[1] Montecatini has recently merged with Edison, another major chemical producer.

IRI. The industry, which relies mainly on raw materials from the USA, employs some 150,000 workers.

The woollen industry, which employs something over half of this total, is also heavily concentrated in the North. The majority of the woollen cloth and worsted is produced in the Biellese and to a less degree in the Bergamasque Sub-Alpine valleys, while a high proportion of the country's knitting wool, hosiery and knit-wear is made along the Sub-Alpine fringe of Vicenza province at Valdagno (Lanerossi, Marzotto), Schio, Thiene and Vicenza itself as well as at Padua and Venice. In Tuscany the biggest producer is Prato which specializes in regenerated cloth (shoddy). Italian woollens, especially fashionable knitwear, enjoy a high reputation which earns them a place in western European markets. The vast majority of the raw wool used is imported; the fibre obtainable from Italy's own flocks is unsuitable for the finer fabrics now in demand and is largely used for mattresses, felts and upholstery.

The silk industry, which once had a much wider distribution, is now concentrated in an arc of towns to the north of Milan from Varese through Como to Treviglio; this area accounts for most of the spinning and almost all the weaving carried out. Regular lines of mulberries still provide a familiar element in much of the Northern Plain and parts of the Marche but they are being slowly sacrificed to the demands of mechanization as raw silk production declines with rising living standards. The only significant producing areas now are Lombardy and above all Veneto and Venezia Giulia where some processing is also carried on. The manufacture of silk has been a declining activity for several decades and now employs only about 20,000 operatives; it has been the victim of Asian competition and of rayon and synthetic substitutes. There is no doubt that the quality of Italian goods is high and there is still a modest export to the USA and western Europe. The main hope of the industry seems to lie in the restoration of silk's image as a prestige fibre.

Between the wars Italy emerged as a major producer of rayon. Much of the necessary raw material, in the form of cane, poplar and eucalypt, is home-produced. Rayon is a manufacture demanding massive capital investment, and production is concentrated in the hands of a few firms (notably Snia–Viscosa) operating a few large plants, for example at Varedo and Torviscosa; the latter may be considered a company town. Since the war Italy, while retaining her rank as a rayon manufacturer, has shared in the expansion in synthetic fibres some of which were invented by Italian firms. As with rayon, production is in large, heavily capitalized units controlled by a few firms chief among which are Snia-Viscosa and Montecatini (there is rough parallel between these two companies and Courtaulds and ICI respectively). In the North the main centres interested in synthetic fibres are Turin, Chatillon, Verbania, Vercelli, Pavia, Padua, Magenta and Forli; the South is represented at Caserta, Colleferro (Frosinone province), Pisticci and most recently at Manfredonia. Most of the firms involved are also concerned with producing a wide range of synthetic products including plastics, fibre glass and paints. Among the less important textiles, flax and hemp manufacturing is concentrated mainly in southern Lombardy, but Naples also shares in this activity and is outstanding in jute processing.

Italians with their long traditions in the field have a strong feeling for textiles and they excel in colour and design. Exports have benefited from the creation of a fashionable image for Italian goods (in knitwear, for example) which has been assisted by the reputation of Rome as a centre of *haute couture* – a development which owes something to the film industry. The ready-made clothing industry, with its dependence on chain stores to retail its goods, is still much less important than in Britain; it is gaining ground but there is still an understandable preference for the individual dressmaker and tailor.

As a craft industry shoemaking survives almost everywhere in Italy but the factory production of footwear is concentrated heavily in the North, notably at Vigevano (the biggest single centre), Varese, Milan, Montebelluna and Bologna, but Tuscany and Umbria also share in the trade. Italian manufacturers have been particularly successful in imposing their fashions on the rest of Europe—to the benefit of exports. A speciality of Cornuda is the manufacture of skiing and climbing boots, an activity demanding skilled craftsmanship.

*Wood industries*

The furniture industry has benefited from the rise in living standards and from a boom in building since the early fifties. It is represented in most large consuming areas but the factories of Lombardy, especially in the Brianza, have more than local importance. The Marche and Tuscany also have a stake in the industry.

The paper industry too, with its large demands on water, is also mainly a northern activity in which Turin, Milan, Como, Varese, Vercelli, Cuneo and Novara have an interest; Liguria produces mainly wrapping paper. The Centre's contribution (about 25% of the total) is mainly provided by Lazio (Tivoli, Isola di Liri, Cassino), where rag and waste paper are the raw materials used, and by the Marche. Fabriano was Europe's first producer of paper.

*Alimentary industries*

Were it possible to calculate accurately the workers effectively employed in food processing, ranging from the provision of the humblest necessities of life at the village level to the sophisticated factory product, it would probably emerge as the largest single employer of labour. Despite their importance in the internal economy the alimentary industries have shared less than most in the post-war expansion of production and exports. There have been changes, of course, notably a swing towards standardized branded products, and a concentration of production in larger units. Since Italy is capable of producing a greater range of products and is less dependent on imports than Britain, food manufacturing has a wider distribution and such activities as milling, malting, sugar refining and oil seed and meat processing are less obviously concentrated at the ports; indeed, there are hundreds of little concerns scattered throughout the country engaged in milling, olive oil pressing, wine making, cheese making, etc. from local produce and for local needs. The possibility of taking one's own sack of wheat to the village mill and of taking away flour from which the miller has removed nothing may seem primitive economics but it ensures a quality of bread quite unobtainable in more sophisticated countries. The Northern Plain, the area with the most productive agriculture as well as the biggest concentration of consumers, has a high proportion of the large processing concerns. Sugar refining from its very nature favours large units and is particularly important in Emilia–Romagna, Veneto and Lombardy. The same regions are also engaged in the packing and canning of fruit. Most cities of the plain, particularly those along the Via Emilia, share in milling and pasta making and in the manufacture of preserves, essences, liqueurs, sauces, biscuits and confectionery. Milan, with such well-known enterprises as Motta and Alemagna, is particularly important. Emilia is famous for its pork meats (*zampone, salame, mortadella*, etc.) and sausages, and no city in Italy has a higher reputation with gourmets than Bologna. Although Gorgonzola and Parma bear the most famous names in Italian cheese making, this activity is shared by Lodi, Pavia, Piacenza, Cremona, Bergamo and Milan in a zone which also produces Bel Paese, *stracchino* and *provolone*. The characteristic cheese of peninsular Italy (and Sardinia) is *pecorino*; it is made from sheep's milk and is often used as a substitute in cooking for the more expensive parmesan. Outside the Northern Plain Campania is the most important food-processing area. Apart from the packing and despatch of fresh fruit and vegetables, Campania specializes in the manufacture of pasta, preserves and tomato essences. Apulia, Tuscany and Liguria are foremost in olive oil refining. In a country where wine is so cheap, beer is something of a luxury but breweries are to be found in most of the larger cities, especially in the North. The bottling and distribution of mineral water (Nepi, Fiuggi, Chianciano, etc.) at scores of local plants is a sizeable industry in Italy where the discussion of one's liver is as much a topic of conversation as is one's rheumatism in England. The list of local food specialities is almost inexhaustible – the *panettone* of Milan, the *panforte* of Siena, the *mozzarella* of Campania, the almond confectionery of Sicily – but they find only a limited sale abroad. The existence of communities of Italian origin overseas as well as the spread of more cosmopolitan tastes (a by-product of tourism) help to maintain the export of some types of manufactured foodstuffs.

Frequent reference has already been made to the wine industry in earlier sections.

*The fishing industry*

As might be expected in a Roman Catholic country, fish is a regular feature of the Italian diet. Unfortunately the Mediterranean provides no fishing grounds comparable with those of the northern Atlantic and northern Pacific, where the presence of extensive continental shelves and the mingling of waters of differing temperature and salinity are conducive to the growth of plankton and other fish foods in great abundance. In consequence the demand for fish cannot be met from home waters and in recent years the traditional imports of dried and salted herring and cod have been supplemented by more expensive pre-packed frozen fish. Although fishing on a full-time or part-time basis helps to provide a living for tens of thousands of Italians the value of the catch is normally only about one-fifth of that of the UK. There is no concentration of activity in highly specialized ports like Grimsby or Bergen with their elaborate processing facilities; each port serves a limited hinterland from limited fishing grounds. The vast majority of the boats in use have a restricted range and little accommodation for storage or the crew; indeed about a third of the boats in use are without engines. At present only a handful of deep-sea trawlers, most of them based on Leghorn, operate outside the Mediterranean waters. The unsatisfactory state of the industry and the need for large-scale investment have prompted various government schemes (most recently the so-called Blue Plan) aimed at the provision of better processing facilities ashore and of more modern vessels capable of a much greater range. The waters of the Mediterranean are overfished and at the best of times provide no shoals on the scale encountered in the Atlantic and North Sea; the normal rewards of a night's fishing are a mixed catch of sardines, mackerel, anchovies, dentex and mullet; apart from tunny the swordfish is the biggest fish landed. Oysters, mussels, prawns, shrimps and cuttlefish abound in the shallower waters and provide the ingredients for mixed fries and fish soups rivalling those of Marseilles. The majority of the tunny landed is caught in Sardinian and Sicilian waters although the processing is largely in the hands of Ligurian concerns. The sponges of the Messina Straits and Lampedusa and the corals of Sardinia are of only minor importance. Eels are a speciality of the Po and its tributaries, and among fresh-water fish the trout of Garda is perhaps the best known.

## COMMUNICATIONS

RAILWAYS. Out of a network totalling 21,143 km (UK 29,500 km), 16,380 km are operated by the state and the rest by concessionaires. Almost all the state mileage is of standard gauge, roughly half is electrified and over a quarter consists of double track. Of the private lines totalling 4763 km half the mileage is of standard gauge and about one-third is electrified. The overall density is about two-thirds of that of the United Kingdom and somewhat less than that of France; the much closer network in the North compared with that of the rest of the country is yet another indication of that area's relative prosperity. Quite apart from the difficulty of much of the terrain, which made railways difficult to build and makes them expensive to maintain, the Italian administration is faced with most of the economic and social problems plaguing operators elsewhere in Europe. Italy lacks the heavy mineral traffic which makes up such a large proportion of British railway freight and this goes some way to explaining why in recent years the tonnage carried on the Italian system annually has only been about one-quarter of the British total and the number of ton-kilometres about one-half.

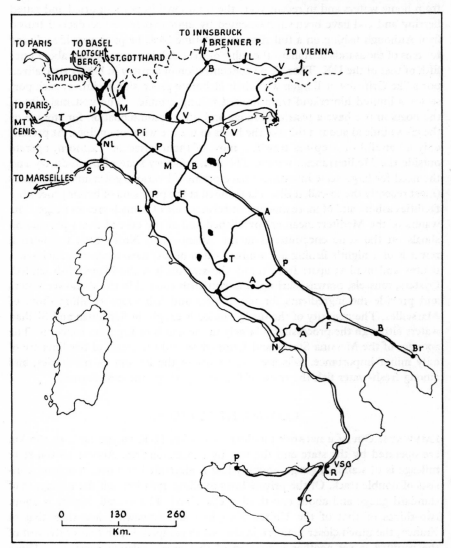

*Fig. 52.* The trunk routes of the Italian railway network

Moreover, although a railway system for the whole country must be provided and maintained, large areas outside the North are incapable of furnishing enough traffic to meet running costs; in fact, the railways operate at a very substantial annual loss. For many years they have been losing ground to coach operators and road hauliers not only in the remoter areas but on the medium and long distances, and this tendency is being accelerated by the spread of the motorway network. The popularity of the car and the motor scooter has also cut deeply into the railways' passenger traffic. Although nothing so drastic as the Beeching plan has ever been mooted some of the remoter feeder lines have been abandoned and new investment is being directed towards the improvement of long-distance trunk routes on which the railways may hope to operate competitively. To this end electrification has been pushed ahead (for example from Salerno to Palermo) and on several sections the track has been (Battipaglia–Reggio Calabria) or is in process of being doubled (the Adriatic coast route). The operation of fast air-conditioned 'super-trains', for example between Rome and Milan and between Turin and Lyons, is another feature of the modernization programme.

The major trunk routes and the essential links through the Alps and Apennines are summarized in fig. 52.

ROADS. The volume of both passenger and goods traffic on the roads vastly exceeds that carried by the railways and there seems every prospect that the disparity will increase. Between 1957 and 1961 the number of cars and lorries on the roads increased by 83% to nearly 3 million and the number of motor cycles and tricycles increased by 28% to over 4 million. Four main types of road may be recognized – motorways (*autostrade*), national trunk roads, provincial roads and communal roads. Italy was the pioneer of motorways in Europe but those built before the war (mainly radiating from Milan), although guarded against cross traffic, were not dual carriageways. Since 1956 they have been doubled and incorporated into a much more ambitious network radiating from Milan to Genoa, Turin, Sesto Calende, Varese, Como and Venice (the *Serenissima*), and penetrating deep into the peninsula as far as Salerno (the *Strada del Sole*). Private enterprise (notably Fiat) has an interest in part of the system but the majority of it is being financed through IRI. There is no doubt that a timely expenditure on motorways has provided an economic asset of the first order and at the same time is making a contribution, particularly by means of the Strada del Sole, to national integration. The links between the Italian motorway system and that of her trans-Alpine neighbours is so far unsatisfactory but the extension of the auto-strada from Aosta to the entrances of the Mt Blanc and Great St Bernard tunnels and the construction of the proposed motorway up to the Brenner should do much to remedy this weakness. Tolls are levied according to engine capacity; that for a 1500-cc car works out at about one penny per mile. The motorways supplement a comprehensive national system of conventional highways; they are best exemplified in the famous consular roads leading to Rome. Like similar roads in Britain, they are often quite inadequate for the volume of traffic but the motorways have done much to relieve the congestion. The subsidiary network maintained by the provincial and local authorities varies greatly in quality and density; on the whole the British counterpart provides a much more satisfactory coverage.

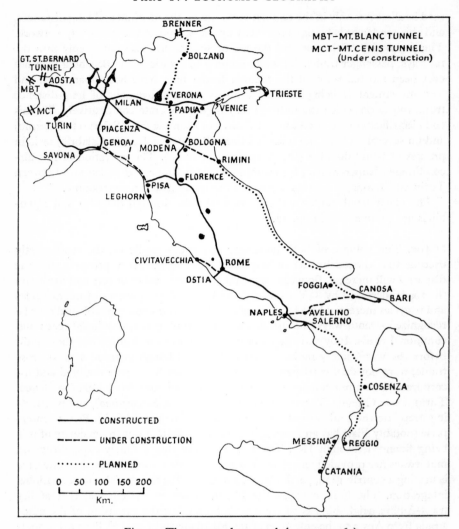

*Fig. 53.* The autostrada network (summer 1965)

INLAND WATERWAYS. This form of transport plays only a minor rôle in Italian communications. Except for one or two short stretches, notably on the lower Arno and lower Tiber, the rivers of peninsular Italy are unsuited to all but the smallest craft. In the North, even the Po system, which is navigable for 600 ton barges as far as Mantua and Pavia upstream, is of only modest importance. From time to time plans for connecting Milan to the Adriatic by a satisfactory waterway are aired but so far the project has been repeatedly shelved. The heaviest traffic is to be found among the Venetian lagoons and on the three main Alpine lakes where steamers operate regular services.

INTER-ISLAND COMMUNICATIONS. In the absence of the Messina Straits bridge now under discussion, the principal link with Sicily is provided by the train ferry between Villa S. Giovanni and Messina; car ferries operate on the same route and between Reggio and Messina. Much of the freight bound for the mainland is shipped by regular services from Palermo to Naples. The main packet service to Sardinia operates between Civitavecchia and Olbia but there are also services between Cagliari and Naples and much of the island's freight traffic falls within the orbit of Genoa. Even the smaller Tyrrhenian islands have regular sailings to the mainland, at least in summer; Portoferraio is reached from Piombino (a car ferry service), Ischia and Capri from Naples, Giglio from Porto S. Stefano and the Lipari islands from Milazzo. On some of these routes, which would seem to offer scope for hovercraft, the normal steamer services are supplemented by hydrofoil 'taxis'.

AIRWAYS. Through Alitalia the state operates an airline of world rank with services to the main cities of Europe, to North and South America, the Middle and Far East, and most parts of Africa. The majority of this international traffic is concentrated on Rome and to a lesser degree on Milan, but Florence, Genoa, Turin, Venice, Pisa, Naples and Alghero also enjoy direct air links with several European capitals, at least in the summer. An excellent internal network links the country's main cities.

THE MERCANTILE MARINE. At the end of the war the Italian mercantile marine had been reduced to one-tenth of its pre-war total of $3\frac{1}{2}$ million tons. Thanks to the acquisition of surplus American tonnage, now largely replaced, and to an ambitious building programme, the pre-war total was surpassed within a decade, and although the pace of expansion has slackened in recent years the shipping registered under the Italian flag now approaches 6 million deadweight tons. Tankers account for about 40% of the total and passenger and passenger–cargo liners 15%; the rest is dry cargo tonnage (including several ore carriers) engaged in transporting essential raw materials. The disastrous situation in the industry in 1945 left the government little alternative but to intervene with financial support, and the state has retained a large interest, particularly in the passenger and passenger–cargo trade through IRI (Finmare), and more recently has acquired a further stake with the expansion of the ENI tanker fleet. The most important lines, all part of Finmare, are the Italia line operating to North and South America; the Lloyd Triestino to East, West, and South Africa, Australia and the Far East; the Adriatica to the eastern Mediterranean and the Black Sea; and the Tirrenia to the western Mediterranean, North Africa and north-west

Europe. In common with the railways and airlines, Italian shipping companies benefit from a lively emigrant traffic.

Ignoring internal movements, the ports handling most passengers are in order Naples, Genoa, Brindisi, Trieste and Venice. Genoa and Naples are also outstanding in freight handling with Venice, Augusta, Ravenna, Savona, Leghorn, La Spezia, Trieste and Bari well behind. Augusta and Ravenna owe their newfound rank to their selection as oil terminals; similar developments elsewhere (for example at Taranto, Bari and Brindisi) will no doubt cause other radical changes in the order of ports as classified by tonnage handled.

## TRADE

Although there was no hope of its ever being achieved, the avowed policy of the pre-war Italian government was one of self-sufficiency within the Empire; to this end grain production was expanded to the utmost, imports were restricted to a minimum, industry, particularly that of a strategic nature, was subsidized and protected by high tariffs, and emigrants were sent out to open up the African territories. The revival of such a policy after the war was quite unthinkable, and particularly since 1950, as far as the structural weaknesses in her economy would allow, Italy has staked her hopes of achieving higher living standards for her rising population on an expansion of industry and trade. In this respect she has been assisted by an improvement in the world economic climate which has facilitated the availability of international capital for development projects, has furnished outlets for emigration, and has prospered the tourist trade. Furthermore, the desirability of more trade unimpeded by quotas and tariffs has become widely accepted among the western countries and has found expression in such organizations as GATT and OECD, and in more restricted spheres in the ECSC, EEC and EFTA. Traditionally a high protection country, Italy committed herself as a founder member of EEC to a progressive reduction of her tariffs to the lower level favoured by the Community. This policy has presented Italy's more efficient large-scale industries with an excellent opportunity but has inevitably caused some disruption in certain sectors (textiles, shipbuilding), particularly those in which too many small units are engaged and the processes employed have not kept pace with technical advances. Even some of the larger firms have been forced by competition into association with foreign concerns (Alfa Romeo, Ferrania, Olivetti). Italy's political and economic aspirations are not completely fulfilled by her membership of EEC; she would prefer some wider association with American links.

Although still lagging behind most western European countries in trade *per capita*, Italy between 1953 and 1963 enjoyed a spectacular trade expansion to which the engineering industries (especially vehicles) and the chemical industry made a major contribution. Since the recession of 1963, with its credit squeeze and balance of payments difficulties – an unpleasant reminder of the hazards inherent in the policy of industrial expansion to which she is committed – Italy's exports have risen much more slowly and it seems unlikely that the pace of expansion in the fifties will be regained. The accompanying tables underline Italy's increasing dependence on imports of raw materials, fuels and foodstuffs. The inability of agriculture to satisfy the increasing demand for meat and the more expensive foodstuffs, which had risen with increasing affluence, was a contributory factor in the 1963 balance of payments crisis. Tourist receipts (in recent years equalling about 15% of those from visible exports[1]) and emigrant remittances are important items in the balance of payments.

[1] In 1964 Italy earned $826 million more from foreign tourists than her own tourists spent abroad.

## TABLE 4

### MEAN MONTHLY TEMPERATURES FOR TYPICAL STATIONS (see fig. 14)

| Climatic type | Station | Ht metres | I | II | III | IV | V | VI | VII | VIII | IX | X | XI | XII |
|---|---|---|---|---|---|---|---|---|---|---|---|---|---|---|
| Ia | Bardonecchia | 1275 | -1·6 | -0·4 | 2·4 | 6·1 | 9·9 | 14·4 | 17·7 | 16·2 | 13·1 | 8·2 | 3·3 | 0·0 |
|  | Bormio | 1225 | -1·4 | 0·7 | 3·9 | 7·7 | 11·5 | 15·5 | 17·3 | 16·5 | 13·8 | 8·7 | 3·3 | -0·7 |
|  | Cortina | 1275 | -2·3 | -1·3 | 1·8 | 5·2 | 9·1 | 13·5 | 15·8 | 15·4 | 12·7 | 7·6 | 2·8 | -1·6 |
|  | Desenzano | 74 | 4·0 | 4·6 | 8·9 | 13·2 | 17·3 | 21·8 | 24·5 | 23·7 | 20·4 | 14·7 | 10·0 | 5·3 |
| Ib | Milan | 122 | 1·2 | 3·7 | 8·3 | 13·1 | 17·7 | 21·9 | 24·3 | 23·3 | 20·0 | 13·3 | 6·9 | 2·7 |
|  | Mantua | 20 | 0·8 | 3·2 | 8·5 | 13·4 | 17·7 | 22·5 | 24·8 | 24·0 | 20·1 | 13·9 | 7·6 | 2·3 |
|  | Venice | 3 | 3·8 | 4·1 | 8·2 | 12·6 | 17·1 | 21·2 | 23·6 | 23·3 | 20·4 | 15·1 | 10·5 | 5·5 |
| IIa | Genoa | 21 | 8·4 | 8·7 | 11·5 | 14·5 | 17·8 | 21·9 | 24·6 | 25·0 | 22·8 | 18·1 | 13·3 | 9·5 |
| IIb | Florence | 50 | 5·6 | 5·8 | 9·9 | 13·3 | 17·4 | 22·1 | 25·0 | 24·5 | 21·2 | 15·8 | 11·2 | 6·0 |
|  | Rome | 51 | 7·4 | 8·0 | 11·5 | 14·4 | 18·4 | 22·9 | 25·7 | 25·5 | 22·4 | 17·7 | 13·4 | 8·9 |
|  | Naples | 149 | 8·7 | 8·7 | 11·4 | 14·3 | 18·1 | 22·3 | 24·8 | 24·8 | 22·3 | 18·1 | 14·5 | 10·3 |
| IIc | Rimini | 7 | 3·3 | 4·5 | 8·7 | 12·9 | 17·2 | 21·7 | 24·3 | 23·8 | 20·4 | 15·3 | 10·1 | 5·1 |
|  | Bari | 12 | 8·4 | 8·5 | 10·8 | 13·9 | 17·5 | 21·9 | 24·5 | 24·3 | 21·7 | 18·2 | 14·8 | 10·2 |
| IId | Verghereto | 812 | 1·7 | 2·8 | 5·6 | 9·4 | 13·0 | 17·5 | 20·6 | 20·3 | 17·0 | 12·0 | 7·7 | 2·9 |
|  | Aquila | 735 | 2·1 | 2·6 | 6·8 | 10·8 | 14·8 | 19·6 | 21·8 | 21·9 | 18·4 | 13·3 | 8·5 | 3·7 |
|  | Potenza | 826 | 3·5 | 3·7 | 6·6 | 10·5 | 14·4 | 19·3 | 21·8 | 21·0 | 18·8 | 14·1 | 10·1 | 5·3 |
| IIe | Reggio Calabria | 15 | 11·1 | 11·1 | 13·2 | 15·4 | 19·0 | 23·1 | 25·9 | 26·3 | 23·9 | 19·3 | 17·3 | 13·2 |
|  | Taormina | 260 | 11·0 | 10·6 | 13·1 | 16·2 | 20·1 | 24·1 | 27·1 | 27·1 | 23·7 | 20·0 | 16·0 | 12·6 |
| IIf | Cagliari | 73 | 9·9 | 10·3 | 12·9 | 15·3 | 18·6 | 22·8 | 25·8 | 25·7 | 23·3 | 19·5 | 15·6 | 11·8 |

## TABLE 5

### MEAN MONTHLY PRECIPITATION FOR TYPICAL STATIONS (*see* fig. 14)

| Climatic type | Station | I | II | III | IV | V | VI | VII | VIII | IX | X | XI | XII | Total |
|---|---|---|---|---|---|---|---|---|---|---|---|---|---|---|
| Ia | Bardonecchia | 22 | 41 | 42 | 84 | 65 | 38 | 35 | 46 | 59 | 98 | 73 | 57 | 660 |
| | Bormio | 19 | 23 | 39 | 47 | 75 | 79 | 90 | 100 | 80 | 74 | 69 | 33 | 728 |
| | Cortina | 50 | 47 | 82 | 138 | 132 | 128 | 148 | 117 | 115 | 119 | 116 | 59 | 1252 |
| | Desenzano | 50 | 48 | 63 | 70 | 99 | 75 | 67 | 66 | 78 | 67 | 71 | 61 | 815 |
| Ib | Milan | 60 | 59 | 73 | 89 | 102 | 83 | 72 | 81 | 87 | 121 | 105 | 76 | 1007 |
| | Mantua | 49 | 41 | 54 | 54 | 83 | 71 | 40 | 40 | 68 | 68 | 71 | 46 | 685 |
| | Venice | 48 | 43 | 63 | 61 | 81 | 75 | 45 | 56 | 68 | 84 | 82 | 51 | 757 |
| IIa | Genoa | 109 | 105 | 101 | 82 | 61 | 42 | 35 | 62 | 63 | 135 | 206 | 112 | 1113 |
| IIb | Florence | 61 | 68 | 65 | 74 | 62 | 49 | 23 | 38 | 54 | 96 | 107 | 72 | 769 |
| | Rome | 74 | 87 | 79 | 62 | 57 | 38 | 6 | 23 | 66 | 123 | 121 | 92 | 828 |
| | Naples | 87 | 77 | 76 | 55 | 37 | 33 | 14 | 16 | 56 | 102 | 135 | 105 | 793 |
| IIc | Rimini | 51 | 67 | 52 | 51 | 59 | 64 | 35 | 42 | 89 | 89 | 73 | 74 | 746 |
| | Bari | 39 | 39 | 50 | 35 | 38 | 32 | 19 | 24 | 40 | 111 | 110 | 67 | 604 |
| IId | Verghereto | 115 | 111 | 115 | 108 | 112 | 81 | 38 | 47 | 95 | 159 | 158 | 155 | 1294 |
| | Aquila | 49 | 62 | 59 | 81 | 54 | 38 | 38 | 39 | 65 | 82 | 88 | 80 | 735 |
| | Potenza | 130 | 88 | 67 | 82 | 95 | 62 | 28 | 43 | 82 | 71 | 125 | 123 | 996 |
| IIe | Reggio Calabria | 74 | 76 | 56 | 52 | 26 | 13 | 6 | 9 | 36 | 53 | 70 | 97 | 568 |
| | Taormina | 103 | 94 | 82 | 61 | 16 | 13 | 6 | 4 | 49 | 91 | 92 | 126 | 737 |
| IIf | Cagliari | 54 | 59 | 50 | 43 | 39 | 5 | 3 | 10 | 32 | 53 | 57 | 74 | 479 |

## TABLE 6

### EMPLOYED LABOUR FORCE (IN THOUSANDS)

### 1951, 1961 AND 1963

(Source: Compendio Statistico Italiano)

| | 1951 | | 1961 | | 1963 | | of which | | | |
| --- | --- | --- | --- | --- | --- | --- | --- | --- | --- | --- |
| | | | | | | | Men | % | Women | % |
| | Number | % | Number | % | Number | % | | | | |
| Agriculture | 6,227 | 42·5 | 5,907 | 29·1 | 5,295 | 27·0 | 3,515 | 25·2 | 1,780 | 31·3 |
| Industry | 4,913 | 33·5 | 8,012 | 39·5 | 7,986 | 40·6 | 6,173 | 44·2 | 1,813 | 31·9 |
| Other activities | 3,523 | 24·0 | 6,348 | 31·3 | 6,346 | 32·4 | 4,264 | 30·6 | 2,085 | 36·6 |
| Total | 14,663 | 100·0 | 20,267 | 100·0 | 19,630 | 100·0 | 13,952 | 100·0 | 5,678 | 100·0 |

## TABLE 7

### DETAILS OF THE LAND REFORM ZONES

| Agency (Ente) | Total area under jurisdiction | Expropriated area available for assignment | Otherwise acquired | Total area available assignment | Area assigned PODERI | | Area assigned QUOTE | | Area assigned TOTAL | |
| --- | --- | --- | --- | --- | --- | --- | --- | --- | --- | --- |
| | | | | | Number | Area | Number | Area | Number | Area |
| Po Delta | 260,000 | 44,233 | 3,263 | 47,496 | 6,160 | 38,151 | 257 | 352 | 6,417 | 38,503 |
| Maremma | 956,638 | 177,350 | 2,533 | 179,883 | 7,940 | 122,025 | 11,103 | 39,654 | 19,043 | 162,243 |
| Fucino | 155,000 | 15,864 | 111 | 15,975 | | | 9,146 | 13,475 | 9,146 | 13,475 |
| Campania | 121,431 | 8,327 | 8,040 | 16,367 | 1,670 | 12,319 | 1,608 | 2,489 | 3,278 | 15,020 |
| Apul-Luc-Molise | 1,453,181 | 189,458 | 7,693 | 197,151 | 16,084 | 135,276 | 15,023 | 36,872 | 31,107 | 172,148 |
| Calabria | 503,779 | 75,423 | 10,494 | 85,917 | 11,411 | 61,276 | 7,491 | 14,735 | 18,902 | 77,373 |
| Sardinia | 2,126,025 | 48,352 | 52,959 | 101,311 | 2,810 | 54,094 | 756 | 3,297 | 3,566 | 57,675 |
| Sicily | 2,392,672 | 74,256 | 893 | 75,149 | | | | | 16,971 | 74,256 |
| TOTAL | 7,968,726 | 633,263 | 85,986 | 719,249 | 46,075 | 423,141 | 45,384 | 110,874 | 108,430 | 610,693 |

## TABLE 8

### FORM OF OPERATION, OWNERSHIP AND DEGREE OF FRAGMENTATION OF THE ITALIAN AGRICULTURAL AND FOREST AREA, 1961

*(1961 Agricultural Census)*

| Form of operation | Farm units | | Area | | Percentage farm area owned by operator | | Percentage of farm area in | | Fragmented into | | | |
|---|---|---|---|---|---|---|---|---|---|---|---|---|
| | Number | % | Hectares | % | Wholly | In part | Consolidated units | Fragmented | 2–3 plots | 4–5 plots | 6–10 plots | Over 10 plots |
| Direct by cultivator whether owner or not | 3,485,968 | 81·2 | 13,218,337 | 49·8 | 56·4 | 13·1 | 38·1 | 61·9 | 31·2 | 12·9 | 11·3 | 6·5 |
| With hired labour or share croppers (*compartecipanti*) | 330,060 | 7·7 | 9,158,660 | 34·4 | 87·9 | 4·7 | 49·0 | 51·0 | 30·0 | 10·2 | 7·1 | 3·7 |
| On share tenant basis on consolidated holdings (*mezzadria appoderata*) | 316,549 | 7·4 | 3,125,536 | 11·8 | 93·7 | 1·2 | 58·8 | 41·2 | 26·8 | 8·0 | 5·0 | 1·7 |
| Other forms including *mezzadria non-appoderata* | 161,347 | 3·7 | 1,069,132 | 4·0 | 90·0 | 1·4 | 51·2 | 48·8 | 32·4 | 9·9 | 5·2 | 1·3 |
| | 4,293,924 | 100·0 | 26,571,665 | 100·0 | | | 41·0 | 59·0 | 30·8 | 12·2 | 10·3 | 5·7 |

TABLE 9

LAND-USE, FORM OF FARM OPERATION
AND SIZE OF FARM UNITS FOR SELECTED PROVINCES

*(1961 agricultural census)*

*Land-use of selected provinces expressed as percentages of each province (1961)*

| Province | Rotated field crops | of which | | Tree and bush crops | Permanent pasture | Woods | Productive uncultivated | Total forest and farmland | Other uses | Total area '000 ha. |
|---|---|---|---|---|---|---|---|---|---|---|
| | Total | Cereals | Forage | | | | | | | |
| Bolzano | 4·2 | 58·7 | 23·0 | 2·6 | 34·5 | 40·1 | 3·1 | 84·5 | 15·4 | 740 |
| Cremona | 80·9 | 38·0 | 53·5 | 0·8 | 5·8 | 3·5 | — | 91·1 | 8·9 | 176 |
| Padua | 75·3 | 51·8 | 25·3 | 8·9 | 4·1 | 2·4 | 0·5 | 91·3 | 8·7 | 214 |
| Ferrara | 57·2 | 38·1 | 25·5 | 19·8 | 1.2 | 1·5 | 0·9 | 80·6 | 19·4 | 263 |
| Savona | 9·5 | 39·6 | 16·5 | 10·4 | 10·1 | 63·7 | 1·1 | 95·0 | 5·0 | 154 |
| Arezzo | 47·5 | 37·2 | 38·3 | 3·9 | 7·7 | 32·8 | 3·6 | 95·3 | 4·7 | 323 |
| Siena | 58·9 | 35·6 | 31·8 | 0·3 | 3·5 | 32·8 | 3·0 | 96·3 | 3·7 | 382 |
| Terni | 44·8 | 41·9 | 48·3 | 2·3 | 13·4 | 36·2 | 0·2 | 96·0 | 4·0 | 212 |
| Teramo | 63·9 | 45·7 | 35·7 | 1·9 | 9·1 | 13·6 | 6·2 | 94·9 | 5·1 | 194 |
| Foggia | 59·4 | 65·7 | 11·3 | 11·8 | 15·3 | 6·4 | 1·6 | 94·6 | 5·4 | 719 |
| Bari | 31·3 | 64·0 | 9·6 | 47·4 | 14·5 | 3·2 | — | 96·6 | 3·4 | 513 |
| Potenza | 39·5 | 64·2 | 6·4 | 3·5 | 30·4 | 18·4 | 2·7 | 94·8 | 5·2 | 655 |
| Caserta | 56·0 | 54·6 | 19·0 | 10·0 | 9·1 | 17·4 | 0·6 | 92·5 | 7·5 | 264 |
| Reggio | 20·8 | 20·0 | 23·3 | 27·0 | 14·0 | 24·8 | 7·8 | 94·4 | 5·6 | 318 |
| Enna | 63·0 | 52·4 | 19·0 | 16·2 | 11·3 | 4·3 | 0·7 | 95·9 | 4·1 | 256 |
| Nuoro | 15·9 | 28·5 | 5·0 | 3·4 | 57·1 | 13·0 | 6·2 | 96·6 | 3·4 | 727 |
| Italy | 42·7 | 38·1 | 20·6 | 9·1 | 16·8 | 19·4 | 3·4 | 91·5 | 8·5 | 30,122 |

| Percentage of provincial productive area according to form of operation | | | | Percentage of provincial productive area according to size of units | | | |
|---|---|---|---|---|---|---|---|
| Direct | With hired labour or comparteci-panti | Mezzadria appoderata | Other forms | Under 1 ha | 1–5 ha | 5–25 ha | Over 25 ha |
| 51 | 48 | — | — | 4 | 4 | 14 | 76 |
| 57 | 39 | 3 | — | 2 | 9 | 31 | 58 |
| 84 | 10 | 5 | — | 5 | 37 | 39 | 19 |
| 55 | 29 | 15 | — | 1 | 9 | 49 | 41 |
| 63 | 29 | 5 | 3 | 2 | 17 | 42 | 36 |
| 25 | 38 | 37 | — | 1 | 10 | 45 | 44 |
| 14 | 44 | 40 | — | 1 | 6 | 35 | 58 |
| 21 | 39 | 39 | — | 1 | 10 | 39 | 49 |
| 33 | 24 | 43 | — | 1 | 21 | 52 | 26 |
| 62 | 34 | 2 | 3 | 2 | 11 | 33 | 54 |
| 67 | 19 | — | 14 | 6 | 27 | 32 | 35 |
| 59 | 32 | 5 | 3 | 1 | 16 | 31 | 52 |
| 60 | 32 | 5 | 2 | 6 | 32 | 29 | 33 |
| 33 | 58 | — | 9 | 7 | 19 | 21 | 53 |
| 45 | 20 | 4 | 29 | 2 | 20 | 34 | 33 |
| 54 | 44 | — | 1 | 1 | 5 | 15 | 79 |
| 49 | 34 | 12 | 45 | 3 | 18 | 33 | 46 |

## TABLE 10

### LAND-USE AND PRINCIPAL CROP AREAS
### 1953 AND 1963

(*Source: Annuario di Statistica Agraria*)

| | Area in '000 ha | | Percentage agric-forest land (1963) | Yield per ha quintals (1963) |
|---|---|---|---|---|
| | *1953* | *1963* | | |
| *Rotated field crops* | *13,211* | *12,674* | *46·0* | |
| Cereals | | 5,867 | 21·3 | |
|   Soft wheat | 4,770 | 3,033 | | 22·3 |
|   Hard wheat | 1,370 | 1,361 | | 12·2 |
|   Rye | 93 | 53 | | 14·6 |
|   Barley | 250 | 204 | | 13·7 |
|   Oats | 457 | 400 | | 13·7 |
|   Rice | 176 | 115 | | 51·2 |
|   Maize | 1,272 | 1,116 | | 33·2 |
| Leguminous crops | | 689 | 2·5 | |
| Potatoes | 393 | 292 | 1·1 | 113·6 |
| Vegetables | | 316 | 1·1 | |
|   Onions | 21 | 30 | | |
|   Artichokes | 23 | 47 | | |
|   Cabbage | 53 | 46 | | |
|   Cauliflowers | 30 | 36 | | |
|   Salads | | 41 | | |
|   Tomatoes | 90 | 127 | | |
| Industrial crops | | 322 | 1·2 | |
|   Sugar beet | 210 | 230 | | 343·4 |
|   Tobacco | 50 | 49 | | |
|   Hemp | 54 | 12 | | |
|   Flax | 18 | 6 | | |
|   Cotton | 26 | 16 | | |
| Rotated forage | 4,461 | 3,346 | 12·1 | |
| *Tree crops* | *2,468* | *2,741* | *9·9* | |
|   Vines (specialized) | 1,048 | 1,139 | 4·1 | |
|   Olives (specialized) | 872 | 899 | 3·3 | |
|   Citrus and other fruits | | 567 | 2·0 | |
| *Permanent pasture* | *5,090* | *5,095* | *18·5* | |
|   Meadows | | 875 | | |
|   Other grazing | | 4,220 | | |
| *Woodlands* | *5,710* | *6,029* | *21·9* | |
|   Stands (*fustaie*) | | 2,424 | 8·8 | |
|     of which conifers | | 1,135 | 4·1 | |
|     deciduous and mixed | | 1,289 | 4·7 | |
|   Coppice (*cedui*) | | 3,605 | 13·1 | |
| *Productive uncultivated* | *1,244* | *1,010* | *3·7* | |
| Total agricultural and forest area | 27,786 | 27,549 | 100·0 | |
| Other uses | | 2,574 | | |
| Total national territory | | 30,123 | | |

280

TABLE II

ITALIAN MINERAL PRODUCTION 1953 AND 1963
IN THOUSANDS OF METRIC TONS (EXCEPT NATURAL GAS,
IN MILLIONS OF CUBIC METRES)

*(Source: Compendio Statistico Italiano)*

| Mineral | '000 metric tons 1953 | '000 metric tons 1963 | '000 metric tons 1964 | Producing areas |
|---|---|---|---|---|
| Anthracite | 68 | 13 | 9 | Valle d'Aosta |
| Sulcis coal | 1,062 | 574 | 462 | Sulcis, Sardinia |
| Lignite | 754 | 1,365 | 1,200 | Tuscany, Umbria |
| Oil | 85 | 1,834 | 2,687 | Sicily, Abruzzi |
| Natural gas | 2,279 | 7,264 | 7,667 | Po Valley, Basilicata |
| Iron ore | 991 | 1,005 | 914 | Elba, La Nurra |
| Bauxite | 271 | 268 | 236 | Abruzzi, Apulia |
| Lead ore | 67 | 51 | 52 | Iglesiente, La Nurra |
| Zinc ore | 161 | 205 | 221 | Iglesiente, La Nurra |
| Manganese ore | 38 | 45 | 47 | Iglesiente |
| Mercury ore | 194 | 256 | 276 | M. Amiata |
| Antimony | 2 | 0·5 | 0·8 | Sardinia |
| Arsenic | 3 | — | — | Sardinia |
| Sulphur | 1,922 | 967 | 698 | Central Sicily |
| Pyrites | 1,234 | 1,398 | 1,396 | Tuscany |
| Potash | — | 1,263 | 1,470 | San Cataldo, Sicily |

TABLE 12

THE DISTRIBUTION OF INDUSTRIAL AND COMMERCIAL MANPOWER
1951 AND 1961 (IN THOUSANDS)

*(Industrial Censuses 1951 and 1961)*

| | 1951 | 1961 |
|---|---|---|
| *Extractive industries* | *119* | *104* |
| *Manufacturing industries* | *3,498* | *4,492* |
| Food and tobacco | 412 | 433 |
| Textiles | 651 | 592 |
| Clothing and shoes | 412 | 527 |
| Furniture | 102 | 134 |
| Wood industries | 193 | 244 |
| Metal industries | 145 | 192 |
| Machines, non-electric | 336 | 503 |
| Machines, electric | 95 | 172 |
| Precision machinery | 51 | 83 |
| Mechanical workshops | 227 | 376 |
| Vehicles | 188 | 235 |
| Non-metallic minerals | 207 | 312 |
| Chemical industries | 149 | 227 |
| *Construction* | *532* | *919* |
| *Gas, electricity and water undertakings* | *93* | *108* |
| *Commerce* | *1,803* | *2,392* |
| *Transport and communications* | *579* | *747* |
| *Credit, insurance, finance* | *162* | *219* |
| *Social services, etc.* | *207* | *314* |
| TOTAL | 6,995 | 9,427 |

## TABLE 13

### THE NATURE OF ITALIAN TRADE IN THOUSANDS OF MILLIONS OF LIRE

(*Source: Annuario Statistico Italiano*)

| | *Imports* | | | | | *Exports* | | | | |
|---|---|---|---|---|---|---|---|---|---|---|
| | *1957* | *1959* | *1961* | *1963* | *1964* | *1957* | *1959* | *1961* | *1963* | *1964* |
| *Farm, forest and fishery products* | 520 | 678 | 746 | 908 | 880 | 244 | 238 | 267 | 287 | 305 |
| Agricultural | 284 | 371 | 454 | 497 | 502 | 235 | 229 | 256 | 274 | 291 |
| Animal | 171 | 196 | 176 | 270 | 249 | 3 | 3 | 4 | 4 | 5 |
| Forest | 52 | 90 | 93 | 105 | 95 | 5 | 5 | 6 | 7 | 7 |
| Fish | 13 | 21 | 23 | 35 | 35 | 1 | 1 | 1 | 1 | 1 |
| *Products of extractive industries* | 638 | 558 | 598 | 719 | 780 | 17 | 20 | 20 | 17 | 19 |
| Metalliferous minerals | 160 | 140 | 153 | 155 | 135 | 4 | 4 | 3 | 2 | 5 |
| Fossil fuels | 444 | 382 | 404 | 516 | 591 | — | 4 | 4 | 1 | — |
| Coals | 154 | 93 | 88 | 100 | 102 | — | — | — | — | — |
| Crude oil | 290 | 289 | 315 | 416 | 489 | — | 4 | 4 | 1 | — |
| Non-metalliferous minerals | 34 | 36 | 42 | 48 | 53 | 12 | 12 | 13 | 13 | 14 |
| *Manufactures* | 1,108 | 1,714 | 1,920 | 3,084 | 2,859 | 1,326 | 1,562 | 2,330 | 2,850 | 3,399 |
| Based on agriculture | 344 | 484 | 423 | 792 | 789 | 475 | 506 | 750 | 901 | 1,003 |
| Foods | 199 | 293 | 216 | 477 | 472 | 142 | 104 | 134 | 145 | 144 |
| Drinks | 3 | 5 | 6 | 10 | 9 | 25 | 25 | 31 | 40 | 43 |
| Tobacco | 2 | 3 | 4 | 6 | 7 | — | — | — | — | — |
| Textiles | 72 | 83 | 88 | 150 | 153 | 220 | 256 | 380 | 456 | 516 |
| Clothing and leather | 12 | 21 | 24 | 38 | 45 | 72 | 100 | 173 | 222 | 254 |
| Wood and cork | 56 | 78 | 85 | 111 | 102 | 16 | 19 | 31 | 37 | 46 |
| Based on minerals | 498 | 817 | 1,047 | 1,692 | 1,449 | 542 | 696 | 1,071 | 1,316 | 1,614 |
| Metal products | 180 | 329 | 386 | 506 | 413 | 104 | 118 | 128 | 129 | 210 |
| Machinery | 286 | 444 | 609 | 1,110 | 963 | 408 | 542 | 883 | 1,112 | 1,310 |
| Machines and equipment | 179 | 259 | 361 | 634 | 585 | 146 | 193 | 381 | 507 | 596 |
| Precision machinery | 28 | 50 | 71 | 106 | 110 | 36 | 44 | 97 | 135 | 148 |
| Other metal machinery | 28 | 41 | 53 | 105 | 88 | 178 | 54 | 87 | 106 | 122 |
| Vehicles and means of transport | 51 | 94 | 124 | 265 | 182 | 47 | 251 | 317 | 364 | 444 |
| Non-metal mineral-based manufactures | 32 | 44 | 53 | 75 | 72 | 31 | 37 | 60 | 74 | 94 |
| Other manufactures | 266 | 414 | 450 | 601 | 622 | 309 | 361 | 509 | 633 | 782 |
| Chemical | 120 | 213 | 226 | 285 | 306 | 94 | 138 | 219 | 256 | 316 |
| Coal and oil derivatives | 36 | 55 | 62 | 73 | 57 | 116 | 129 | 143 | 174 | 194 |
| Artificial and synthetic fibres | 14 | 19 | 18 | 22 | 25 | 10 | 10 | 15 | 22 | 33 |
| Paper products | 32 | 58 | 70 | 100 | 105 | 6 | 8 | 12 | 14 | 20 |
| Natural and synthetic rubber goods | 4 | 9 | 11 | 18 | 19 | 7 | 17 | 36 | 50 | 65 |
| Others | 45 | 60 | 62 | 102 | 108 | 60 | 57 | 85 | 117 | 152 |
| TOTAL | 2,266 | 2,950 | 3,264 | 4,712 | 4,520 | 1,588 | 1,820 | 2,617 | 3,154 | 3,723 |

## TABLE 14

### THE DIRECTION OF ITALIAN TRADE IN THOUSANDS OF MILLIONS OF LIRE

*(Source: Annuario Statistico Italiano)*

| | Imports | | | | | Exports | | | | |
|---|---|---|---|---|---|---|---|---|---|---|
| | 1957 | 1959 | 1961 | 1963 | 1964 | 1957 | 1959 | 1961 | 1963 | 1964 |
| France | 121 | 162 | 299 | 458 | 446 | 101 | 112 | 199 | 327 | 406 |
| Belgium–Luxembourg | 41 | 48 | 76 | 150 | 132 | 39 | 46 | 72 | 114 | 146 |
| Netherlands | 47 | 57 | 77 | 139 | 163 | 34 | 48 | 80 | 115 | 156 |
| Fed. Germany | 277 | 293 | 509 | 799 | 737 | 222 | 295 | 465 | 564 | 707 |
| *EEC* | *486* | *561* | *963* | *1,547* | *1,478* | *396* | *501* | *817* | *1,120* | *1,416* |
| United Kingdom | 112 | 116 | 179 | 289 | 247 | 99 | 135 | 175 | 169 | 208 |
| Sweden | 43 | 45 | 63 | 92 | 87 | 45 | 43 | 63 | 66 | 72 |
| Switzerland | 66 | 71 | 93 | 120 | 114 | 122 | 131 | 180 | 213 | 225 |
| Austria | 98 | 91 | 111 | 131 | 106 | 53 | 51 | 73 | 82 | 88 |
| Yugoslavia | 33 | 38 | 49 | 101 | 83 | 49 | 41 | 87 | 71 | 108 |
| *Rest of Western Europe* | *435* | *473* | *652* | *964* | *849* | *412* | *554* | *809* | *872* | *1,042* |
| USSR | 32 | 49 | 93 | 110 | 92 | 27 | 27 | 56 | 71 | 57 |
| *Communist Europe* | *59* | *97* | *191* | *265* | *231* | *61* | *74* | *135* | *169* | *172* |
| South African Republic | 32 | 22 | 31 | 48 | 45 | 19 | 19 | 24 | 33 | 46 |
| *Africa* | *158* | *178* | *204* | *320* | *307* | *129* | *131* | *165* | *229* | *235* |
| USA | 424 | 234 | 539 | 642 | 612 | 143 | 216 | 239 | 297 | 317 |
| Canada | 38 | 19 | 43 | 53 | 42 | 18 | 21 | 29 | 30 | 37 |
| *North America* | *462* | *253* | *588* | *695* | *654* | *161* | *237* | *268* | *327* | *354* |
| Brazil | 17 | 27 | 25 | 44 | 51 | 23 | 19 | 28 | 26 | 13 |
| Argentina | 60 | 63 | 84 | 134 | 167 | 39 | 44 | 68 | 73 | 71 |
| *Latin America* | *158* | *146* | *174* | *310* | *341* | *147* | *161* | *193* | *199* | *208* |
| Iraq | 46 | 64 | 97 | 98 | 70 | 5 | 2 | 5 | 5 | 8 |
| Saudi Arabia | 129 | 69 | 64 | 83 | 101 | 7 | 4 | 5 | 8 | 11 |
| Kuwait | 62 | 81 | 87 | 122 | 185 | 6 | 4 | 6 | 8 | 9 |
| *Asia* | *364* | *329* | *397* | *512* | *553* | *148* | *146* | *204* | *210* | *259* |
| Australia | 86 | 55 | 81 | 76 | 82 | 12 | 12 | 17 | 23 | 31 |
| TOTAL | 2,266 | 2,105 | 3,264 | 4,712 | 4,520 | 1,588 | 1,821 | 2,614 | 3,154 | 3,723 |

# Bibliography

# PART I

L. BARZINI: *The Italians*

M. CARY: *The Geographical Background of Greek and Roman History*. OUP, 1949

A. CERVESATO: *The Roman Campagna*. Fisher Unwin, 1913

THOS CORYAT: *Coryat's Crudities*

T. FRANK: *An Economic History of Rome*. J. Cape, 1927

D. GIOFFRE: *Il commercio d'importazione genovese alla luce dei registri del dazio (1495–1537)*. Milan, 1962

M. GRINDROD: *Italy*. OUP, 1964

W. E. HEITLAND: *Agricola*. OUP, 1921

J. HEURGON: *The Daily Life of the Etruscans*. Hachette, 1964

G. LUZZATO: *Storia economica di Venezia dall' XI al XVI secolo*. Venice, 1962

MONTAIGNE: *The Journal of Montaigne's Travels in Italy (1580–1581)*

J. MOORE: *A View of Society and Manners in Italy*, 1780

FYNES MORISON: *Itinerary (1594)*

M. NEWBIGIN: *The Mediterranean Lands*. Methuen, 1927

IRIS ORIGO: *The Merchant of Prato*

D. RANDALL-MACIVER: *Italy before the Romans*. Clarendon, 1928

M. ROSTOVTZEFF: *The Social and Economic History of the Roman Empire*. OUP.

L. T. SMITH (ed.): *Itinerary of John Leland*

D. MACK SMITH: *Italy*. University of Michigan Press, 1961

J. TOUTAIN: *Economics in the Ancient World*

A. A. M. VAN DER HEYDEN and H. H. SCULLARD: *Atlas of the Classical World*. Nelson, 1959

VON VACANO: *The Etruscans in the Ancient World*. Arnold, 1960

A. G. WOODHEAD: *The Greeks in the West*. Thames & Hudson

ARTHUR YOUNG: *Travels in France and Italy*

P. BIROT and J. DRESCH: *La Méditerranée et Le Moyen Orient. Vol I. La Méditerranée Occidentale*. Presses Univ. de France, 1953

A. DE PHILIPPIS: 'Il clima d'Italia meridionale nei suoi rapporti con la vegetazione'. *Atti Congresso Geog. Ital*. 1957

P. GABERT: 'Une tentative d'evaluation du travail de l'érosion sur les massifs montagneux qui dominent la plaine du Pô'. *Rev. de Géog. Alp*. 1960

BIBLIOGRAPHY

M. D. GENTILESCHI: 'Fenomeni carsici nell' alto bacino del Corno'. *Boll. Soc. Geog. Ital.* 1961

H.M.S.O.: *Weather in the Mediterranean*. Vol. I

B. KAYSER: *Recherches sur les sols et l'erosion en Italie meridionale; Lucanie*. Paris, 1961

F. MANCINI: *Carta dei suoli d'Italia* (commentary on 1/1,500,000 map). Edizioni Agricole Bologna, 1961

A. MANISCALO and G. PASQUINI: 'L'idrologia e il carsismo nel Matese meridionale'. *Boll. Soc. Geog. Ital.* 1963

M. PINNA: 'La carta dell'indice di aridità per l'Italia'. *Atti Congresso Geog. Ital.* 1957

A. SESTINI: 'Delimitazione delle grandi regioni orografico-morphologiiche dell' Italia'. *Riv. Geog. Ital.* 1943–4

TOURING CLUB ITALIANO: *Conosci l'Italia*. Vol. I. *L'Italia fisica*. 1957. Vol. III. *La flora*. 1958

G. T. TREWARTHA: *The World's Problem Climates*. Chaps. 15 and 16. Methuen, 1960


PART III

R. ALMAGIÀ: *L'Italia*. Vols. I and II. UTET, 1961

O. BALDACCI: *Puglia*. UTET, 1962

G. BARBERO: *Land Reform in Italy*. FAO, Rome, 1961

E. BEVILACQUA: *Marche*. UTET, 1961

A. BRUSA: 'Il decentramento portuale e industriale a Genova'. *Boll. Soc. Geog. Ital.* 1964

CONSORZIO AUTONOMO DEL PORTO DI GENOVA: *Il Porto di Genova*. 1963

M. COQUERY: 'Aspects démographiques et problèmes de croissance d'une ville "millionaire"; le cas de Naples'. *Ann. Géog.* 1963

C. L. DOZIER: 'Establishing a framework for development in Sardinia; the Campidano.' *Geog. Rev.* 1957

ENTE MAREMMA: *La riforma fondiari in Maremma*. 1951–4

'Excursion Géographique Interuniversitaire. Vieille et nouvelle Sardaigne'. *Ann. Géog.* 1960

G. FERRO: 'L'alpeggio al Passo di S. Pelligrino'. *Boll. Soc. Geog. Ital.* 1962

G. FORTUNATO: *Considerazioni geografiche sulla questione meridionale; il Mezzogiorno e lo stato italiano*. Florence, 1926

P. GABERT: *Turin, ville industrielle*. Paris, 1964

A. GIARRIZZO: 'La piana del Garigliano'. *Boll. Soc. Geog. Ital.* 1965

D. GRIBAUDI: *Piemonte de Val d'Aosta*. UTET, 1960

J. M. HOUSTON: *The Western Mediterranean World*. Longmans, 1965

M. LE LANNOU: *Pâtres et Paysans de la Sardaigne*. Tours, 1941

C. MERLO: *Liguria*. UTET, 1961

BIBLIOGRAPHY

E. MIGLIORINI: *Veneto*. UTET, 1962

F. MILONE: *Sicilia; la natura e l'uomo*. Boringhieri, 1961

F. MILONE: *L'Italia nell' economia delle sue regioni*. Einaudi, 1958

A. MORI: *Studi geografici sull' isola d'Elba*. Inst. Geog. Univ. Pisa, 1960

M. ORTOLANI: 'Il Subappennino Abruzzese'. *Riv. Geog. Ital.* 1960

R. PARMEGIANI: 'L'Albania salentina'. *Boll. Soc. Geog. Ital.* 1962

M. R. P. PEDRINI: *Umbria*. UTET, 1963

M. PINNA: 'Il piano di rinascita della Sardegna'. *Riv. Geog. Ital.* 1965

R. PRACCHI: *Lombardia*. UTET, 1960

L. RANIERI: *Basilicata*. UTET, 1961

R. RICCARDI: 'La diminuzione della populazione nella provincia di Rieti tra 1951 e 1961'. *Boll. Soc. Geog. Ital.* 1963

V. RICCHIONI: *Studi storici di economia dell' agricoltura meridionale*. Florence, 1952

V. RICCHIONI: 'Aspetti della transformazione fondiaria nella Murgia dei Trulli'. *Atti Congresso Geog. Ital.* 1957

C. J. ROBERTSON: 'Agricultural regions of the North Italian Plain'. *Geog. Rev.* 1938

R. ROCHFORT: 'La pétrole en Sicile'. *Ann. Géog.* 1960

C. RUINI: *Le vicende del latifondo siciliano*. Florence, 1946

D. RUOCCO: *La geografia industriale della Campania*. Inst. Geog. Univ. Napoli, 1964

A. TIZZONI: 'Distribuzione topografica delle grandi industrie di Milano'. *Atti. Congresso. Geog. Ital.* 1957

U. TOSCHI: *Emilia-Romagna*. UTET, 1961

TOURING CLUB ITALIANO: *Saggio di un atlante del paesaggio italiano*. 1928

TOURING CLUB ITALIANO: *Conosci l'Italia*. Vol. VII. *Il Paesaggio*. 1963

L. UNGER: 'Rural settlement in Campania'. *Geog. Rev.* 1953

G. VALUSSI: *Friuli–Venezia Giulia*. UTET, 1961

L. E. VIONE and R. VOLPI: *Borgo a Mozzano*. Geog. Pub. Ltd, 1963


PART IV

A. BRUSA: *Gli idrocarburi in Italia*. Ist. Geog. Univ. Genova, 1961

J. P. COLE: *Italy*. Chatto & Windus, 1964

C. COLOMONICO: Editor of various memoirs commenting on the *Carta della Utilizzazione del Suolo* (see below)

G. DAINELLI: *Atlante fisico economico d'Italia*. Milan, 1940

E. DALMASSO: 'L'industrie électrique en Italie'. *Ann. Géog.* 1964

H. DESPLANQUES: 'La réforme agraire Italienne.' *Ann. Géog.* 1957

R. E. DICKINSON: *The Population Problem in Southern Italy*. Syracuse Univ. Press, 1955

R. DUMONT: *Types of Rural Economy*. Chap. VII. 'Overpopulation and unemployment in the Italian countryside'. Methuen, 1957

### BIBLIOGRAPHY

G. FERRO: 'La viticoltura italiana'. *Boll. Soc. Geog. Ital.* 1962
G. FERRO: 'La olivicoltura italiana'. *Boll. Soc. Geog. Ital.* 1962
ISTAT: *Annuario di statistica agraria*
    *Annuario statistico italiano*
    *Compendio statistico italiano*
    *Censimento generale dell' agricoltura* – 1961
    *10° Censimento generale della populazione* – 1961
ISTITUTO NAZIONALE DI ECONOMIA AGRARIA: *La distribuzione della proprietà fondiaria in Italia*. Rome, 1947
VERA LUTZ: *Italy: a Study in Economic Development*. OUP, 1962
G. MEDICI: *Carta dei tipi d'impresa nell' agricoltura italiana*. INEA, Rome, 1958
G. MEDICI: *L' agricoltura e la riforma agraria*. INEA, Rome, 1946
G. MERLINI: *Le regioni agrarie in Italia*. Bologna, 1948
A. MOLINARI: *Survey of the Southern Italian Economy*. SVIMEZ, 1950
A. MORI: 'Osservazioni sull' emigrazione vitalizia nell' Italia meridionale'. *Boll. Soc. Geog. Ital.* 1961
M. PINNA: *Carta della densità della populazione in Italia* (census 1961)
M. J. WISE: 'Population pressure and national resources: some observations upon the Italian population problem'. *Econ. Geog.* 1954


### MAPS

*Istituto Geografico Militare.* 1/25,000, and 1/100,000
*Istituto Geografico Militare* and *Ufficio Geologico. Carta Geologica d'Italia,* scale 1/1,000,000 in two sheets; scale 1/100,000 for most areas
*Consiglio Nazionale delle Ricerche. Carta della Utilizzazione del Suolo.* Scale 1/200,000. 26 sheets. Pub. Touring Club Italiano

# Index